ASTRONOMY

REGION OF ORION

The photograph was made with a small lens with an exposure of 10 hours.
The Hyades are near the upper right corner. Sirius is at the lower left.
Nebulae are abundant in the Orion region. (*Photograph by Edwin Hubble*)

8TH
EDITION

ASTRONOMY

ROBERT H. BAKER
AUTHOR OF An Introduction to Astronomy

D. VAN NOSTRAND COMPANY, INC.
PRINCETON, NEW JERSEY
Toronto / London

Van Nostrand Regional Offices: *New York, Chicago, San Francisco*

D. Van Nostrand Company, Ltd., *London*

D. Van Nostrand Company (Canada), Ltd., *Toronto*

First Published, May 1930
Second Edition, May 1933
Third Edition, June 1938
Fourth Edition, April 1946
Fifth Edition, March 1950
Sixth Edition, March 1955
Seventh Edition, February 1959
Eighth Edition, January 1964

PRINTED IN THE UNITED STATES OF AMERICA

PREFACE TO THE EIGHTH EDITION

The considerable revision of ASTRONOMY in the new edition is intended to keep the book up to the times. The scope and arrangement of the material remain practically as before. This is a textbook for two-semester introductory courses in astronomy at the college level.

Among the developments in this science since the appearance of the previous edition are new data obtained from spacecraft. These include the extensive radiation belt surrounding the earth, the photographs of the extreme ultraviolet solar spectrum, and the first views of the far side of the moon. New geological evidence has appeared in support of the impact theory of lunar craters. The timing of radio echoes from Venus has given a value of the scale of celestial distances somewhat greater than is presently adopted from optical observations.

Other new developments noted in this edition include the growing dependence on magnetic fields in interpretations of celestial phenomena. The use of pulsating stars as distance indicators has received further refinement. Young, populous star clusters are recognized in addition to the more familiar globular clusters of older stars. Increasing objection is noted to the hypothesis of colliding galaxies as explanations of S0 galaxies and the powering of certain radio sources. Opinions are heard more frequently that planetary systems may be abundant throughout the universe.

The author is indebted to a number of colleagues for helpful suggestions for this new edition.

ROBERT H. BAKER

Claremont, California
December 1963

CONTENTS

INTRODUCTION

Astronomy, the "science of the stars," is concerned with the physical universe. This science deals with planets and their satellites, including the earth and moon, with comets and meteors, with the sun, the stars and clusters of stars, with the interstellar gas and dust, with the system of the Milky Way and the other galaxies that lie beyond the Milky Way.

The most comprehensive of the sciences, astronomy is also regarded as the oldest of all. People of ancient times were attentive watchers of the skies. They were attracted by the splendor of the heavens, as we are today, and by its mystery that entered into their religions and mythologies. Astrology, the pseudo-science which held that the destinies of nations and individuals were revealed by the stars, provided at times another incentive for attention to the heavens.

An additional incentive to the early cultivation of astronomy was its usefulness in relation to ordinary pursuits. The daily rotation of the heavens furnished means of telling time. The cycle of the moon's phases and the westward march of the constellations through the year were convenient for calendar purposes. The pole star in the north served as a faithful guide to the traveler on land and sea. These are some of the ways in which the heavens have been useful to man from the earliest civilizations to the present.

The value of this science, however, is not measured mainly in terms of economic applications. Astronomy is concerned primarily with an aspiration of mankind, which is fully as impelling as the quest for survival and material welfare, namely, the desire to know about the universe around us and our relation to it. The importance of this service is demonstrated by the widespread public interest in astronomy and by the generous financial support that has promoted the construction and operation of large telescopes in increasing numbers. Nowhere in the college curricula can the value of learning for its own sake be more convincingly presented than in the introductory courses in astronomy.

It is the purpose of astronomy to furnish a description of the

1

physical universe, in which the features and relationships of its various parts are clearly shown. At present the picture is incomplete. Doubtless it will always remain incomplete, subject to improvements in the light of new explorations and viewpoints. The advancing years will bring added grandeur and significance to the view of the universe, as they have in the past.

The Sphere of the Stars. As early as the 6th century B.C., Greek scholars regarded the earth as a globe standing motionless in the center of the universe. The boundary of their universe was a hollow globe, having the stars set on its inner surface. This celestial sphere was supported on an inclined axis through the earth, on which the sphere rotated daily, causing the stars to rise and set. Within the sphere seven celestial bodies moved around the earth; they were the sun, the moon, and the five bright planets.

This view of the universe remained practically unchanged for more than 2000 years thereafter. The chief problem of astronomy was to account for the observed motions of the seven wandering bodies. The outstanding solution of the problem, on the basis of the central, motionless earth, was the Ptolemaic system.

Copernicus, in the 16th century, proposed the theory that the planets revolve around the sun rather than the earth and that the earth is simply one of the planets. The rising and setting of the stars were now ascribed to the daily rotation of the earth. The new theory placed the sun and its family of planets sharply apart from the stars. With its gradual acceptance, the stars came to be regarded as remote suns at different distances from us and in motion in various directions. The ancient sphere of the stars remained only as a convention; and the way was prepared for explorations into the star fields, which have led to the more comprehensive view of the universe that we have today.

The Solar System. The earth is one of a number of relatively small planets that revolve around the sun; the planets are accompanied by smaller bodies, the satellites, of which the moon is an example. These are dark globes, shining only as they reflect the sunlight. The nine principal planets, including the earth, have average distances from the sun ranging from 0.4 to 40 times the earth's distance. Thousands of smaller planets, the asteroids, describe their orbits mainly in the middle distances. Comets and meteor streams also revolve around the sun; their orbits are usually more elongated than are those of the planets, and they often extend to greater distances from the sun.

These bodies together comprise the solar system, the only known system of its kind, although others may well exist. A similar planetary system surrounding the very nearest star could not be discerned with the largest telescope. Likewise, the telescopic view of our own system from the nearest star would show only the sun, then having the appearance of a bright star.

The Stars. The sun is one of the multitude of stars, representing a fair average of the general run. It is a globe of intensely hot gas, 864,000 miles in diameter, and a third of a million times as massive as the earth. Some stars are much larger than the sun and some others are much smaller. Blue stars are hotter than the sun, which is a yellow star. Red stars are cooler; but all are hot as compared with ordinary standards, and they are radiating great amounts of energy. The stars are the power plants and building blocks of the universe.

Vast spaces intervene between the stars. If the size of the sun is represented by one of the periods on this page, the sun's nearest neighbor among the stars, the double star Alpha Centauri, would be shown on this scale by two dots 10 miles away. The actual distance exceeds four light years; that is, a ray of light, having a speed of 186,300 miles a second, spends more than four years in traveling from that star to the sun. This is a sample of the spacing of stars in the sun's neighborhood.

The interstellar spaces are not perfectly empty. In our vicinity and in many other regions they contain much gas and dust. Clouds of this material made luminous by nearby stars constitute the bright nebulae. The dust clouds can be detected by their dimming and reddening of stars behind them; they are responsible for the dark rifts that cause most of the variety in the Milky Way.

Our Galaxy is the assemblage of 100,000 million stars to which the sun belongs. Its most striking feature, as we view it from inside, is the glowing band of the Milky Way. This system consists in the main of a spheroidal central stellar region surrounded by a flat disk of stars 80,000 light years in diameter. Imbedded in this disk are spiral arms, containing stars, gas, and dust. The sun is near the principal plane of the Galaxy; it is distant about 30,000 light years from the center, which is situated in the direction of the constellation Sagittarius.   The sun is included in a spiral arm.

As would be inferred from its flattened form, the Galaxy is rotating around an axis through its center.   In the rotation the sun is now moving swiftly toward the direction of Cygnus.   The period of the rotation in the sun's neighborhood is of the order of 200 million years.   The more nearly spherical and more slowly rotating halo of the Galaxy includes the globular clusters.

The Exterior Galaxies.   Our spiral galaxy is one of the major building blocks of the universe.   Millions of other galaxies extend into space as far as the largest telescopes can explore, and many of these are also spirals.   They are retreating from us, and their speeds of recession increase as their distances are greater.   This is the basis for the spectacular theories of the expanding universe.

Astronomy is a physical science closely related to the others.   Its interests range from the structure and transmutation of the atom to the constitution and evolution of the universe.   Its large optical telescopes are cameras for recording the proceedings in the laboratory of space, where quantities of material, extremes of conditions, and lengths of time involved in the experiments transcend those of operations in the terrestrial physical and chemical laboratories. The telescopes also have important uses in collecting the radiations of celestial bodies and in funneling them into physical apparatus, such as the spectroscope and photoelectric cell.

Radio telescopes of increasing effectiveness are recording cosmic radiations of longer wavelength, extending the inquiries into the daytime and through cloudy skies.   They inform us of features of the universe that may be entirely concealed from optical telescopes.

1

ASPECTS OF THE SKY

THE CELESTIAL SPHERE; ITS APPARENT DAILY
ROTATION — DIURNAL CIRCLES OF THE STARS
— THE SUN'S APPARENT ANNUAL PATH — THE
CONSTELLATIONS

At the beginning of the study of astronomy it is convenient to
regard the earth as a sphere situated at the center of a vast spherical
shell on which the stars are set. The stars may accordingly be
represented on the surface of a globe and their positions may be
referred to circles on the globe, just as the positions of towns and
ships are denoted on the globe of the earth. It is in order at first
to recall the circles that are employed on the earth's surface.

1·1. Circles of the Terrestrial Sphere. The earth rotates daily from
west to east on an axis joining the north and south poles. Because
of its rotation the earth is somewhat flattened at the poles and
bulged at the equator. For the present purpose the flattening and
also the surface irregularities are neglected. If the earth is regarded
as a sphere, any plane passing through its center cuts the surface
in a *great circle*. A plane through the earth but not through the
center cuts the surface in a *small circle*.

The *equator* is the great circle of the terrestrial sphere halfway
between the north and south poles and therefore 90° from each.
Meridians are halves of great circles joining the poles and are therefore perpendicular to the equator. The *meridian of Greenwich*,
which passes through the original site of the Royal Greenwich
Observatory in England, is taken as the *prime meridian* for reckoning longitude. *Parallels of latitude* are small circles parallel to the
equator, which diminish in size with increasing distance from the
equator.

1·2. Longitude and Latitude. The position of a point on the
earth's surface is denoted by the longitude and latitude of the point.
The *longitude* is measured in degrees along the equator east or west

from the prime meridian to the meridian through the point. Its value ranges from 0° to 180° either way, and the direction is indicated by the abbreviation E. or W., or by the minus or plus sign. If the longitude is 60° W., the point is somewhere on the meridian 60° west from the Greenwich meridian.

The *latitude* of a point is its distance in degrees north or south from the equator, measured along the meridian through the point. Its value ranges from 0° at the equator to 90° at the poles, and the direction is indicated by the abbreviation N. or S., or by the plus or minus sign. If the latitude is 50° N., the point is somewhere on the parallel 50° north from the equator. When the longitude is also given, the position is uniquely defined. As an example, the Yerkes Observatory is in longitude 88° 33′ W. and latitude 42° 34′ N.

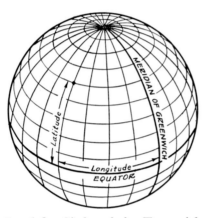

Fig. 1·2. Circles of the Terrestrial Sphere. The position of a point on the earth is denoted by its longitude and latitude.

Positions of stars on the apparent globe of the sky are similarly denoted. Although a single system of circles based on the equator suffices for the earth, four different systems are required in the sky for the various purposes of astronomy. The three to be described in this chapter are based on the horizon, celestial equator, and ecliptic.

THE CELESTIAL SPHERE; ITS APPARENT DAILY ROTATION

1·3. The Celestial Sphere is the conventional representation of the sky as a spherical shell on which the celestial bodies appear projected. Evidently of very great size, it has the properties of an infinite sphere. Its center may be anywhere at all and is often taken as the observer's position. Parallel lines, regardless of their distance apart, are directed toward the same point of the sphere, just as the rails of a track seem to converge in the distance. Each star has its *apparent place* on the sphere, where it appears to be; this specifies only the star's direction. The *apparent distance* between two stars is their difference in direction, which may be regarded as angular distance on the celestial sphere.

Apparent places and distances are always expressed in angular measure, such as degrees, minutes, and seconds of arc. For estimating angular distances in the sky it is useful to remember that the apparent diameters of the sun and moon are about half a degree. The pointer stars of the Great Dipper are somewhat more than 5° apart.

1·4. Horizon and Celestial Meridian. The *zenith* is the point of the celestial sphere that is vertically overhead. The *nadir* is the opposite point, vertically underfoot. These points are located by sighting along a plumb line, or vertical line.

The *celestial horizon* is the great circle on the celestial sphere halfway between the zenith and nadir and, therefore, 90° from each. This is the *horizon* of astronomy as distinguished from the visible horizon, the frequently irregular line where the earth and sky seem to meet. The horizon is an example of the circles that are imagined on the celestial sphere for the purpose of denoting the places of celestial bodies, just as circles such as the equator are imagined on the terrestrial sphere. The horizon is the basis of the horizon system of circles.

Vertical circles are great circles that pass through the zenith and nadir and are, therefore, perpendicular to the horizon. One of these is the observer's *celestial meridian,* the vertical circle that crosses his horizon at the north and south points. Another is the *prime vertical,* which crosses the horizon at the east and west points.

Celestial circles and coordinates may be somewhat confusing to the reader at first, because they often have unfamiliar names and also because they are represented in two dimensions in the diagrams. The use of a celestial globe or of a blank globe on which the circles can be drawn is likely to contribute to a clearer understanding of features of the sky described in this and other chapters. It should preferably be a globe that can be rotated and that has a movable meridian, so that the direction of the rotation axis can be varied.

1·5. Azimuth and Altitude. The position of a star is denoted in the horizon system by its azimuth and altitude. The *azimuth* of a star is the angular distance measured from the north point toward the east along the horizon to the vertical circle of the star. It is measured completely around the horizon from 0° to 360°. Azimuth is often reckoned from the south instead of the north.

The *altitude* of a star is its angular distance from the horizon. Altitude is measured along the vertical circle through the star, generally having values from 0° at the horizon to 90° at the zenith. Its complement, *zenith distance,* is measured downward from the zenith along the vertical circle. When its azimuth and altitude are

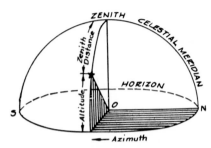

FIG. 1·5. Location of a Star by Azimuth and Altitude. Azimuth is measured from the north point eastward along the horizon. Altitude is the star's angular distance above (or below) the horizon. Zenith distance is the complement of altitude.

given, the star's place in the sky is known, as the following examples illustrate.

(1) Point to a star in azimuth 90° and altitude 45°.
Answer: The star is directly in the east, halfway from the horizon to the zenith.
(2) Point to a star in azimuth 180° and altitude 30°.
Answer: The star is directly in the south, one third of the way from the horizon to the zenith.
(3) State the azimuth and altitude of a star that is exactly in the southwest and two thirds of the way from the horizon to the zenith.
Answer: Azimuth 225°, altitude 60°.

The simplicity of the horizon system recommends it for various purposes in astronomy, navigation, and surveying. It is easy to visualize these circles and coordinates in the sky. The navigator's sextant or octant and the engineer's transit operate in this system. The lack of permanence of the coordinates, however, necessitates the use of other systems as well. Azimuths and altitudes of the celestial bodies are always changing, because of the apparent daily rotation of the celestial sphere; and at the same instant they vary with the observer's position on the earth.

1·6. Apparent Daily Rotation of the Celestial Sphere. The westward movement of the sun across the sky, which causes the sun to rise and set, is an example of the motion in which all the celestial bodies share. It is as though the celestial sphere were rotating daily around the earth from east to west. This apparent daily rotation, or *diurnal motion,* of the heavens is an effect of the earth's rotation on its axis from west to east.

Every star describes its *diurnal circle* around the sky daily. All diurnal circles of the stars are parallel and are described in the same period of time; but those of the sun, moon, and planets, which change their places among the stars, are not quite parallel and have somewhat different periods. The rapidity with which a star proceeds along its diurnal circle depends on the size of the circle that is described. The motion is fastest for stars that rise exactly in the east; it becomes progressively slower as the rising is farther from the east point, and vanishes at two opposite points in the sky around which the diurnal circles are described.

1·7. The Celestial Poles. The two points on the celestial sphere having no diurnal motion are the *north and south celestial poles.*

FIG. 1·7. Circumpolar Star Trails. The exposure time was 1 hour. The brighter trail below the center is that of Polaris. (*Yerkes Observatory photograph*)

They are the points toward which the earth's axis is directed. For observers in the northern hemisphere, the north celestial pole is situated vertically above the north point of the horizon; its place is marked approximately by Polaris, the *pole star,* or *north star,* at the end of the handle of the Little Dipper. Polaris is now about 1° from the pole, or twice the apparent diameter of the moon.

The south celestial pole is depressed below the south horizon as much as the north pole is elevated in the northern sky. Its place is not marked by any bright star. This is the elevated pole for observers in the southern hemisphere.

It is interesting to photograph the diurnal trails of stars around the pole with an ordinary camera. Set the camera so that it points toward the pole star and expose a film for several hours on a clear evening, using the full aperture of the lens and having the focus adjusted for distance. The trails in the picture are arcs of diurnal circles, which have the celestial pole as their common center. Increasing the exposure makes the trails longer, but shows no more stars.

1·8. Celestial Equator; Hour Circles. The *celestial equator* is the great circle of the celestial sphere halfway between the north and south celestial poles. It is in the plane of the earth's equator and

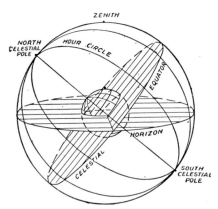

FIG. 1·8. The Celestial Equator in the Plane of the Earth's Equator. It crosses the horizon at the east and west cardinal points at an inclination equal to the complement of the observer's latitude.

is the largest of the diurnal circles. For a particular place on the earth, the celestial equator has nearly the same position in the sky throughout the day and year; it is traced approximately by the sun's diurnal motion on March 21 or September 23.

Hour circles pass through the celestial poles and are, therefore, at right angles to the celestial equator. They are half circles from pole to pole, like meridians of the terrestrial sphere; and they may be considered as fixed either on the turning celestial sphere or with respect to the observer, like his celestial meridian.

1·9. Directions in the Equator System. In the system of circles based on the celestial equator, north is the direction along an hour circle toward the north celestial pole. South is the opposite direction. West is the direction of the diurnal motion, which is parallel to the celestial equator. With these definitions in mind there will be no confusion about directions in the sky, even in the vicinity of the pole. As one faces north, the stars circle daily in the counterclockwise direction. From a star directly above the pole, north is downward and west is toward the left; from a star below the pole, north is upward and west is toward the right.

1·10. Right Ascension and Declination. The *right ascension* of a star is the angular distance measured in hours, or degrees, from the

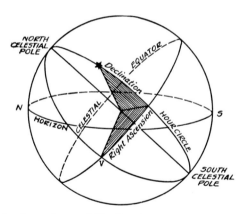

Fig. 1·10. Right Ascension and Declination. Right ascension is measured eastward from the vernal equinox along the celestial equator. Declination is measured north or south from the celestial equator along an hour circle.

vernal equinox eastward along the celestial equator to the hour circle of the star. The vernal equinox is the point where the sun's center crosses the celestial equator at the beginning of spring; the hour circle through this point serves the same purpose as the prime meridian of the earth. Unlike terrestrial longitude, which is measured both east and west from the prime meridian, right ascension is always measured toward the east, from 0^h or $0°$ at the vernal equinox to 24^h or $360°$ at the equinox again.

The *declination* of a star is its angular distance north or south from the celestial equator. Declination is measured along the hour circle of the star, its value ranging from $0°$ at the equator to $90°$ at the poles. If the star is north of the equator, the sign of the declination is plus; if the star is south of the equator, the sign is minus. The places of the celestial bodies are generally denoted by their right ascensions and declinations in maps and catalogs.

As an example, the right ascension of the bright star Sirius is $6^h 43^m$, and the declination is $-16° 39'$; the star is therefore $6^h 43^m$, or $100° 45'$, east of the vernal equinox and $16° 39'$ south of the celestial equator. The following relations can be employed in changing from hours to degrees of right ascension, or conversely:

$$1^h = 15° \qquad\qquad 15° = 1^h$$
$$1^m = 15' \qquad\qquad 1° = 4^m$$
$$1^s = 15'' \qquad\qquad 1' = 4^s$$

1·11. Hour Angle. The place of a star is also denoted in the equator system by its hour angle and declination. In this case the observer's celestial meridian is the circle of reference and is considered to have two branches. The *upper branch* of the celestial meridian is the half between the celestial poles that includes the observer's zenith; the *lower branch* is the opposite half that includes the nadir. A star is at *upper transit* when it crosses the upper branch of the celestial meridian, and at *lower transit* when it crosses the lower branch.

The *local hour angle* of a star is the angular distance measured along the celestial equator westward from the upper branch of the observer's celestial meridian to the hour circle of the star; or it is the corresponding angle at the celestial pole. The value of the hour angle ranges from $0°$ to $360°$. Unlike the right ascension of a star, which remains nearly unchanged during the day, the hour angle increases at the rate of about $15°$ an hour, and at the same instant has different values in different longitudes.

The *Greenwich hour angle* of a star is its local hour angle as observed at the meridian of Greenwich. Greenwich hour angles of celestial bodies are tabulated in nautical and air almanacs at convenient intervals of the day throughout the year.

DIURNAL CIRCLES OF THE STARS

1·12. The Observer's Latitude Equals the Altitude of the North Celestial Pole. The *astronomical latitude* of a place on the earth is defined as the angle between the vertical line at the place and the plane of the earth's equator. Evidently this is also the angle between the directions of the zenith and celestial equator. As is

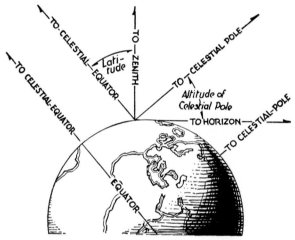

FIG. 1·12. The Latitude of a Place on the Earth Equals the Altitude of the North Celestial Pole at That Place. Astronomical latitude is defined as the angle between the vertical line and the equator plane. This angle equals the altitude of the north celestial pole, because both are complements of the angle between the zenith and the celestial pole. It also equals the declination of the zenith.

seen in Fig. 1·12, this angle equals the altitude of the north celestial pole as well as the declination of the zenith at the place. Here we have the basic rule for all determinations of latitude by sights on celestial objects.

Where irregularities of the earth affect the direction of the vertical line, the astronomical latitude requires a slight correction to obtain the *geographical latitude*. The correction rarely exceeds 30″ and is usually much smaller.

When the latitude of a place is given, the altitude of the celestial pole is an equal number of degrees, according to the rule. Thus the positions of the celestial poles and of the celestial equator midway between them become known relative to the horizon of the place. Because the diurnal circles of the stars are parallel to the equator, we may now consider how these circles are related to the horizon for observers at different places on the earth.

1·13. At the Pole, Diurnal Circles Are Parallel to the Horizon. Viewed from the north pole, latitude 90° N., the north celestial

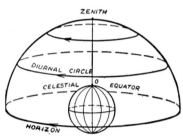

pole is in the zenith and the celestial equator coincides with the horizon. Here the diurnal circles are parallel to the horizon. Stars north of the celestial equator never set, and those in the south celestial hemisphere are never seen. The sun, moon, and planets, which change their places among the stars, come into view when they move north across the equator and set when they cross

FIG. 1·13. Diurnal Circles Observed at the North (or South) Pole Are Parallel to the Horizon.

to the south. At the south pole, of course, the south celestial pole is in the zenith and everything is reversed.

It will be noted later that some statements in this chapter require slight modification because of refraction of starlight in the earth's atmosphere.

1·14. At the Equator, Diurnal Circles Are Perpendicular to the Horizon. Viewed from the equator, latitude 0°, the celestial poles

are on the horizon at its north and south points. The celestial equator crosses at right angles to the horizon at its east and west points and passes directly overhead. All diurnal circles, since they are parallel to the equator, are also perpendicular to the horizon and are bisected by it. Thus every star is above the horizon for about 12 hours and is below

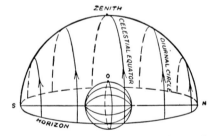

FIG. 1·14. Diurnal Circles Observed at the Equator Are Perpendicular to the Horizon.

for the same interval; the daily duration of sunlight is about 12 hours throughout the year.

It is to be noted that places on the equator are the only ones from which the celestial sphere can be seen from pole to pole, so that all parts of the heavens are brought into view by the apparent daily rotation.

1·15. Elsewhere, Diurnal Circles Are Oblique. From points of observation between the pole and the equator, the north celestial pole is elevated a number of degrees equal to the latitude of the place, and the south celestial pole is depressed the same amount.

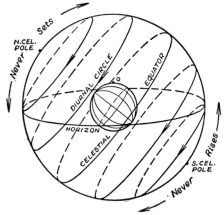

Fɪɢ. 1·15.   Diurnal Circles Observed in Latitude 40° N. Are Oblique.

Although the celestial equator still crosses the horizon at the east and west points, it no longer passes through the zenith, but leans toward the south, in the northern hemisphere, by an angle equal to the latitude.   Thus the diurnal circles of the stars cross the horizon obliquely.

The celestial equator is the only one of these circles that is bisected by the horizon.   Northward, the visible portions of the diurnal circles become progressively greater, until the entire circles are in view; southward from the celestial equator they diminish in size, until they are wholly out of sight.   The changing daily duration of sunlight from summer to winter serves as an example.

In this oblique aspect of the diurnal motion with respect to the horizon, the celestial sphere is conveniently divided into three parts: (1) A cap around the elevated celestial pole, having its radius equal to the latitude of the place, contains the stars that are always above the horizon; (2) a cap of the same size around the depressed pole contains the stars that never come into view; (3) a band of the heavens symmetrical with the celestial equator contains the stars that rise and set. In latitude 40° N., for example, the two caps are 40° in radius, and all stars within 50° of the celestial equator rise and set.

As one travels south, the circumpolar caps grow smaller and finally disappear when the equator is reached. As one travels north, the circumpolar caps increase in radius, until they join when the pole is reached. Here none of the stars rises or sets.

1·16. Circumpolar Stars. If a star is nearer the celestial pole than the pole itself is to the horizon, the star does not cross the horizon; it is a *circumpolar star*. Consequently, for an observer in the

Fig. 1·16. The Midnight Sun at Etah, Greenland. The exposures were made in July at intervals of 20 minutes while the sun was describing the lowest part of its diurnal circle above the north horizon. (*Photograph by Donald B. MacMillan*)

northern hemisphere, a star never sets if its north polar distance (90° minus its declination) is less than the observer's latitude; and it never rises if its south polar distance is less than the latitude. The following examples illustrate the rule:

(1) The Southern Cross, Decl. −60°, never rises in latitude 40° N., because its south polar distance of 30° is less than the latitude. It becomes visible south of latitude 30° N., in Florida and southern Texas.

(2) The bowl of the Great Dipper, Decl. +58°, never sets in latitude

40° N., because its north polar distance of 32° is less than the latitude. Under the celestial pole its center is still 8° above the horizon. It rises and sets south of latitude 32° N.

(3) The sun on June 22, Decl. +23½°, rises and sets in latitude 40° N., because its north polar distance of 66½° is not less than the latitude. North of about latitude 66½° N. the sun is circumpolar on that date.

The *midnight sun* is an example of a circumpolar object. The sun may be seen at midnight on June 22 about as far south as the arctic circle. Farther north it remains above the horizon for a longer period, and at the north pole it does not set for six months.

THE SUN'S APPARENT ANNUAL PATH

1·17. Westward Advance of the Constellations Through the Year. In addition to their daily westward circling around us, the stars are a little farther west each evening than they were at the same time the evening before. A constellation steps forward gradually, until it has finally disappeared in the west at that time. For example, the familiar oblong figure of Orion is seen rising in the east in the early evening in December. Late in the winter, Orion has moved into the south at the same hour of the night. As spring advances, it comes out in the western sky and sets soon after nightfall.

This steady westward march of the constellations with the changing seasons results from the sun's apparent eastward movement among the stars. If the stars were visible in the daytime, as they are in the sky of the planetarium, we could watch the sun's progress among them. We would observe that the sun is displaced toward the east about twice its diameter from day to day, and completely around the heavens in the course of a year. The sun's apparent annual movement around the celestial sphere is a consequence of the earth's annual revolution around the sun.

Not only does the sun move eastward with respect to the stars, but it oscillates to the north and south as well during the year. The sun's apparent path is inclined to the celestial equator.

1·18. The Ecliptic; Equinoxes and Solstices. The *ecliptic* is the apparent annual path of the sun's center on the celestial sphere. It is a great circle inclined 23½° to the celestial equator.

Four equidistant points on the ecliptic are the two *equinoxes*, where the circle intersects the celestial equator, and the two *solstices*, where it is farthest from the equator. The *vernal equinox* is the sun's position about March 21, when it crosses the celestial equator going north; the *autumnal equinox* is the sun's position about September 23, when it crosses on the way south. The *summer solstice* is the most northern point of the ecliptic, the sun's position about June 22; the *winter solstice* is the southernmost point, the sun's position about December 22. These dates vary slightly because of the plan of leap years.

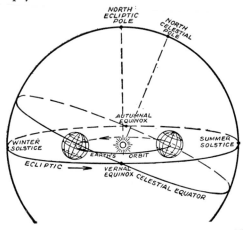

FIG. 1·18. Relation of Ecliptic and Celestial Equator. The inclination of the ecliptic to the celestial equator is the same (23½°) as the inclination of the earth's orbit to its equator.

The north and south *ecliptic poles* are the two points 90° from the ecliptic. They are 23½° from the celestial poles.

The relation between the ecliptic and celestial equator is explained in Fig. 1·18, in which the earth's orbit is viewed nearly edgewise. Because parallel lines meet in the distant sky, the celestial poles, toward which the earth's axis is directed, are not displaced by the earth's revolution around the sun; similarly the celestial equator is unaffected. Evidently the angle between the ecliptic and celestial equator is the same as the angle between the earth's orbit and equator. This inclination, or *obliquity,* of the ecliptic is 23° 27′; it is at present decreasing at the rate of 1′ in 128 years.

1·19. Relation Between Ecliptic and Horizon. The inclination of the celestial equator to the horizon of a particular place remains almost unaltered; this angle is the complement of the latitude of the place. Thus in latitude 40° N. the celestial equator is inclined 50° to the horizon. The ecliptic, however, takes different positions in the sky during the day.

Because the ecliptic is inclined 23½° to the celestial equator, its inclination to the horizon can differ as much as 23½°, either way, from that of the equator. It can be seen with the aid of a globe that the greatest and least angles between the ecliptic and the horizon in middle northern latitudes occur when the equinoxes are rising and setting.

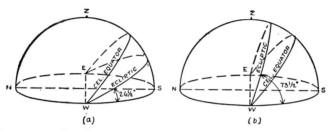

FIG. 1·19. Relation Between Ecliptic and Horizon. (a) The ecliptic is least inclined to the horizon in middle northern latitudes when the vernal equinox is rising and the autumnal equinox is setting. (b) The ecliptic is most inclined when the autumnal equinox is rising and the vernal equinox is setting.

In latitude 40° N., when the vernal equinox is rising and the autumnal equinox is setting, as at sunset on September 23, the angle between the ecliptic and horizon is 50° − 23½° = 26½°. The visible half of the ecliptic lies below the celestial equator. When the autumnal equinox is rising and the vernal equinox is setting, as at sunset on March 21, the angle is 50° + 23½° = 73½°. The visible half of the ecliptic is then above the celestial equator.

It will be noted later that the variation in the angle between the ecliptic and horizon is involved in the explanations of the harvest moon, the appearance of the planet Mercury as evening and morning star, and the favorable seasons for observing the zodiacal light.

1·20. Celestial Longitude and Latitude. The observations of early astronomers were confined for the most part to the sun, moon, and bright planets, which are never far from the ecliptic. It was accordingly the custom to denote the places of these objects with reference to the ecliptic by giving their celestial longitudes and latitudes. *Celestial longitude* is angular distance from the vernal equinox, measured eastward along the ecliptic to the circle through the object

that is at right angles to the ecliptic. *Celestial latitude* is the angular
distance of the object from the ecliptic, measured to the north or
south along the perpendicular circle.

The earlier coordinates still find use in problems of planetary
motions. They have been supplanted for most purposes by right
ascension and declination, which are the counterparts of terrestrial
longitude and latitude. The newer coordinates might well have
been named celestial longitude and latitude instead, except that
these names had already been appropriated.

THE CONSTELLATIONS

1·21. The Primitive Constellations. The stars form interesting
patterns, which are well known to many people. There are dippers,
crosses, and a variety of other figures easy to identify and to remem-

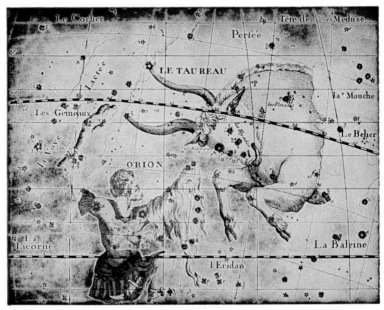

Fig. 1·21. Orion and Taurus. (*Atlas Celeste de Flamsteed, 1776*)

ber. In the original sense, the *constellations* are these configurations
of stars.

Two thousand years ago, the Greeks recognized 48 constellations
with which they associated the names and forms of heroes and ani-

mals of their mythology. The earliest nearly complete account of them that can be found in libraries today is contained in the *Phenomena,* written about 270 B.C. by the poet Aratus. In the writings of Hesiod, more than 500 years earlier, and in the Homeric epics the more conspicuous figures, such as Orion, the Pleiades, and the Great Bear, are mentioned familiarly. There are reasons for supposing that practically the whole scheme of primitive constellations was transmitted to the Greeks, having originated several thousand years before among the peoples of the Euphrates valley. The 48 original constellations, with certain changes made by the Greeks, are described in Ptolemy's *Almagest* (about A.D. 150), which specifies the positions of stars in the imagined creatures.

The ancient star-creatures have nothing to do with the science of astronomy. Their names, however, are still associated with striking groupings of stars, which attract the attention now just as they interested people long ago.

1·22. Constellations as Regions of the Celestial Sphere. The original constellations did not cover the entire sky. Of the 1028 stars

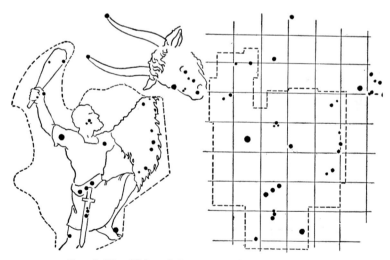

FIG. 1·22. Old and New Boundaries of Orion.

listed by Ptolemy, 10 per cent were "unformed," that is, not included within the 48 figures. Moreover, a large area of the celestial sphere in the south, which never rose above the horizons of the Greeks, was uncharted. In various star maps that appeared after the beginning of the 17th century, new configurations were added to fill the vacant spaces and received names not associated with mythology. At present, 88 constellations are recognized (Table 1·I), of which 70 are visible at least in part from the latitude of New York in the course of a year.

For the purposes of astronomy, the constellations are regions of the celestial sphere set off by arbitrary boundary lines. These divisions are useful for describing the approximate positions of the stars and other celestial bodies. The statement that Vega is in the constellation Lyra serves the same purpose as the information that a town is in Ohio. We know about where it can be found.

The boundaries of the majority of the constellations were formerly irregular. Revised by action of the International Astronomical Union, in 1928, the boundaries are now parts of circles parallel and perpendicular to the celestial equator. The boundary lines are not shown in the star maps of this book.

1·23. Names of Individual Stars. Fifty or more of the brighter stars are known to us by the names given them long ago. Some star names, such as Sirius and Capella, are of Greek and Latin origin; others, such as Vega, Rigel, and Aldebaran, are of Arabic derivation. The influence of the Arabs in the development of astronomy is indicated by the frequent appearance of their definite article *al* in the names of stars (Algol, Altair, etc.).

Some star names now regarded as personal were originally expressions giving the positions of stars in the imagined constellation characters. These descriptive terms, translated from Ptolemy's catalog into Arabic, degenerated later into single words. Examples are Betelgeuse (perhaps meaning armpit of the Central One), Fomalhaut (mouth of the Fish), Deneb (tail, of the Bird).

1·24. Designations of Stars by Letter and Number. The star maps of Bayer's *Uranometria* (1603) introduced the present plan of designating the brighter stars of each constellation by small letters of the Greek alphabet. In a general way, the stars are lettered in order of brightness, and the Roman alphabet is drawn upon for further letters. The full name of a star in the Bayer system is the letter followed by the possessive of the Latin name of the constellation. Thus α Tauri is the brightest star in Taurus. When several stars in the constellation have nearly the same brightness, they are lettered in order of their positions in the mythological figure, beginning at the head. Thus the seven stars of the Great Dipper, which are not much different in brightness, are lettered in order of position.

Another plan, adopted in Flamsteed's *Historia Coelestis* (1729), in which the stars are numbered consecutively from west to east across a constellation, permits the designation of a greater number of stars. The star 61 Cygni is an example. In modern maps of the lucid stars it is usual to employ the Bayer letters as far as they go, giving the specific names of the brightest and most notable stars, and to designate some fainter stars by the Flamsteed numbers.

These are means of identifying the few thousand stars visible to the unaided eye. Stars are also often referred to by their running numbers in the catalogs. The position of the star HD 32416 can be found by turning to that number in the *Henry Draper Catalogue*.

1·25. Magnitudes of the Stars. It is easier to identify a star correctly when its brightness is known as well as its place in the sky. From Ptolemy's early catalog to the modern catalogs and maps of the stars, it has been the custom to express the relative brightness of a star by stating its *magnitude*. At first, the stars were divided arbitrarily into six classes, or magnitudes, in order of diminishing brightness. About 20 of the brightest stars were assigned to the 1st magnitude; Polaris and stars of the Great Dipper were representatives of the 2nd magnitude; and so on, until stars barely visible to the naked eye remained for the 6th magnitude.

With the invention of the telescope, permitting the observation of still fainter stars, the number of magnitudes was increased, while greater precision in measurement of brightness began to call for the use of decimals in denoting the magnitudes. Eventually, a factor slightly greater than 2.5 was adopted as the ratio of brightness corresponding to a difference of 1 magnitude. Thus a star of magnitude 3.0 is about 2½ times as bright as a star of magnitude 4.0.

The magnitudes assigned to the naked-eye stars by the early astronomers are not altered greatly by modern practice, except those of the very brightest stars. The original 1st-magnitude stars range so widely in brightness that the more brilliant ones have been promoted by the modern rule to brighter classes, and so to smaller numbers. The visual magnitude of the brightest star, Sirius, is −1.4; Canopus is −0.7; Arcturus, Vega, and Capella, the brightest stars of the north celestial hemisphere, are not far from magnitude 0; Spica is of magnitude +1.0.

In the maps that follow, the brightness of stars is denoted to whole magnitudes by the symbols, the meanings of which are given in the key adjoining the circular maps. In the interest of simplicity, two stars of around the minus 1st magnitude are designated as of magnitude 0, and a few 5th-magnitude stars as of magnitude 4. Stars fainter than the 4th magnitude are not generally shown in these maps.

1·26. The North Circumpolar Map. Map 1 represents the appearance of the heavens to one facing north in middle northern latitudes. At the center is the north celestial pole, the altitude of which equals the observer's latitude. Hour circles radiating from the center are numbered with hours of their right ascensions. Parallels of declination appear as circles at intervals of 10°, from declination +90° at the center of the map to +50° at its circumference.

The names of the months around the circumference of the map facilitate its orientation to correspond with the sky at any time. If the map is turned so that the date of observation is uppermost, the vertical line through the center of the map represents the observer's celestial meridian at about 9 P.M., standard time. The constellations then have the same position in the map as they have in the northern sky at that hour.

To orient the map for a later hour, turn it counterclockwise through as many hours of right ascension as the standard time is later than 9 P.M. For an earlier hour, turn the map clockwise. Thus the map may be made to represent the positions of the constellations in the northern sky at any time during the year.

1·27. Star Maps for the Different Seasons. Maps 2, 3, 4, and 5 show the constellations that appear in the vicinity of the observer's celestial meridian in the evening during each of the four seasons. The maps extend from the north celestial pole, at the top, down to the south horizon of latitude 40° N. Hour circles radiating from the pole are marked in hours of right ascension near the bottom of the map. Circles of equal declination go around the pole; their declinations are indicated on the central hour circle.

Select the map for the desired season and hold it toward the south. The hour circle above the date of observation coincides with the celestial meridian at about 9 o'clock in the evening, standard time. The stars near this hour circle are at upper transit at about this time. If the observer is in middle northern latitudes and is facing south, the stars represented in the upper part of the map are behind him. The northern constellations are arranged more conveniently, however, in Map 1; they are repeated in the seasonal maps to show how they are related to the constellations farther south.

Map 6 shows the region around the south celestial pole that is not visible from latitude 40° N.

1·28. Zenith Distance of a Star at Upper Transit. Having learned from the map that a certain star is crossing the celestial meridian at 9 P.M., we may wish to know how far from the zenith one must

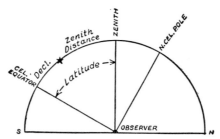

Fig. 1·28. Zenith Distance of a Star at Upper Transit. It equals the observer's latitude minus the star's declination.

look to find the star. The required rule follows from the relation of Section 1·12.

The zenith distance of a star at upper transit equals the observer's latitude minus the star's declination (Fig. 1·28). If the resulting zenith distance is positive, the star is south of the zenith; if it is negative, the star is north of the zenith. In the following examples the observer is in latitude 40° N.

(1) How close to the zenith does the bowl of the Great Dipper pass? Answer: The declination is +58°. At upper transit the zenith distance is 40° − 58° = −18°, north of the zenith.

(2) What declination must a star have in order to pass through the zenith? Answer: If the zenith distance is zero, the star's declination must equal the observer's latitude (40°). Thus stars having declinations less than 40° pass south of the zenith; stars having declinations greater than 40° pass north of the zenith. The sun passes directly overhead in the latitude that equals the sun's declination at that time.

(3) State the sun's zenith distance at its upper transit on June 22. Answer: The sun's declination is then +23½°. Its zenith distance is 40° − 23½° = +16½°, south of the zenith.

TABLE 1·1 NAMES OF THE CONSTELLATIONS

Latin Name	Possessive	English Equivalent	Map
*Androm'eda	Androm'edae	Andromeda	4, 5
Ant'lia	Ant'liae	Air Pump	
A'pus	A'podis	Bird of Paradise	
*Aqua'rius	Aqua'rii	Water Carrier	4
*Aq'uila	Aq'uilae	Eagle	3, 4
*A'ra	A'rae	Altar	6
*A'ries	Ari'etis	Ram	4, 5
*Auri'ga	Auri'gae	Charioteer	5
*Boö'tes	Boö'tis	Herdsman	2, 3
Cae'lum	Cae'li	Graving Tool	
Camelopar'dalis	Camelopar'dalis	Giraffe	
*Can'cer	Can'cri	Crab	2, 5
Ca'nes Vena'tici	Ca'num Venatico'rum	Hunting Dogs	2
*Ca'nis Ma'jor	Ca'nis Majo'ris	Larger Dog	5
*Ca'nis Mi'nor	Ca'nis Mino'ris	Smaller Dog	5
*Capricor'nus	Capricor'ni	Sea-Goat	4
†Cari'na	Cari'nae	Keel	6
*Cassiope'ia	Cassiope'iae	Cassiopeia	1, 4
*Centau'rus	Centau'ri	Centaur	2, 6
*Ce'pheus	Ce'phei	Cepheus	1, 4
*Ce'tus	Ce'ti	Whale	4, 5
Chamae'leon	Chamaeleon'tis	Chameleon	
Cir'cinus	Cir'cini	Compasses	
Colum'ba	Colum'bae	Dove	5
Co'ma Bereni'ces	Co'mae Bereni'ces	Berenice's Hair	2
*Coro'na Austra'lis	Coro'nae Austra'lis	Southern Crown	
*Coro'na Borea'lis	Coro'nae Borea'lis	Northern Crown	3
*Cor'vus	Cor'vi	Crow	2
*Cra'ter	Crater'is	Cup	2
Crux	Cru'cis	Cross	6
*Cyg'nus	Cyg'ni	Swan	3, 4
*Delphi'nus	Delphi'ni	Dolphin	4
Dora'do	Dora'dus	Dorado	
*Dra'co	Draco'nis	Dragon	1, 3
*Equu'leus	Equu'lei	Little Horse	
*Erid'anus	Erid'ani	River	5, 6
For'nax	Forna'cis	Furnace	
*Gem'ini	Gemino'rum	Twins	5
Grus	Gru'is	Crane	4
*Her'cules	Her'culis	Hercules	3
Horolo'gium	Horolo'gii	Clock	
*Hy'dra	Hy'drae	Sea Serpent	2
Hy'drus	Hy'dri	Water Snake	6
In'dus	In'di	Indian	
Lacer'ta	Lacer'tae	Lizard	
*Le'o	Leo'nis	Lion	2

TABLE 1·I NAMES OF THE CONSTELLATIONS—*Continued*

Latin Name	Possessive	English Equivalent	Map
Le'o Mi'nor	Leo'nis Mino'ris	Smaller Lion	
*Le'pus	Le'poris	Hare	5
*Li'bra	Li'brae	Scales	3
*Lu'pus	Lu'pi	Wolf	3
Lynx	Lyn'cis	Lynx	
*Ly'ra	Ly'rae	Lyre	3, 4
Men'sa	Men'sae	Table Mountain	
Microsco'pium	Microsco'pii	Microscope	
Monoc'eros	Monocero'tis	Unicorn	
Mus'ca	Mus'cae	Fly	6
Nor'ma	Nor'mae	Level	
Oc'tans	Octan'tis	Octant	
*Ophiu'chus	Ophiu'chi	Serpent Holder	3
*Ori'on	Orio'nis	Orion	5
Pa'vo	Pavo'nis	Peacock	6
*Peg'asus	Peg'asi	Pegasus	4
*Per'seus	Per'sei	Perseus	4, 5
Phoe'nix	Phoeni'cis	Phoenix	4
Pic'tor	Picto'ris	Easel	
*Pis'ces	Pis'cium	Fishes	4
*Pis'cis Austri'nus	Pis'cis Austri'ni	Southern Fish	4
†Pup'pis	Pup'pis	Stern	5
†Pyx'is	Pyx'idis	Mariner's Compass	
Retic'ulum	Retic'uli	Net	
*Sagit'ta	Sagit'tae	Arrow	3, 4
*Sagitta'rius	Sagitta'rii	Archer	3
*Scor'pius	Scor'pii	Scorpion	3
Sculp'tor	Sculpto'ris	Sculptor's Apparatus	4
Scu'tum	Scu'ti	Shield	
*Ser'pens	Serpen'tis	Serpent	3
Sex'tans	Sextan'tis	Sextant	
*Tau'rus	Tau'ri	Bull	5
Telesco'pium	Telesco'pii	Telescope	
*Trian'gulum	Trian'guli	Triangle	4, 5
Trian'gulum Austra'le	Trian'guli Austra'lis	Southern Triangle	6
Tuca'na	Tuca'nae	Toucan	6
*Ur'sa Ma'jor	Ur'sae Majo'ris	Larger Bear	1, 2
*Ur'sa Mi'nor	Ur'sae Mino'ris	Smaller Bear	1, 3
†Ve'la	Velo'rum	Sails	2, 6
*Vir'go	Vir'ginis	Virgin	2
Vo'lans	Volan'tis	Flying Fish	
Vulpec'ula	Vulpec'ulae	Fox	

* One of the 48 constellations recognized by Ptolemy.

† Carina, Puppis, Pyxis, and Vela once formed the single Ptolemaic constellation Argo Navis.

1·29. Examples of the Use of the Star Maps.

(1) On what date is the bowl of the Great Dipper (Map 1) directly above the celestial pole at 9 P.M., standard time?

Answer: May 1.

(2) Read from Map 1 the right ascension and declination of δ Ursae Majoris (where the handle and bowl of the Dipper join).

Answer: Right ascension 12ʰ 12ᵐ, declination +57°.

(3) On what date is Antares (Map 3) at upper transit at 9 P.M., standard time? What is its zenith distance at that time in latitude 40° N.?

Answer: July 13. The star is 66° south of the zenith.

(4) Locate with respect to the constellations (Map 5) a planet in right ascension 5ʰ 30ᵐ and declination +24°.

Answer: The planet is midway between β and ζ Tauri.

(*Continued on page 34*)

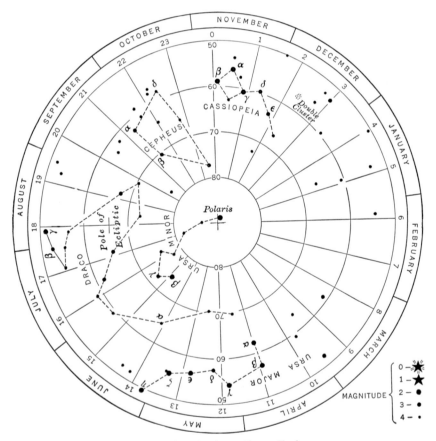

MAP 1. The Northern Constellations.

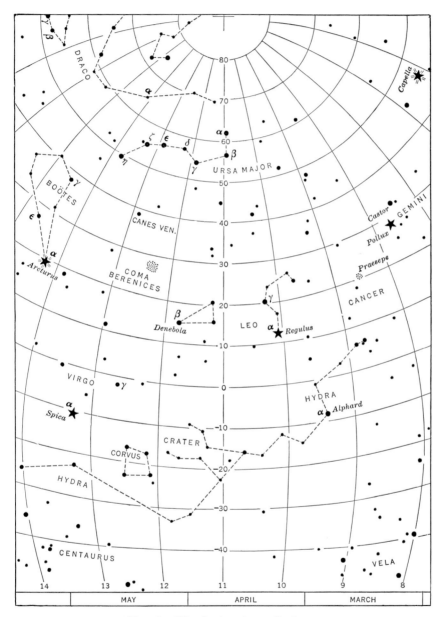

MAP 2.   The Spring Constellations.

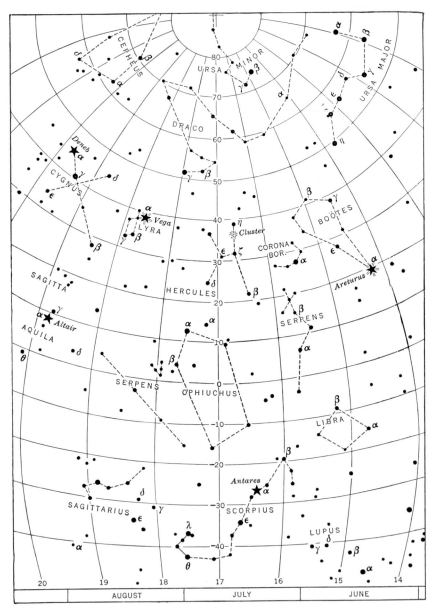

MAP 3. The Summer Constellations.

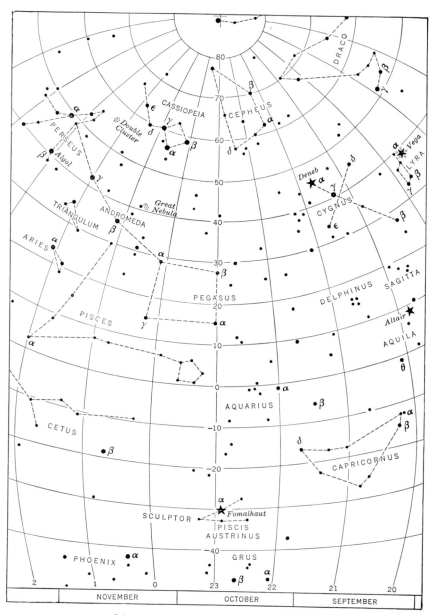

MAP 4. The Autumn Constellations.

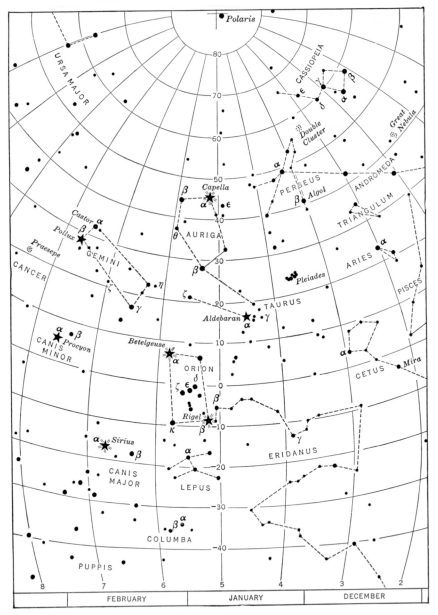

MAP 5. The Winter Constellations.

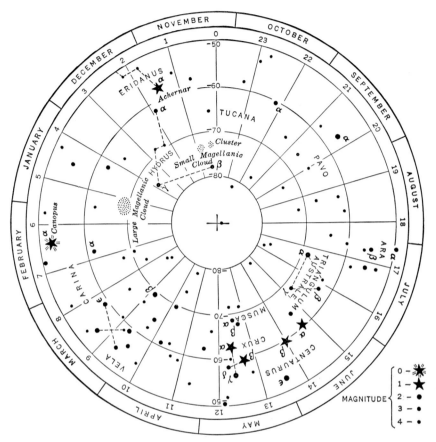

MAP 6. The Southern Constellations.

TABLE 1·II GREEK ALPHABET (SMALL LETTERS)

α	alpha	ι	iota	ρ	rho
β	beta	κ	kappa	σ	sigma
γ	gamma	λ	lambda	τ	tau
δ	delta	μ	mu	υ	upsilon
ε	epsilon	ν	nu	φ	phi
ζ	zeta	ξ	xi	χ	chi
η	eta	o	omicron	ψ	psi
θ	theta	π	pi	ω	omega

(5) At what time is Orion (Map 5) directly in the south on March 1?

Answer: Orion is at upper transit at 7 P.M., standard time, on March 1.

(6) When Orion has been recognized, how can its stars be used for finding Sirius and Procyon?

Answer: The line of Orion's belt (δ, ε, and ζ Orionis) leads to Sirius. Procyon completes an equilateral triangle with Sirius and Betelgeuse in Orion.

(7) How far south must we be in order to view Canopus, Crux, and the Large Magellanic Cloud (Map 6)?

Answer: At least as far south as latitudes 37°, 30°, and 21° N., respectively.

1·30. The Planetarium is a remarkably successful device for showing a replica of the heavens indoors where many people may view it. The word *planetarium* refers either to the projection apparatus or to the structure that houses it. The Adler Planetarium in Chicago, opened to the public in 1930, first employed apparatus of the Zeiss type in America. Others of this type now in operation in the United States are the Fels Planetarium in Philadelphia, the Griffith Observatory in Los Angeles, the American Museum–Hayden Planetarium in New York, the Buhl Planetarium in Pittsburgh, and the Morehead Planetarium at the University of North Carolina.

Fig. 1·30. The Charles Hayden Planetarium, Science Museum, Boston. The stars in this composite picture have been added by an artist.

The Morrison Planetarium in San Francisco has a somewhat similar apparatus. The Charles Hayden Planetarium in Boston has a Korkosz instrument.

The larger Spitz planetariums, model B, are comparable in size and effectiveness with the other large installations; one of these is at the U.S. Air Force Academy, Colorado Springs. For all the large planetariums the domes that represent the sky are 60 to 80 feet in diameter.

More than 100 smaller Spitz planetariums are employed for instruction in astronomy in colleges and museums in this country. Many of these as well as the larger ones are listed occasionally in the periodical *Sky and Telescope* with the hours when the demonstrations are scheduled.

REVIEW QUESTIONS

1. What are the longitude and latitude of the place where you are? Define these terms.

2. State the azimuth and altitude of a star in each of the following places: (a) Directly in the northeast and halfway from horizon to zenith; (b) at the south point of the horizon; (c) directly in the west and 30° from the zenith.

3. Name the celestial circle or coordinate corresponding to each of the following definitions:

(a) The vertical circle that is also an hour circle.
(b) The sun's apparent annual path.
(c) The circle 90° from the north celestial pole.
(d) Angular distance measured westward from the celestial meridian along the celestial equator.
(e) Angular distance measured eastward from the vernal equinox along the celestial equator.

4. State the right ascension and declination of the vernal equinox; summer solstice; autumnal equinox; winter solstice. Locate these points in the maps and give their positions relative to the constellations.

5. From what places on the earth are the following situations true?

(a) Diurnal circles of the stars are parallel to the horizon.
(b) South celestial pole is 30° above the horizon.
(c) All stars rise and set.
(d) The sun passes through the zenith once a year.
(e) All stars north of declination 50° N. are circumpolar.

6. Which of the following stars never set, never rise, or rise and set at your latitude: γ Draconis (Map 1), Arcturus (Map 3), Capella (Map 5), Canopus and Achernar (Map 6)?

7. Name six bright stars not mentioned in Question 6 and the constellation containing each.

8. Describe the characteristic geometrical figures formed by the prominent stars of the constellations Ursa Major, Leo, Boötes, Cygnus, Pegasus, and Orion.

9. Name a constellation that is near your zenith in the evening at each of the four seasons. During what month is each one nearly overhead at 9 P.M. standard time?

10. On what date is Deneb (α Cygni) at upper transit at 9 P.M. standard time? At 7 P.M.? What is its distance then from your zenith?

11. Orion and Auriga (Map 5) cross the celestial meridian at the same time. Do they also rise and set at the same time? Explain.

12. Find in an astronomical almanac the right ascensions and declinations of the sun, moon, and bright planets for a particular date and locate these objects in the maps with reference to the constellations.

REFERENCES

Allen, Richard H., *Star-Names and Their Meanings,* 1899.

Baker, Robert H., *Introducing the Constellations.* Revised edition. The Viking Press, New York, 1957.

Norton, Arthur P., *A Star Atlas.* Fourteenth edition. Also the simpler *Popular Star Atlas.* Sky Publishing Corporation, Cambridge, Mass.

Russell, H. N., R. S. Dugan, and J. Q. Stewart, *Astronomy.* Two volumes; vol. 1 revised in 1945. Ginn and Company, Boston, 1938.

Shapley, Harlow, editor, *Source Book in Astronomy.* Harvard University Press, Cambridge, 1960.

Shaw, R. William, and Samuel L. Boothroyd, *Manual of Astronomy.* A guide to observation and laboratory interpretation in elementary astronomy. Third edition. F. S. Crofts and Co., New York, 1947.

2

THE EARTH IN MOTION

THE EARTH — THE EARTH'S ROTATION — THE EARTH'S
REVOLUTION — THE EARTH'S PRECESSION — THE
SEASONS

The earth is a globe of rock about 7900 miles in diameter, which
is slightly flattened at the poles and bulged at the equator. Its
irregular surface is 70 per cent covered with water, and it is en-
veloped by an atmosphere to a height of several hundred miles. In
addition to principal features of the earth itself, three motions of
the earth and some of their consequences are described in this chapter. These are: (1) the earth's daily rotation on its axis; (2) the
earth's annual revolution around the sun; (3) the earth's precession,
which resembles the gyration of a spinning top.

THE EARTH

2·1. The Earth's Globular Form. If the earth were a perfect sphere,
after mountains and depressions are smoothed, all meridians would
be circles, so that 1° of latitude would have the same value in statute
miles wherever the degree is measured. Because the latitude of a
place (1·12) equals the altitude of the north celestial pole at that
place, the length of 1° of latitude is the distance we must go along
the meridian in order to have the pole rise or drop 1°; this distance
may be measured by the appropriate method of surveying and is corrected to average sea level. Many such measurements, usually over
longer arcs, show that 1° of latitude is everywhere nearly equal to
69 statute miles. The results are:

At the equator, latitude 0°, 1° of latitude	=	68.7 miles
At latitude 20°		68.8
40°		69.0
60°		69.2
At the poles, latitude 90°		69.4 miles

The *statute mile,* which is commonly used for measuring land distances, is a unit in which distances are expressed in astronomy. It

equals 5280 feet. The *nautical mile,* employed in marine navigation, is the length of 1′ of a great circle of the earth, regarded as a
sphere for this purpose. It equals 6080 feet.

2·2. The Earth as an Oblate Spheroid. Although the length of a
degree of latitude is everywhere about 69 miles, the steady increase

in its value from the equator
to the poles is significant. The
greater length near the poles
shows that the meridians curve
less rapidly there than at the
equator. The meridians are ellipses, and the earth itself ap-
proximates an oblate spheroid.
The figure is also an ellipsoid
of revolution, generated by the
rotation of an ellipse around its
minor axis, or in this case of a
meridian around the earth's axis.

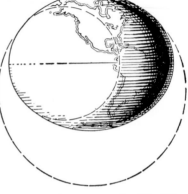

**2·3. Dimensions of the Earth;
Its Oblateness.** The dimensions
of the earth are considered to
be the dimensions of the regular spheroid having a surface

Fig. 2·2. Curvature of a Meridian
at the Pole and Equator. The
greater length of 1° of latitude at
the pole, which is exaggerated in
the diagram, shows that the meridian is there a part of a larger circle.

that most nearly fits the irregular surface of the earth. The dimensions of the *international spheroid* that follow were calculated in
1909 by the U.S. Coast and Geodetic Survey. This remains the
standard spheroid of reference, although later surveys have given
slightly different values. The dimensions of this spheroid are:

> Equatorial diameter = 7926.68 statute miles
> Polar diameter   = 7899.98
> ─────────────────────────────────
> Difference   =   26.70

The longest arc of a meridian ever surveyed extends from Finland
to the southern end of South Africa, a distance of 5777½ nautical
miles. By the calculations of the U.S. Army Map Service from these
data, completed in 1954, the earth's equatorial diameter is found to
be 7926.52 statute miles, so that the circumference at the equator
would be nearly 24,902 miles.

The *oblateness,* or *ellipticity,* of the spheroid is found by dividing the difference between the equatorial and polar diameters by the equatorial diameter. It is the conventional way of denoting the degree of flattening at the poles. The small value of this fraction, $\frac{1}{297}$, for the earth shows that its flattening is slight. If the earth is represented by a globe 18 inches in diameter, the radius at the poles is only a thirty-second of an inch less than the equatorial radius, and the highest mountain is less than an eightieth of an inch above sea level. It has been said that the earth is more nearly spherical than are most of the balls in a bowling alley.

2·4. The Interior of the Earth. The earth's mass is 5.98×10^{27} grams, or 6.6×10^{21} tons. This value is calculated from the acceleration of gravity at the surface by use of an appropriate formula (7·21). Dividing the mass in grams by the volume, which is 1.083×10^{27} cm³, we find that the average density of the earth is $5\frac{1}{2}$ times the density of water. This is one of the few data of observation we have concerning the earth's interior. Other information comes from its transmission of earthquake waves at different depths to distant seismographs.

Aside from its atmosphere and hydrosphere, the earth consists mainly of two parts: the *mantle,* extending 1800 miles below the crust, and the *core.* The *crust* is the relatively thin layer from the solid surface to the mantle. The continental crust has an average thickness of 20 miles, but the subocean crust may be as thin as $2\frac{1}{2}$ miles in some places. The crust is composed of igneous rocks such as granite and basalt, overlain with sedimentary rocks such as sandstone and limestone, all together about three times as dense as water. The mantle is believed to be composed mainly of silicates of magnesium and iron.

The outer 1000 miles of the core behaves like a liquid; it does not transmit earthquake waves of the type resembling light waves. The inner core, 18 times as dense as water and supposedly very hot, is frequently said to consist mainly of nickel-iron such as occurs in many meteorites. This impression goes along with the idea that the heavier materials sank to the bottom when the earth was entirely molten.

Much of the increase in the density of the earth toward its center is caused by increasing compression. Near the center the pressure of the overlying material rises to the order of 50 million pounds to the square inch, or more than 3 million atmospheres. W. H. Ramsey has suggested that the very dense core may not differ

greatly in composition from the regions above it. The higher
density may begin abruptly at the distance from the center where
the pressure becomes great enough to collapse the molecules.

2·5. The Lower Atmosphere.   The earth's atmosphere is a mixture
of gases surrounding the earth's surface to a height of several hundred miles.   From its average pressure of 15 pounds to the square
inch at sea level, the mass of the entire atmosphere is calculated to
be 6×10^{15} tons, or somewhat less than a millionth the mass of the
earth itself.   The air becomes rarefied with increasing altitude so
rapidly that half of it by weight is within $3\frac{1}{2}$ miles from sea level.
The lower atmosphere is divided into two layers: the troposphere
and the stratosphere.

The *troposphere* extends to heights ranging from 10 miles at the
equator to 5 miles at the poles.   It is the region of rising, falling,
and swirling currents, and of clouds that seem too frequently to
obstruct our view of the heavens.   The turbulent air makes the stars
twinkle and often causes serious blurring of the view with the telescope.   Its chief constituents are nitrogen and oxygen in the proportion of 4 parts to 1 by volume, carbon dioxide, and water vapor;
there are other gases in relatively small amounts and dust in variable quantity.   By their strong absorption of infrared radiations,
water vapor and carbon dioxide are especially useful in preventing
rapid escape of heat from the ground.

The *stratosphere* rises above the troposphere to an altitude of 45
miles.   Here the currents are horizontal, and only a little water
vapor remains.   Ozone, having molecules composed of 3 instead of
2 atoms of oxygen, is formed by action of the sun's extreme ultraviolet radiations on ordinary oxygen molecules, mainly in the
lower stratosphere.   The molecules are thereby dissociated into
atoms, which by collision with unaffected oxygen molecules produce ozone.   The ozone is subsequently dissociated by the radiations.   By these and other processes the sun's destructive ultraviolet radiations are attenuated before they can reach the ground.
These radiations are now studied spectroscopically in photographs
from above the absorbing levels of the atmosphere to determine
what information they bring about the sun itself.

The stratosphere contains one fifth of the entire air mass.   To
its upper limit it is still dense enough to make some contribution
to twilight, as is known from the duration of this effect. *Twilight*

is sunlight diffused by the air onto a region of the earth's surface where the sun has already set or has not yet risen. Astronomical twilight ends in the evening and begins in the morning when the sun's center is 18° below the horizon; the fainter stars are then visible overhead in a clear sky. The times of sunset and sunrise and of the end and beginning of astronomical twilight can be found in some of the almanacs for any date and latitude.

2·6. The Upper Atmosphere. The *ionosphere* is the region of the atmosphere that is most affected by impacts of high-frequency radiations and high-speed particles from outside. Here the molecules of the gases are largely reduced to separate atoms, and the atoms themselves are shattered into ions and electrons. The ionosphere is often regarded as the layer between altitudes of 45 and 200 miles, where the ionized gases are more abundant, but the designation may be extended to include the entire upper atmosphere.

Three or more fluctuating ionized (12·6) layers of the upper atmosphere occur at successively higher altitudes. The D layer at the height of 45 to 55 miles is attributed to the sun's Lyman-alpha radiation. The E layer, at 60 to 80 miles, is ionized mainly by X rays from the sun's corona. The F region, at 125 to 150 miles, is attributed to far ultraviolet radiations by helium in the sun. By repeated reflections from these layers and the ground, radio waves longer than 30 meters emitted from the ground can travel considerable distances over the earth before they are dissipated. The shortest of these are reflected from the top layer; they are employed for long-distance communications, which are interrupted when this layer is disturbed during a severe geomagnetic storm. Radio waves having lengths shorter than 30 meters generally penetrate all layers and escape. These also can come through from outside the earth to be received by radio telescopes.

The influx of electrified particles from the sun illuminates the gases of the upper atmosphere in the airglow and the aurora (10·35). In the lower ionosphere the resistance of the denser air to the swift flights of meteors heats these bodies to incandescence, so that they make bright trails across the sky.

2·7. The Earth's Magnetic Field resembles the field of a bar magnet thrust through the earth's center at a considerable angle to the

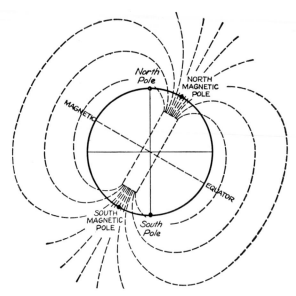

FIG. 2·7. The Earth's Magnetic Field. The axis of the field is inclined to the earth's rotation axis. (*Adapted from a schematic diagram in H. E. White's* Modern College Physics)

axis of rotation. The north *geomagnetic pole,* where the axis of the field intersects the earth's surface, has been located at various points in the Canadian Archipelago around 1200 miles from the north pole of rotation. Soviet scientists report that, in fact, the magnetic meridians run close together across the Arctic Ocean from the Archipelago nearly to the Taimyr Peninsula in Siberia. At any particular place on the earth the direction of the compass needle oscillates, and it becomes especially unsteady during a geomagnetic storm.

Among the achievements of the International Geophysical Year, which began in 1957 and extended through 1958, was the unexpected discovery of a belt of high density of electrified particles encircling the earth. This effect was first reported, in May 1958, by James A. Van Allen of the State University of Iowa from studies with his associates of Geiger counts gathered by artificial satellites.

The *Van Allen radiation belt* has its greatest density in two zones at heights of 2000 and 10,000 miles above the earth's surface and disappears almost completely at 40,000 miles. Charged particles,

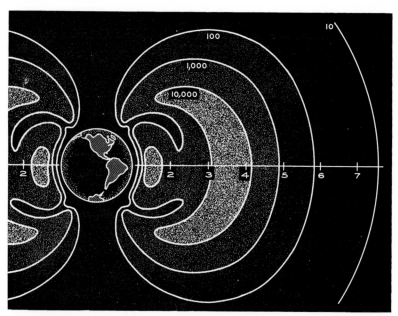

FIG. 2·7A. The Van Allen Radiation Belt. Distances are given in earth-radii. Radiation intensities, represented by the contours, are in Geiger counts per second. This diagram appeared in *Sky and Telescope* for June, 1959.

presumed to be mainly electrons and protons from the sun, are trapped by the earth's magnetic field, where they are believed to spiral rapidly back and forth along lines of force. The belt reaches down toward the earth around two circles 23° from the magnetic poles. Here the particles "slop over," causing the displays of auroras and other effects accompanying geomagnetic storms. Explorations of the earth's field by space craft have been extended to more than 100,000 miles from the earth into the region dominated by the interplanetary magnetic field.

2·8. The Earth as a Celestial Body. Because we live here instead of somewhere else in the planetary system, we do not view the earth in its proper relation to the rest of our community. From the nearest planets the earth would look like a brilliant star moving through the constellations; from Mars it would be a fine evening and morning star. From the outer planets it would be lost in the glare of the sun. From the nearest star all the planets would be

Fig. 2·8. The Earth from an Altitude of 101 Miles. The distance from the curving horizon to the bottom of the picture is 900 miles. The dark area near the top is the Gulf of California. Photographed from a rocket launched in 1947 from White Sands, New Mexico. (*Naval Research Laboratory photograph*)

invisible with the largest telescope, and the sun itself would be only one of the brighter stars.

Through the telescope the observer from a neighboring planet would view the earth as a disk. He would see it marked by bright regions of snowfields and clouds, and by dark areas of water. He could determine the direction and period of the earth's rotation from the movement of surface markings and would note twilight zones between the day and night hemispheres. The observer would probably be unable to detect optical evidence of human life here. He could only consider, as we do for the other planets, whether conditions on the earth seem suitable for people like himself.

Observed from the moon with the unaided eye the earth would appear among the constellations, having a diameter nearly 4 times as great as the moon's apparent diameter in our skies. The photograph from a rocket at the altitude of 101 miles (Fig. 2·8) gives an idea of how the earth would look from the moon through a telescope magnifying 2400 times. It would appear as a globe on which its main features would be visible. As indicated by the Gulf of California at the upper left in the picture, the water areas would contrast clearly with the land.

2·9. Recording Apparatus Above the Earth. The direct probing of space around the earth began effectively in the late 1940's with the launching of single-stage rockets. Among the records recovered after the rockets returned to the ground were photographs of the earth from heights up to more than 100 miles (Fig. 2·8).

The second step was a spectacular feature of the International Geophysical Year. This was the launching by multistage rocket assemblies of vehicles containing apparatus for recording conditions at the higher altitudes and for transmitting the information to radio stations on the ground. The vehicles were given horizontal speeds of about 5 miles a second and were placed thereby in elliptical orbits around the earth as temporary artificial satellites, until they spiraled down into denser atmosphere and were burned up, like meteors. Artificial satellites and other space probes are often designated by the year of their launching followed by a small Greek letter in order of the launchings during that year, or else by the class of craft followed by a Roman numeral.

The first of the artificial earth-satellites was 1957-alpha (Sputnik I) launched by the Russians on October 4, 1957; it went down about January 4, 1958. The first American satellite, 1958-alpha

Fig. 2·9. Trail of the 3rd-Stage Rocket of Artificial Satellite 1957-Alpha in the Vicinity of the Pleiades. A 3-second exposure with a 4-inch camera at 5:13 A.M., C.S.T. on October 19, 1957. The camera vibrated slightly at the beginning of the exposure. (*Photograph by Kenneth M. Yoss and associates, Louisiana State University*)

(Explorer I), was launched on February 1, 1958; its radio became silent on May 23 of that year. The second American satellite, 1958-beta (Vanguard I), continues to return information from its small solar-powered radio.

The third step in the program was the launching of space probes with speeds of nearly 7 miles a second, so that the vehicles could escape from the earth's gravitational field and orbit the sun as artificial planets. The first of these, the Russians' Lunik I, went into orbit on January 2, 1959, and continued radio contact to a distance of 373,000 miles. The second artificial planet was the Americans' Pioneer IV launched on March 3, 1959; it continued radio contact to 410,000 miles. The space probe Lunik II, launched on September 12, 1959, crashlanded on the moon the following day. The probe Lunik III, launched on October 4, 1959, curved part way around the moon and, on October 7 at the distance of 40,000 miles from the moon, made photographs of its far side, which were then transmitted to the earth. The artificial planet 1960-alpha (Pioneer V) was launched on March 11, 1960, into an orbit between those of the earth and Venus. With its greater transmitting power it maintained radio contact until June 26, when its distance from the earth exceeded 22 million miles.

The launchings in 1961 and 1962 of manned vehicles into limited orbits above and around the earth were among the preparations for more extensive human space flights. Early features of the proposed programs are a voyage to the moon and an orbiting astronomical observatory.

THE EARTH'S ROTATION

Rotation is turning on an axis, whereas *revolution* is motion in an orbit. Thus the earth rotates daily and revolves yearly around the sun. The earth rotates from west to east on an axis joining its north and south poles. Among the effects of the rotation are the behavior of the Foucault pendulum, the directions of prevailing winds, the spinning of cyclones, and the oblateness of the earth.

2·10. Absence of Earlier Proof of the Rotation. Although the early Greek scholars cited evidence that the earth is a globe, they believed with few exceptions that it was motionless. As late as the time of Copernicus and in fact beyond it, no convincing proof was available that the earth had any motion at all. The alternation of day and night and the rising and setting of the stars could mean either that the heavens are turning daily from east to west or that the earth is rotating from west to east; but the second interpretation was generally dismissed as unreasonable.

Copernicus favored the earth's rotation because it seemed to him more probable that the smaller earth would be turning rather than the larger celestial sphere. His conviction that the earth also revolves around the sun was likewise unsupported by rigorous proof. In more recent times, many conspicuous effects of the earth's rotation have become known.

2·11. The Foucault Pendulum. A freely swinging pendulum affords a simple and effective demonstration of the earth's rotation. The experiment was first performed for the public by the French physicist J. B. L. Foucault in 1851 under the dome of the Pantheon in Paris. This pendulum consisted of a large iron ball freely suspended from the center of the dome by a wire 200 feet long and set swinging along a line marking the meridian. Those who watched the oscillating pendulum saw its plane turn slowly in the clockwise direction. They were observing in fact the progressive change in the direction of the meridian caused by the earth's rotation under the invariable swing of the pendulum.

The demonstration was widely acclaimed as convincing proof of the earth's rotation, a fact that had not been universally accepted even at that late date. Similar demonstrations are often given today in planetariums, museums, and elsewhere.

The behavior of the Foucault pendulum is most easily understood if we imagine it suspended directly above the pole. A meridian there is turned completely around in a day with respect to the unvarying swing of the pendulum, always toward and away from the same star. In general, the observed deviation of the pendulum

Fig. 2·11. The Foucault Pendulum. (*Drawing by Russell W. Porter*)

from the meridian in 1 hour is 15° times the sine of the latitude. At the pole the rate is 15° an hour. In the latitude of Chicago it is 10° an hour, so that the plane of the swing seems to go around there once in 36 hours. The deviation is clockwise in the northern hemisphere and counterclockwise in the southern hemisphere. At the equator there is no deviation at all, because the meridian also keeps the same direction as the earth rotates.

2·12. Deflection of Objects Moving Horizontally. Because all parts of the earth's surface rotate in the same period, the linear speed of the rotation varies with the latitude; it is greatest at the equator and diminishes toward the poles.

In its flight toward the target, a projectile retains the speed of the eastward rotation at the place from which it started, aside from air resistance. Fired northward in the northern hemisphere, the projectile moves toward a place of slower rotation; it is therefore deflected ahead of, or to the east of, the target. If it is fired southward instead, the projectile moves toward a place of faster rotation; it now falls behind, or to the west of the target. In either event the deflection is to the right when the observer faces in the direction of the flight. If the projectile is fired in the southern hemisphere, the deflection will evidently be to the left.

In general, objects moving horizontally above the earth's surface are deflected to the right in the northern hemisphere and to the left in the southern hemisphere. The deflection is relative to a meridian, which is skewed meanwhile by the earth's rotation. Although this consequence of the rotation is not conspicuous in the case of short-range projectiles, convincing deflections are found in prevailing winds and in cyclones.

2·13. Deflection of Surface Winds. The general circulation of the atmosphere shows the effect of the earth's rotation on the transport of heat from the equatorial to the polar regions. The warmer air near the equator rises and flows toward the poles. Cooled at the higher altitudes, the currents descend, especially around latitudes 30°, and flow over the surface. Thus we have the easterly trade winds of the tropics and the westerlies of the temperate zones (Fig. 2·13) as these currents are deflected by the earth's eastward rotation. In addition, there are easterly surface winds in the polar regions, where the colder air moves toward the equator.

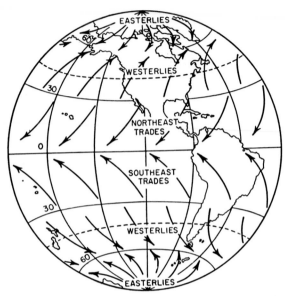

Fɪɢ. 2·13.   Prevailing Surface Winds.   The moving air is deflected to the right in the northern hemisphere and to the left in the southern hemisphere.

By this account the prevailing currents in the mid-latitudes, where the temperature gradients are steepest, are frequently dynamically unstable and break into large eddies.   These are the large-scale cyclonic and anticyclonic vortices of the temperate zones.

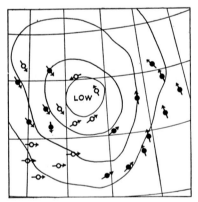

Fɪɢ. 2·14.   A Cyclone in the Northern Hemisphere.   The whirl is counterclockwise.

2·14. Cyclones Show the Deflection Effect.   The *cyclones* of the temperate zones are great vortices in the atmosphere averaging 1500 miles in diameter, which migrate eastward and are likely to bring stormy weather. Marked "low" in the weather map, they are areas of low barometric pressure into which the surface air is moving.   The inflowing currents are deflected like projectiles by the earth's rotation, so that they spiral inward in the counterclockwise direction in the northern hemisphere and clockwise in the southern hemisphere.

Anticyclones, marked "high" in the weather map, are areas from which the surface air is moving. The outflowing currents are deflected by the earth's rotation so that they spiral outward, clockwise in the northern hemisphere and counterclockwise in the southern hemisphere. Thus the vortex motions of cyclones and anticyclones are consequences of the earth's rotation.

This deflection of moving objects relative to the surface of the rotating earth is known as the *Coriolis effect* after the French engineer who first discussed it a century ago. Its importance extends beyond its meteorological consequences. Correction for the effect is required in the control of long-range missiles and in the use of the level bubble, as in the bubble octant employed on a moving plane.

Another effect of the earth's rotation is found in the behavior of the gyrocompass, which brings the axis of its rotor into the plane of the geographical meridian and thus shows the direction of true north. Still another effect is the bulging of the earth's equator.

2·15. Cause of the Earth's Oblateness. The effort of a stone to escape when it is whirled around at the end of a string is an example of the centrifugal tendency of whirling bodies. Similarly, all parts of the rotating earth tend to move away from the earth's axis; the action is greatest at the equator and diminishes to nothing at the poles. This effect at any place may be regarded as the resultant of two effects operating at right angles to each other:

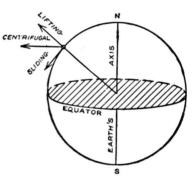

FIG. 2·15. Effect of the Earth's Rotation on a Body at Its Surface. The centrifugal effect directed away from the earth's axis is resolved into two effects at right angles. One diminishes the weight of the body; the other urges it toward the equator.

(1) *The lifting effect* is opposed to the earth's attraction and therefore diminishes the weight of an object at that place. This would cause an object weighed on a spring balance to weigh less at the equator than at the poles by 1 pound in 289 if the earth

were a sphere. The actual reduction in weight is 1 pound in 190. An object at the equator also weighs less than at the poles because it is farther from the center of the earth. Here we have additional evidence of the earth's oblateness.

(2) *The sliding effect* of the earth's rotation is directed along the surface toward the equator. Yet things that are free to move— the water of the oceans, for example—have not assembled around the equator, as they would have done if the earth were a sphere. The centrifugal effect of the earth's rotation has produced enough oblateness of the earth itself to compensate this sliding effect.

2·16. Gravity at the Earth's Surface. *Gravity* is the result of the earth's attraction (gravitation) directed nearly toward its center and diminished by the lifting effect of the earth's rotation. The acceleration of gravity, g, is the rate at which a falling body picks up speed; its value at sea level increases from 32.09 feet/sec² at the equator to 32.26 feet/sec² at the poles. The weight of an object, which equals its mass multiplied by g, is therefore less at the equator than at the poles by 0.17/32.26, or 1 pound in 190.

Values of the acceleration of gravity are precisely determined by timing the swing of a pendulum at different places. For the simple pendulum, $g = 4\pi^2 l/t^2$, where l is the length of the pendulum in centimeters and t is the time in seconds of a complete oscillation.

2·17. The Variation of Latitude. The declination of the zenith of a place on the earth and therefore the latitude of the place (1·12) can be determined with remarkable accuracy by observations of the transits of stars with a photographic zenith telescope. The difference between the latitudes of two widely separated stations can be measured by this means within 0″.01, or about 1 foot on the earth's surface. When the latitudes of two places on opposite sides of the earth are measured repeatedly, the values prove to be continuously varying; if one latitude is increasing at a particular time, the other is decreasing. Because latitude is reckoned from the equator, which is midway between the north and south poles, it follows that the poles are not stationary points on the earth's surface.

By international cooperation the latitudes of stations at about the same distances north and south of the equator and in different longitudes have been determined persistently over the past 60 years.

The records show how the poles have oscillated during that interval. Each pole describes a complex path, which is always confined within an area smaller than that of a baseball diamond.

The wandering of each pole may be resolved mainly into two nearly circular motions. The first, having a period of 12 months and a diameter of about 20 feet, is ascribed to seasonal variations in the distribution of air masses. The second, having a period around 14 months and a diameter that has varied from 10 to 50 feet, has a cause less well agreed upon. The effects of both are slight shiftings of the earth with respect to its axis, which keeps a constant direction in space as far as these are concerned.

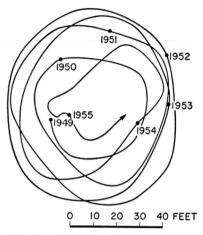

FIG. 2·17. Wandering of the North Pole, 1949 to 1955. The path of the pole on the earth's surface is shown, with its position at the beginning of each year.

There seems to be no possibility of wider migrations of the poles in the past that might account for the marked variations of climates in geologic times.

2·18. Variations in the Earth's Rotation. The earth's rotation has long provided the master clock by which all terrestrial and celestial events have been timed. It has been known for some time, however, that the rate of the rotation is not precisely uniform. This conclusion is based on studies of periodic celestial motions that are independent of the earth's rotation, particularly the monthly revolution of the moon around the earth. If the moon as timed by the earth-clock is forging ahead of its prescribed schedule, the earth is presumably running slow. Periodic variations in the rotation have also been detected with clocks of high precision. The variations in the rate of the earth's rotation are classified as periodic, irregular, and secular.

(1) *Periodic variations* are mainly annual and semiannual; they appear to be caused in large part by winds and tides. The period of the rotation becomes 0s.001 longer in the spring and 0s.001

shorter in the fall than the average for the year. The earth-clock, as compared with crystal-controlled clocks, becomes as much as $0^s.03$ slow in the former season and the same amount fast in the latter.

(2) *Irregular variations.* During the past 200 years, the error of the earth-clock, as determined from studies of the motion of the moon, has accumulated to 30 seconds, first in one direction and then in the other. These variations, according to Dirk Brouwer, are caused by small, cumulative random changes in the rate of the earth's rotation.

(3) *Secular variations.* Moon-raised tides in the oceans and in the earth itself should act as brakes to reduce the speed of the earth's rotation and thus to lengthen the day. Recorded observed times of early eclipses have seemed to show that the earth-clock has run slow by $3\frac{1}{4}$ hours during the past 20 centuries as compared with a clock having a uniform rate.

THE EARTH'S REVOLUTION

2·19. Evidence of the Earth's Revolution. The sun's annual motion among the constellations is not a proof of the earth's revolution around the sun, for by itself it might leave us in doubt as to whether the sun or the earth is moving. With the aid of a telescope, other annually periodic phenomena are observed, which

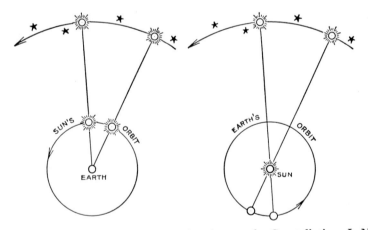

FIG. 2·19. The Sun's Apparent Motion Among the Constellations Is Not a Conclusive Proof of the Earth's Revolution. A similar effect would be observed if the sun revolved around the earth.

provide conclusive evidence of the earth's revolution. Among the effects of this kind are the following.

(1) *The annual parallaxes of the stars* are the periodic changes in the alignments of the nearer stars relative to the more distant ones. This effect, which is described in Chapter 11 in connection with the distances of the stars, is so minute that it was not detected until the year 1837. The failure to observe it had contributed greatly to the persistence of the idea that the earth was stationary, until another effect became known, which serves just as well as a proof of the earth's revolution and is much easier to observe.

(2) *The aberration of starlight* was discovered by the English astronomer James Bradley, in 1727. It is also an annually periodic change in the directions of the stars.

2·20. Aberration of Starlight. Raindrops descending vertically on a calm day strike the face of the pedestrian. Whatever direction he takes, the source of the rain-drops seems to be displaced from overhead in that direction. If he runs instead, the apparent slanting direction of the rain becomes more noticeable; and if he drives rapidly, the direction may seem to be almost horizontal. This is a familiar example of aberration.

Aberration of starlight is the apparent displacement of a star in the direction the earth is moving. The amount of the displacement depends on three factors: (1) It is directly proportional to the speed of the earth. (2) It is inversely proportional to the speed of light.

Fig. 2·20. Aberration of Raindrops. The source of the raindrops is apparently displaced in the direction of the observer's motion. (*Drawing by W. H. Steavenson*)

Whereas the moderate speed of the pedestrian in the rain causes a considerable displacement of the source of the raindrop, very swift movement such as that of the revolving earth is required to produce an appreciable change in the direction of a star. (3) The displacement is greatest when the earth moves at right angles

to the star's direction and becomes zero if the earth moves toward
or away from the star.

If the earth were motionless, there would be no aberration of
starlight. If it had only uniform motion in a straight line, the
displacement of the star would be always the same and might
therefore be unnoticed. If the earth revolves, the changing direction of its motion would cause the star's displacement to change
direction as well, always keeping ahead of us, so that the star would
seem to describe a small orbit. This is precisely what the telescope
shows. The aberration of starlight is convincing evidence of the
earth's revolution around the sun.

2·21. Aberration Orbits of the Stars; the Constant of Aberration.
A star at either pole of the ecliptic has a circular apparent orbit,
because the earth's motion is always perpendicular to the star's
direction. Because the earth's orbit is an ellipse, the true direction
of the star is not precisely at the center of the circle. A star on
the ecliptic oscillates in a straight line. Between the ecliptic and
its poles the aberration orbit is an ellipse. We view these orbits
(Fig. 2·21) flatwise at the ecliptic pole, edgewise on the ecliptic,
and at various angles in between.

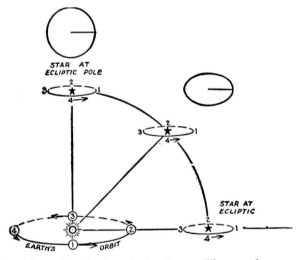

Fig. 2·21. Aberration Orbits of the Stars. The numbers mark corresponding positions of the earth in its orbit and of the stars in their apparent aberration orbits. The outer figures show the observed forms of
the aberration orbits.

The *constant of aberration* is the apparent displacement of a star when the earth is revolving at average speed at right angles to the star's direction. Its value is the same for all stars regardless of their distance or direction; it is the radius of the circle at the ecliptic pole, half the major axis of the ellipse, and half the length of the straight line on the ecliptic. The value of the constant of aberration is about 20″.5. It is nearly 30 times as great for all stars as the parallax effect for even the nearest star and was accordingly the earlier of the two to be detected.

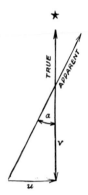

FIG. 2·21A.
Aberration of
Starlight.

The situation is represented by the right triangle of Fig. 2·21A. The side u is the earth's average speed in its orbit, the side V is the speed of light, and the angle a is the aberration constant. The relation is: tan $a = u/V$. If the earth did not revolve, so that u would be zero, a would also be zero. If the light were propagated instantly, so that V would be infinite, a would again be zero. The observed aberration of starlight demonstrates both the earth's revolution and the finite speed of light.

2·22. The Earth's Orbit is an ellipse of small eccentricity with the sun at one focus. It is the path the earth follows in its revolution around the sun and is not to be confused with the ecliptic, the great circle that the sun seems to describe annually on the celestial sphere. The plane of the earth's orbit is also the plane of the ecliptic. Because the orbits of celestial bodies are generally ellipses, the following definitions will be useful here and elsewhere.

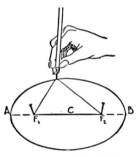

FIG. 2·22. The Ellipse. The sum of the distances from the foci, F_1 and F_2, is constant and equal to the major axis, AB. The eccentricity of the ellipse is the fraction F_1C/AC.

The *ellipse* is a plane curve such that the sum of the distances from any point on its circumference to two points within, the *foci*, is constant and equal to the major axis of the ellipse (Fig. 2·22).

The *eccentricity* of the ellipse is half the distance between the foci divided by half the major axis. It is the conventional way of denoting the degree of flattening of the ellipse. The eccentricity may have any value between 0, when the figure is a circle, and 1, when it becomes a parabola. The eccentricity of the earth's orbit is about 0.017, or $\frac{1}{60}$.

2·23. The Earth's Distance from the Sun. The earth's *mean distance* from the sun is 92,900,000 miles; it is half the length of the

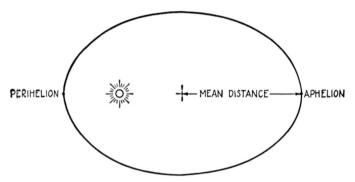

Fig. 2·23. The Earth's Orbit. It is an ellipse of small eccentricity (much exaggerated in the diagram), having the sun at one focus.

major axis of the orbit, or the average between the least and greatest distances from the sun. This distance is known as the *astronomical unit,* because it is frequently taken as the unit in stating the distances of the nearer celestial bodies. The distances of the planets from the sun are given in Table 8·IV in astronomical units as well as in million miles.

Perihelion and *aphelion* are the two points on the earth's orbit respectively nearest and farthest from the sun; they are the extremities of the major axis. The earth is at perihelion early in January, when its distance from the sun is 1.7 per cent, or about 1.5 million miles, less than the mean. It is at aphelion early in July, when its distance is the same amount greater than the mean. The earth is at its mean distance from the sun early in April and October, when it is at the extremities of the minor axis of the orbit.

This preliminary description of the earth's motion relative to the sun neglects effects of the attractions of the earth by neighboring bodies and, of course, the motions of the sun itself.

THE EARTH'S PRECESSION

2·24. Conical Motion of the Earth's Axis. The axis of a spinning top describes the surface of a cone around a line perpendicular to the floor. When it stops spinning, the top falls over. While it continues to spin, the action of gravity does not tip the axis, but

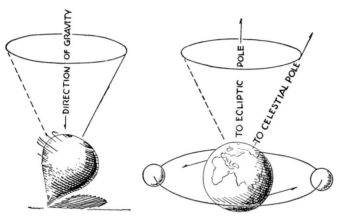

FIG. 2·24. The Earth Resembles a Spinning Top. The effort of the moon, and of the sun, to bring the plane of the earth's equator into the ecliptic plane combines with the earth's rotation to produce the conical precession of the earth's axis.

causes instead the conical motion we observe in the same direction as that of the rotation. This is the precession of the top.

Just as the axis of the spinning top is likely to lean away from the vertical, so the earth's axis is inclined 23½° from the perpendicular to the plane of its orbit, and its equator is inclined to this plane by the same amount. The attractions of the moon and sun, both nearly in the ecliptic plane, for the earth's equatorial bulge tend to bring the equator into the plane of the ecliptic. Because of the earth's rotation, however, the inclination is not much affected. Again, as in the case of the top, there is a conical motion of the axis, but in the opposite direction with respect to the rotation.

The *earth's precession* is a slow conical movement of the earth's axis around a line joining the ecliptic poles, having a period of about 26,000 years.

The effect we are considering is a change in the axis relative to the stars. It is unlike the wandering of the terrestrial poles (2·17), which is caused by a shifting of the earth upon its axis.

2·25. Precessional Paths of the Celestial Poles. The conical movement of the earth's axis causes the celestial poles, toward which

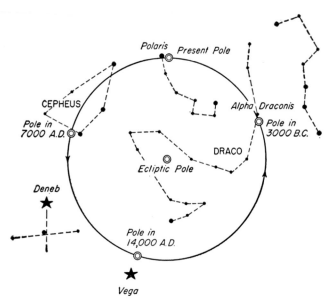

Fɪɢ. 2·25. Precessional Path of the North Celestial Pole. The celestial pole describes a circle of 23½° radius around the ecliptic pole.

the axis is directed, slowly to describe circles around the ecliptic poles; the radii of the two circles are the same and equal to 23½°. This is a movement of the poles among the constellations.

As one faces north, the precessional motion of the north celestial pole is counterclockwise. This pole is now about 1° from the star Polaris, which it will continue to approach until the least distance of slightly less than half a degree is reached, about the year 2100. Thereafter, the diurnal circle of Polaris will grow larger. For those who live in the year 7000, Alpha Cephei will be the nearly invariable pole star, and Polaris will circle daily around it 28° away.

Because the celestial poles are the centers of regions where the stars never set or never rise, the precessional motion shifts the constellations relative to these regions, out of them or into them. The

Southern Cross, which rose and set 6000 years ago throughout the United States, is now visible only from the extreme southern part of this country.

2·26. The General Precession. It is the *lunisolar precession* that has been described. The sun's attraction contributes to this effect as well as the moon's attraction, but in smaller amount. *Planetary precession* is the effect of other planets on the plane of the earth's orbit, so that the ecliptic shifts slowly toward the east along the celestial equator. The result of the two precessions is the *general precession.*

A complete account of precession involves additional factors. Because the inclination of the moon's path to the plane of the earth's equator varies in a period of 18.6 years (5·11), the celestial pole describes a small ellipse in this period around its mean position in the precessional path. The semimajor axis of the ellipse is 9″.2 in the direction of the ecliptic pole. This is the chief term in *nutation,* the nodding of the pole. Thus the precessional path of the celestial pole is irregular; it is not exactly circular and is not precisely the same from one cycle to the next.

2·27. Precession of the Equinoxes. The earth's precession has been defined as a conical movement of the axis. It may also be regarded as a corresponding gyration of the earth's equator and of the celestial equator in the same plane. The celestial equator slides westward on the ecliptic, keeping about the same angle between the

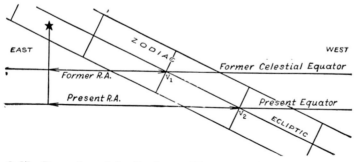

FIG. 2·27. Precession of the Equinox. The westward motion of the vernal equinox, from V_1 to V_2, causes the signs of the zodiac (the 12 equal divisions marked off from the equinox) to shift westward away from the corresponding constellations. Right ascensions and declinations of the stars are altered by precession.

two. The equinoxes, where the two circles intersect, accordingly shift westward along the ecliptic; they move in the general precession at the rate of 50″.26 in celestial longitude in a year. This is the *precession of the equinoxes.*

The annual displacement of the vernal equinox in right ascension is now 46″.09, or 3ˢ.07, and in declination is 20″.05. Thus the equatorial coordinates of the stars on the celestial sphere, which are measured from the vernal equinox, are continuously changing. Accurate catalogs give the right ascensions and declinations of the stars at a stated time and the annual variations of these positions caused by precession as well as by the motions of the stars themselves.

Two other effects of the precession of the vernal equinox are described in the two following sections. These are the displacement of the signs of the zodiac relative to the constellations of the same names and the shortening of the year of the seasons.

2·28. Signs and Constellations of the Zodiac. The *zodiac* is the band of the celestial sphere, 16° in width, through which the ecliptic runs centrally. It contains at all times the sun and moon, and the principal planets, with the exceptions of Venus and Pluto; these two and many asteroids are not confined within its limits.

The *signs of the zodiac* are the 12 equal divisions, each 30° long, which are marked off eastward beginning with the vernal equinox. The signs are named from the 12 *constellations of the zodiac* situated in the respective divisions 2000 years ago. The names of the signs and the seasons in which the sun is passing through them are as follows:

Aries			Libra		
Taurus	}	Spring	Scorpius	}	Autumn
Gemini			Sagittarius		
Cancer			Capricornus		
Leo	}	Summer	Aquarius	}	Winter
Virgo			Pisces		

Because of the precession of the equinoxes, the vernal equinox has moved westward about 30°, and the signs have moved along with it, away from the constellations after which they were named. Thus the signs and constellations of the zodiac of the same names no longer have the same positions. When the sun, on March 21, arrives at the vernal equinox and therefore enters the sign Aries,

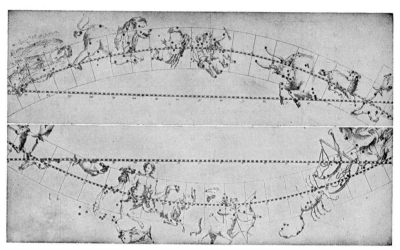

FIG. 2·28.   The Twelve Constellations of the Zodiac.   As described by
Ptolemy about A.D. 150.

it is near the western border of the constellation Pisces and will not
enter the constellation Aries until the latter part of April.

THE SEASONS

2·29. The Year of the Seasons.   The year is the period of the
earth's revolution, or of the sun's apparent motion in the ecliptic.
The kind of year depends on the point in the sky to which the sun's
motion is referred, whether this point is fixed or is itself in motion.
Just as the day in common use is not the true period of the earth's
rotation, so the year of the seasons is not the true period of its
revolution.   Two kinds of year have the greatest use.

The *sidereal year* is the interval of time in which the sun apparently performs a complete revolution with reference to a fixed point
on the celestial sphere.   Its length is $365^d\ 6^h\ 9^m\ 10^s$ ($365^d.25636$) of
mean solar time, which is now increasing at the rate of $0^s.01$ a
century, in addition to any change caused by variations in the rate
of the earth's rotation.   The sidereal year is the true period of the
earth's revolution.

The *tropical year* is the interval between two successive returns
of the sun to the vernal equinox.   Its length is $365^d\ 5^h\ 48^m\ 46^s$
($365^d.24220$) of mean solar time and is now diminishing at the rate
of $0^s.53$ a century.   It is the year of the seasons, the year to which

the calendar conforms as nearly as possible. Because of the westward precession of the equinox, the sun returns to the equinox before it has gone completely around the ecliptic. The year of the seasons is shorter than the sidereal year by the fraction 50″.26/360° of 365.25636 days, or a little more than 20 minutes.

2·30. Cause of the Seasons. Because the earth's equator is inclined 23½° to the plane of its orbit and keeps nearly the same direction

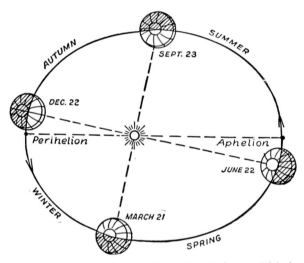

Fig. 2·30. The Seasons in the Northern Hemisphere. This hemisphere is inclined farthest toward the sun at the summer solstice (June 22) and farthest away at the winter solstice (December 22). The earth is nearest the sun early in January.

in space during a complete revolution, each pole is presented to the sun for part of the year and is turned away from it for the remainder of the year. This is the cause of the changing seasons.

The amount of the inclination determines the boundaries of the climatic zones. The *frigid zones* are the regions within 23½° from the poles, in which the sun becomes circumpolar and where the seasons are accordingly extreme. The *torrid zone* has as its boundaries the tropics of Cancer and Capricorn, 23½° from the equator. Here the sun may be overhead at noon; the durations of sunlight and darkness never differ greatly, and temperature changes during the year are not extreme. In the *temperate zones* the sun never appears in the zenith, nor does it become circumpolar, aside from effects of atmospheric refraction (4·3) and the considerable size of the sun's disk.

The inclination of the earth's equator to its orbit causes the sun's annual migration in declination. When the sun is farthest north, at the summer solstice, its altitude at noon is the greatest for our northern latitudes and the duration of sunlight is the longest here for the year. At the winter solstice we have the other extreme, namely, the lowest sun at noon and the shortest duration of sunlight.

2·31. Seasonal Changes in Temperature are produced mainly by differences in the *insolation,* or exposure to sunshine of the regions of the earth's surface. The daily amount of the insolation depends

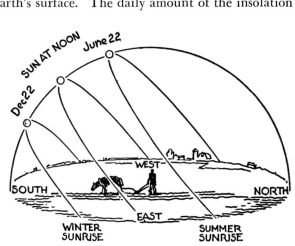

Fig. 2·31. Diurnal Circles of the Sun in Different Seasons. The daily duration of sunshine is longer in the summer, and the sun is higher at noon.

on the intensity of the radiation that is received and the duration of the sunshine.

When the sun is higher in the sky, so that its rays fall more directly on the ground, the radiation is more concentrated. When the sun is lower, so that its rays fall more obliquely, an amount of radiation is spread over more territory and is less effective in heating any part of it. The rays from the lower sun also have to penetrate a greater thickness of the atmosphere and are subject to more absorption. Summer with us is a warmer season than winter because the two factors conspire to produce higher temperatures;

the sun's altitude becomes greater and the daily duration of sun-shine is longer.

At the time of the summer solstice the sun is higher at noon in the latitude of New York than it is at the equator, and it is visible for a longer time, so that the amount of heat delivered in a day is fully 25 per cent greater. Even at the north pole at that time the daily insolation exceeds that at the equator. The uninterrupted radiation from the circumpolar sun compensates its lower altitude; but the temperature is lower at the pole because much of the heat is taken up in the melting of ice.

2·32. Lag of the Seasons. If the temperature depended on insola-tion alone, the warmest days in the United States and Canada should come around June 22 and the coldest part of the winter about December 22. Our experience, however, is that the highest and lowest temperatures of the year are likely to be delayed several weeks after the times of the solstices. The reason is found in the conservation of heat by the earth and its atmospheric blanket.

It is the balance of heat on hand that determines the temperature. As with one's bank balance, the quantity increases as long as the deposits of heat exceed the withdrawals. On June 22 we receive the maximum amount of radiation. Afterward, as the sun moves southward, the receipts grow less, but for a time they exceed the amounts the earth returns into space. As soon as the rate of heating falls below the rate of cooling, the temperature begins to drop. In the winter the sun's altitude at noon and the daily duration of sunshine increase after December 22. It is not until considerably later in the season that the rate of heating overtakes the rate of cooling, so that the temperature begins to rise.

2·33. The Seasons in the Southern Hemisphere differ from those in the northern hemisphere, of course, in that a particular season occurs at the opposite time of year. Another difference might be introduced by the eccentricity of the earth's orbit. Summer in the southern hemisphere begins at the date of the winter solstice, which is only a little while before the earth arrives at perihelion, nearest the sun. It might be supposed that the southern summer would be warmer than the northern summer, which begins when the earth is near aphelion, and similarly that the southern winter would be colder than the northern winter.

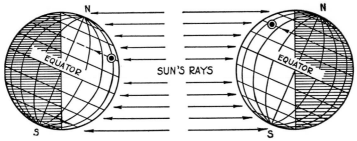

Fig. 2·33. Corresponding Seasons in the Two Hemispheres Occur at Opposite Times of the Year. Northern summer is represented at the left and southern summer at the right.

The earth's distance from the sun at perihelion, however, is only about 3 per cent less than the distance at aphelion; and the slightly greater extremes of temperature that might otherwise be experienced in the southern hemisphere are modified by the greater extent of the oceans in that hemisphere. It will be noted later that the conditions that might produce more extreme temperatures in our southern hemisphere are repeated in the case of the planet Mars. There the effect is observable owing to the greater eccentricity of that planet's orbit.

Review Questions

1. How does the increase in the length of 1° of latitude from the equator to the poles demonstrate the earth's oblateness?

2. State two characteristics of the troposphere; stratosphere; upper atmosphere.

3. How could an observer on the moon detect the earth's atmosphere? the earth's seasonal changes?

4. Describe the behavior of the Foucault pendulum at the north pole and at the equator.

5. What are the means of observing the variable rate of the earth's rotation? State three types of variation and the cause assigned to each.

6. Explain that the aberration of starlight demonstrates both the earth's revolution and the finite speed of light.

7. The precession of an ordinary top is in the direction of the rotation, whereas that of the earth is in the contrary direction. Account for the difference as a consequence of the difference in one of the factors involved.

8. Distinguish between the earth's precessional motion and the motion that causes the variation of latitude.

9. Account for the difference in length between the tropical and the sidereal year.

10. Why is our weather warmer in summer than in winter?

11. Explain that the boundaries between the earth's climatic zones are determined by the inclination of the ecliptic to the equator.

12. Name the term that is defined by each of the following:

(a) The earth's daily turning on its axis.
(b) The displacement of a star in the direction of the earth's motion.
(c) The point in its orbit where the earth is nearest the sun.
(d) The earth's mean distance from the sun.
(e) The twelve equal divisions of the zodiac.

REFERENCES

Jeffries, Harold, *The Earth*. Its origin, history, and physical constitution. Third edition. Cambridge University Press, New York, 1952.

Kuiper, Gerard P., editor, *The Earth as a Planet*. University of Chicago Press, Chicago, 1955.

Mount Stromlo Observatory, Australia.

3

TIMEKEEPING

THE TIME OF DAY – THE CALENDAR

The natural units of time that we find most suitable for our activities are provided by two motions of the earth. The day is the period of the earth's rotation, or of the resulting apparent rotation of the heavens; it is divided arbitrarily into smaller units: the hour, minute, and second. The year is the period of the earth's revolution around the sun; it is divided naturally into the four seasons. The two main units and some arbitrary ones are combined conventionally in the calendar.

The standard time of day in common use is more readily explained if we first consider the kinds of time of day the astronomers read from the clock in the sky in order to derive the correct standard time.

THE TIME OF DAY

3·1. Time Reckoning. Two features on the face of a clock are required for showing the time of day: first, a time reckoner, the hour hand; second, a reference line, the line joining the noon mark to the center of the dial. The angle between the hour hand and the reference line, when it is converted from degrees to hours and minutes, denotes the time of day. Divisions and numerals around the dial are added for convenience, and interpolating devices, the minute and second hands, add accuracy to the reading of the time. In the ordinary clock the hour hand goes around twice instead of once in a day, as it does in the case of the celestial clock.

To observe the time of day from the master clock in the sky, a point on the celestial sphere is chosen as the *time reckoner*. The part of the hour circle joining that point to the celestial pole may be regarded as the hour hand; it circles westward around the pole once in a day. The *reference line* is the observer's celestial meridian.

It is *noon* when the time reckoner is at upper transit (1·11), and *midnight* when it is at lower transit of the meridian. A *day* is the interval between two successive upper or lower transits by the time

reckoner. *Time of day* is either the hour angle of the time reckoner
if the day begins at noon (which is true of the sidereal day), or it is
the hour angle of the time reckoner plus 12 hours if the day begins
at midnight. These definitions apply to any kind of local time.

The three time reckoners in use are the vernal equinox, the
apparent sun, and the mean sun. The corresponding kinds of time
are sidereal time, apparent solar time, and mean solar time.

3·2. The Sidereal Day Is Shorter Than the Solar Day. In the upper
position of the earth, in Fig. 3·2, it is both sidereal and solar noon
about March 21 for the observer at *0*. The vernal equinox and the

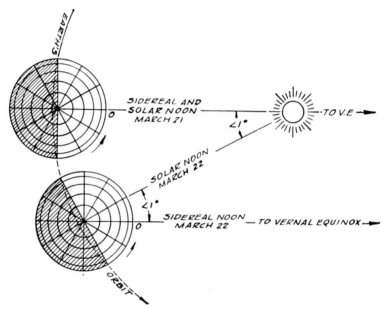

FIG. 3·2. The Sidereal Day Is Shorter than the Solar Day. Because it is
also revolving around the sun, the earth must rotate farther after completing the sidereal day before the solar day is ended.

sun are both at upper transit over his meridian. By the time the
earth has made a complete rotation relative to the equinox, so that
this meridian is very nearly parallel to its original direction, the
earth in its revolution around the sun has moved to its lower position
in the diagram. In the new position it is sidereal noon of the
following day; the vernal equinox on the remote celestial sphere
is again at upper transit, so that the sidereal day is completed.

Because of its revolution, however, the earth must rotate still farther before the solar day is ended.

Now the angle through which the earth revolves in 1 day averages 360°/365.25, or a little less than 1°. It is evident from the figure that this is also the angle through which the earth must rotate after completing the sidereal day before the ending of the solar day. Because the earth rotates at the rate of 15° an hour, or 1° in 4 minutes, the sidereal day is about 4 minutes shorter than the solar day.

More exactly, the difference is $3^m 55^s.909$, so that the length of the sidereal day is $23^h 56^m 4^s.091$ of mean solar time. Owing to the precession of the equinox (2·27), the sidereal day is slightly shorter than the true period of the earth's rotation, which is $23^h 56^m 4^s.099$ of mean solar time.

3·3. Sidereal Time is the local hour angle of the vernal equinox and might have been more correctly called equinoctial time. The sidereal day begins with the upper transit of the equinox and is reckoned through 24 hours to the next upper transit. Sidereal time agrees with our solar time about September 21. It gains on solar time thereafter at the rate of $3^m 56^s$ a day, which accumulates to 2 hours in a month and to a whole day in the course of a year. Evidently the earth rotates once more in a year than the number of solar days in the year.

By our watches a star rises, or crosses the celestial meridian, 4 minutes earlier from night to night, or 2 hours earlier from month to month. Thus a star that rises at 10 o'clock in the evening on November 1 will rise at 8 o'clock on December 1. The westward march of the constellations with the advancing seasons (1·17) is caused by the difference in length between the sidereal and the solar day.

3·4. Determining the Sidereal Time. Sidereal time is kept in the observatories by sidereal clocks, which run about 4 minutes fast of ordinary clocks in the course of a day. The sidereal clocks at the Naval Observatory and elsewhere are corrected frequently by observations of stars. Corrections are required not only for errors in the running of the clocks themselves, but also because of unpredictable irregularities in the earth's rotation. When the correct sidereal time is known, the corresponding standard time clocks may be kept right as well.

Sidereal time is determined by observing transits of stars across the celestial meridian. The rule employed, which can be verified by reference to Fig. 3·4, is as follows: The sidereal time at any instant equals the right ascension of a star that is at upper transit at that instant. In order to apply the rule it is necessary to know precisely when the star is at upper transit. This can be observed by means of a meridian transit instrument.

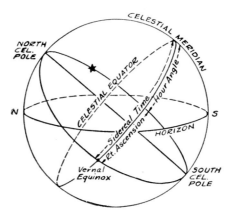

FIG. 3·4. Relation Between the Sidereal Time and the Right Ascension and Hour Angle of a Star. Sidereal time equals the right ascension of a star plus its hour angle. When the star is at upper transit (hour angle zero), the sidereal time equals the star's right ascension.

The *meridian transit instrument* in its simplest form is a rather small telescope mounted on a single horizontal axis, which is set east and west so that the telescope may be pointed only along the observer's celestial meridian. Having directed the telescope to the place where the star will soon transit, the observer looks into the eyepiece and watches the star move toward the middle of the field of view. A vertical wire through the middle of the field marks the celestial meridian. At the instant that the star's image is bisected by the wire, the reading of the sidereal clock is recorded.

Suppose that the clock reading is $6^h 40^m 17^s.2$ and that the star's right ascension is given in an almanac as $6^h 40^m 15^s.7$. The clock is accordingly $1^s.5$ fast, because at the instant of its upper transit the star's right ascension is the correct sidereal time.

Recording devices are employed to time the transits of stars more accurately than can be done by visual observations. The *photographic zenith tube* (Fig. 3·4B) has replaced the simple transit instru-

ment at the Naval Observatory and in other places. This is a fixed
vertical telescope, with which the stars are photographed as they
cross the celestial meridian nearly overhead. The cone of starlight
from the objective is reflected from a mercury surface before coming
to focus on a small photographic plate below the lens. With this

FIG. 3·4A. A Transit Instrument of the Naval Observatory. Formerly
employed for correcting the clocks, it is now replaced for this purpose by
the 8-inch photographic zenith tube.

instrument an error of only about $0^s.003$ is obtained in a time
determination from a set of 18 stars.

3·5. Apparent Solar Time. Although sidereal time is suited to
certain activities of the observatories, it is not useful for civil purposes, because our daily affairs are governed by the sun and not by
the vernal equinox. Sidereal noon, for example, comes at night
during part of the year.

The *apparent sun* is the sun we see. The local hour angle of its
center plus 12 hours is the *apparent solar time,* or simply, apparent
time. The apparent solar day begins at apparent midnight and is

FIG. 3·4B.   The 8-inch Photographic Zenith Tube at the U. S. Naval Observatory.   (*Official U. S. Navy photograph*)

reckoned through 24 hours continuously.   However, the sun itself is not a uniform timekeeper; it runs fast or slow of a regular schedule, at times nearly half a minute a day.   The sundial is the only timepiece adapted to the sun's erratic behavior.   The lengths of the apparent solar day as recorded by ordinary clocks at four different times in the year are about as follows:

Jan. 1	24^h	0^m	29^s
Apr. 1	23	59	42
July 1	24	0	12
Oct. 1	23	59	41

Two factors contribute chiefly to the irregularity in the length of the apparent solar day: (1) The variable speed of the earth's revolution, because of the eccentricity of its orbit; and (2) the inclination of the ecliptic to the celestial equator. We are not considering here the further irregularity caused by variations in the rate of the earth's rotation.

3·6. Effect of the Earth's Variable Revolution. Because the earth's orbit is an ellipse, the speed of the earth in its revolution around the sun is not uniform. The closer it is to the sun, the faster the

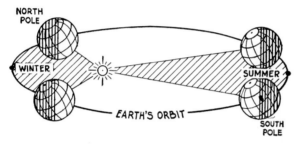

FIG. 3·6. The Earth's Variable Revolution. Since, by Kepler's law of areas, the line joining the earth and sun sweeps over the same area every day, the earth must revolve farther in a day when it is nearer the sun.

earth revolves. This relation is expressed precisely as a particular case of Kepler's law of areas (7·15): The line joining the earth to the sun sweeps over equal areas in equal intervals of time.

When the earth is near perihelion, early in January, it revolves farthest in a day. Because the difference in length between the solar day and the more nearly constant sidereal day depends on the daily progress of the earth's orbital motion (3·2), apparent solar days would then have the maximum length. When the earth is near aphelion, early in July, it makes the smallest advance in its orbit in a day. Apparent solar days would then have the minimum length if this were the only cause of their variation.

This effect can also be considered by shifting the attention from the earth's revolution around the sun to the consequent apparent motion of the sun along the ecliptic. It is this motion that delays the sun's return to the meridian from day to day. The farther the earth revolves in a day, the greater is the sun's displacement along the ecliptic and the greater for this reason would be the length of the apparent solar day.

3·7. Effect of the Obliquity of the Ecliptic. Even if the sun's motion in the ecliptic were uniform, the length of the apparent solar day would still be variable, because the ecliptic is inclined to the celestial equator. It is the projection of the sun's eastward motion upon the celestial equator that determines the delay in completing the apparent solar day.

At the equinoxes, a considerable part of the sun's motion in the ecliptic is north or south, which does not delay the sun's return. At the solstices, where the ecliptic is parallel to the equator, the entire motion is eastward; moreover, the hour circles are closer together here. Therefore, as far as the obliquity of the ecliptic is concerned, apparent solar days would be shortest at the equinoxes and longest at the solstices. Both factors act to make the apparent day longest in winter.

3·8. Mean Solar Time. The *mean solar day,* as its name implies, is the average apparent solar day; its length varied slightly because the earth's rotation is not precisely uniform (2·18). The mean solar day is the interval between two successive upper or lower transits of the mean sun. The *mean sun* is an imaginary point that moves eastward in the celestial equator, completing its circuit of the heavens in the same period as that of the apparent sun in the ecliptic. *Mean solar time* is time by the mean sun. The mean solar second, which is 1/86,400 part of the mean solar day, was formerly the basic unit for all measurements of time.

Mean solar time is reckoned from the beginning of the day at local midnight through 24 hours to the following midnight. The local mean time at a particular place is 12 hours plus the local hour angle of the mean sun. The present usage was adopted in 1925 for astronomical reckoning, which had previously begun the day at noon.

Mean time is commonly reckoned in two 12-hour divisions of the day with the designations A.M. and P.M., but the preference for its continuous reckoning through 24 hours is found in various places. In astronomical practice, 6:30 P.M., is often recorded as $18^h 30^m$, and in the operation of ships and airplanes as 1830.

3·9. The Equation of Time is the difference at any instant between apparent and mean solar time; it is the difference between the hour angles of the apparent and mean sun. Four times a year the two agree. At other times the apparent sun is either fast or slow in the westward diurnal motion. Early in November the sundial is more than a quarter of an hour ahead of local mean time. Table 3·I gives the value of the equation of time at midnight at Green-

TABLE 3·I   EQUATION OF TIME

(Apparent time faster or slower than local mean time)

Jan. 1	3^m 8^s	slow	July 1	3^m 30^s	slow
Feb. 1	13 32	slow	Aug. 1	6 18	slow
Mar. 1	12 40	slow	Sept. 1	0 20	slow
Apr. 1	4 16	slow	Oct. 1	9 57	fast
May 1	2 48	fast	Nov. 1	16 20	fast
June 1	2 28	fast	Dec. 1	11 21	fast

wich on the first of each month in 1955 or, very nearly, in any other year.

The rapid change in the equation of time near the beginning of the year has an effect that can be noticed by everyone. At this time of year the earth is nearest the sun and is accordingly revolving fastest. The sun is then moving eastward along the ecliptic fastest, delaying its rising and setting as timed by the mean sun. For this reason the sun does not begin to rise earlier in the morning by our watches until about 2 weeks after the date of the winter solstice, although it begins to set later in the evening 2 weeks before that date.

3·10. Universal Time and Ephemeris Time. *Universal time* is the local mean solar time at the meridian of Greenwich; it is based on the earth's rotation. This is the kind of time in ordinary use and will remain so, because the observatory clocks that distribute this time will continue to be corrected for irregularities in the earth's rotation by frequent sights on the stars. For the foretelling of celestial events, however, the irregular rate of the rotation makes it impossible to predict with very high precision what the universal times of these events will be.

Beginning with the issues for the year 1960, the *American Ephem-*

eris and Nautical Almanac and the British *Astronomical Ephemeris,* which now conform in other respects as well, tabulate the fundamental positions of the sun, moon, and planets at intervals of ephemeris time.

Ephemeris time runs on uniformly; its constant arbitrary unit equals the length of the tropical year at the beginning of the year 1900 divided by 31,556,925.9747, which was the number of seconds and fraction in the year at that epoch. This invariable unit of time is adopted as the fundamental unit by the International Committee of Weights and Measures. Corrections for converting ephemeris time are determined frequently by observing the universal times when certain celestial bodies arrive at positions in the sky predicted on ephemeris time. In actual practice, observations of the moon's positions among the stars (5·12) seem to be the most suitable. In the present century, ephemeris time has been gaining on universal time and in 1960 was ahead by 35 seconds.

3·11. Atomic Time. The household electric clock is a familiar example of the replacement of the pendulum by a more dependable control of the rate. In this case it is the 60-cycle alternating current of the power-generating station. Greater reliability is attained in the quartz-crystal clock, and a still closer approach is being accomplished by successive forms of atomic clocks.

In the quartz-crystal clock now in use in observatories, a quartz crystal controls the frequency of an electronic oscillator, imposing its natural frequency of vibration on the current. By 1950, this clock had become reliable enough to determine periodic terms in the earth's variable rotation. The rate of the quartz-crystal clock, however, speeds up gradually with age.

As an example of atomic clocks, the cesium-controlled clock employs the frequency provided by the precession of the spinning magnetized atoms of cesium gas to correct slight irregularities in the vibration of the quartz crystal. Cesium frequency standards have developed high precision. It remains to be determined by observation whether the scales of atomic and gravitational time are the same.

3·12. Difference of Local Time Equals Difference of Longitude. In any one of the three kinds of local time, a day of 24 hours is completed when the earth has made one rotation, through 360°, relative to the point in the sky that serves as the time reckoner.

Twenty-four hours of that kind of time equal 360° or 24 hours of longitude on the earth; and there is a difference of 15° or 1 hour between the local times of two places that differ by 15° or 1 hour in longitude.

Thus the difference of local times of the same kind between two places equals the difference of their longitudes. Transposed, this is the basis of longitude determinations.

When the local time at one place is given and the corresponding

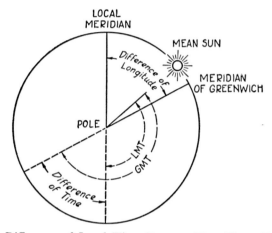

FIG. 3·12.   Difference of Local Time Between Two Places Equals Their Difference of Longitude.

local time at another place is required, add the difference of their longitudes if the second place is east of the first; subtract if it is west.   In Fig. 3·12, the observer is in longitude 60° W., or 4ʰ W. The local mean time (LMT) is 9ʰ, and the Greenwich mean time (GMT), or universal time, is 13ʰ, so that the difference of 4 hours equals the difference between the observer's longitude and that of Greenwich.

3·13. Zone Time.   Because difference of local time equals difference of longitude, local mean time becomes progressively later with increasing distance east of us and earlier west of us.   The inconvenience of continually resetting our watches as we travel east or west is avoided by the use of zone time at sea and standard time on land.   These are conventional forms of mean time.

Standard meridians are marked on the earth at intervals of 15°

or 1 hour in both directions from the meridian of Greenwich. The local mean time of the standard meridian is the time to be kept at sea by timepieces in the entire zone within $7\frac{1}{2}°$ east and west of that meridian if the plan is followed. *Zone time* for any place is accordingly the local mean time of the standard meridian nearest the place. Thus the earth is divided into 24 zones, in which the

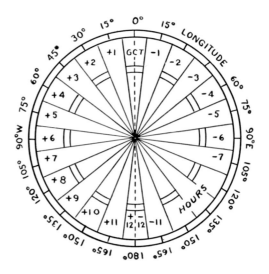

Fig. 3·13. Time Zone Diagram. The numbers outside the circle are the longitudes of the standard meridians. The numbers inside are the corrections in hours from zone time to universal time.

time differs from universal time by whole hours. There are certain exceptions to the rule; a time zone is occasionally modified near land to correspond with the time kept ashore.

3·14. Standard Time on land conforms in a general way with zone time at sea, but its divisions are less uniform. The boundaries of the standard time zones have been determined by local preference and may be altered by legislative action, subject in the United States to approval by the Interstate Commerce Commission. Moreover, the plan is not completely adopted in all parts of the world; the legal times in certain land areas differ from those in adjacent divisions by a fraction of an hour. There is also the frequently arbitrary and nonuniform practice of setting the clocks ahead of the accepted standard time for part of the year. All time divisions are shown in the U.S. Hydrographic Office Time Zone Chart of the World, from which Fig. 3·14 is taken.

Fig. 3·14.   Time Zone Chart of North America.   The large numbers at the top are corrections in hours to universal time.   (*Adapted from H. O. 5192, U.S. Navy Hydrograph Office*)

Four standard times are employed in the greater parts of the United States and Canada, namely, Eastern, Central, Mountain, and Pacific standard times; they are respectively the local mean times of the meridians 75°, 90°, 105°, and 120° west of the Greenwich meridian and are therefore 5, 6, 7, and 8 hours slow as compared with universal time. Newfoundland standard time is 3½ instead of 4 hours slow. Yukon standard time is 9 hours slow, and Alaska standard time is 10 hours slow of universal time.

Certain changes for Canada are shown in the Dominion Operations Map of 1958. Apart from Quebec, Ontario, and the Northwest Territories, each division of Canada has adopted a single standard time.

3·15. The International Date Line. In successive time zones west of the zone including Greenwich, the time becomes progressively earlier than universal time. In successive zones east of the Greenwich zone the time becomes later. Finally, in the zone including the 180° meridian the western half differs by a whole day from the eastern half. The rule for ships and for airplanes over the ocean is to change the date at the 180° meridian. At the westward crossing of this meridian the date is advanced a day, and at the eastward crossing it is set back a day. Thus if the eastward crossing is made on Tuesday, June 7, the date becomes Monday, June 6.

For the land areas in this vicinity the boundary between the earlier and later dates is the *international date line*. This line departs in places from the 180° meridian so as not to divide politically associated areas; it bends to the east of the 180° meridian around Siberia and to the west around the Aleutian Islands.

3·16. Radio Time Service. Time signals based on Naval Observatory time determinations are transmitted from 4 naval radio stations and 2 stations of the National Bureau of Standards. The signals are seconds of universal time, corrected for predicted seasonal variations in the speed of the earth's rotation.

The naval radio stations at Annapolis (NSS) and elsewhere trans-

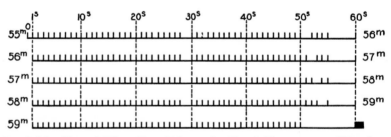

FIG. 3·16. Plan of Time Signals from the Naval Observatory. The short lines represent the seconds signals; these are omitted at the 29th second and before the beginning of each minute.

mit the time signals during the last 5 minutes preceding hours scheduled in the Appendix to *U.S. Naval Observatory Circular Number 49* (1954). The schedule is subject to change. The signals are on a variety of frequencies and represent the seconds beats of the crystal-controlled transmitting clock. These are on continuous waves and can be heard only with receivers suited to code reception. The signals are omitted at certain seconds (Fig. 3·16) so that the listener can readily identify the minute and second of each signal. The beginning of a long dash following the longest break announces the precise beginning of the hour.

The seconds signals from the standard frequency station WWV at Beltsville, Maryland, are transmitted continuously day and night on frequencies of 2.5, 5, 10, 15, 20, and 25 mc. They are heard as clicks superposed on standard audio frequencies; they employ modulated waves and can therefore be heard with ordinary shortwave radiophone receivers. The seconds clicks are interrupted at the 59th second of each minute. At 2 minutes before the beginning of the hour and at each multiple of 5 minutes thereafter, the audio tone is interrupted for exactly 2 minutes for the purpose of making announcements.

The Dominion Observatory at Ottawa supplies continuous time service from three different transmitters on frequencies of 3330, 7335, and 14,670 kc, respectively, adjacent to the amateur bands. The seconds signals are omitted each minute on the 29th second and from the 51st to the 59th second inclusive, when a voice announcement of the time is given. More than 60 broadcast stations across Canada transmit the Dominion Observatory time signal at 1 P.M., EST each day. These are examples of the distribution of the correct time by observatories in various parts of the world.

THE CALENDAR

Calendars have been employed since the beginnings of civilizations as registers on which to record past events and to predict future ones that occur regularly. They have undertaken to combine two or three natural measures of time, the solar day, the lunar month, and the year of the seasons, in the most convenient ways; and they have frequently encountered difficulties, because these measures do not fit evenly one into another. Calendars have generally been of 3 types: the lunar, the lunisolar, and the solar calendar.

3·17. Calendars of Three Types. (1) *The lunar calendar* is the simplest of the 3 types and was the earliest to be used by almost all nations. Each month began originally with the "new moon," the first appearance for the month of the crescent moon after sunset. Long controlled only by observation of the crescent, this calendar was eventually operated by fixed rules. In the fixed lunar calendar the 12 months of the lunar year are alternately 30 and 29 days long, making 354 days in all and thus having no fixed relation to the year of the seasons. The Mohammedan calendar is a survivor of this type.

(2) *The lunisolar calendar* tries to keep in step with the moon's phases and the seasons and is the most complex of the 3 types. It began by occasionally adding a 13th month to the short lunar year to round out the year of the seasons. The extra month was later inserted by fixed rules. The Jewish calendar is the principal survivor of this type.

(3) *The solar calendar* makes the calendar year conform as nearly as possible to the year of the seasons and neglects the moon's phases; its 12 months are generally longer than the lunar month. Only a few early nations, notably the Egyptians and eventually the Romans, adopted this simple type.

3·18. The Early Roman Calendar dates formally from the traditional founding of Rome in 753 B.C. It was originally a lunar calendar of a sort, beginning in the spring and having 10 months. The names of those months, if we use mainly our own style instead of the Latin, were: March, April, May, June, Quintilis, Sextilis, September, October, November, and December. The years for many centuries thereafter were counted from 753 and were designated A.U.C., in the year of the founding of the City. Two months, January and February, were added later and were eventually placed at the beginning, so that the number months have since then appeared in the calendar out of their proper order.

In the 12-month form the Roman calendar was of the lunisolar type. The day began at midnight instead of at sunset as it did with most early people. An occasional extra month was added to keep the calendar in step with the seasons. The calendar was managed so unwisely, however, by those in authority that it fell into confusion; its dates drifted back into seasons different from the ones they were supposed to represent.

When Julius Caesar became the ruler of Rome, he was disturbed by the bad condition of the calendar and took steps to correct it. He particularly wished to discard the lunisolar form with its troublesome extra months. Caesar was impressed with the simplicity of the solar calendar the Egyptians were using, and he knew of their discovery that the length of the tropical year is very nearly 365¼ days. He accordingly formulated his reform with the advice of the astronomer Sosigenes of Alexandria. In preparation for the new calendar the "year of confusion," 46 B.C., was made 445 days long in order to correct the accumulated error of the old one. The date of the vernal equinox was supposed to have been brought thereby to March 25. The Julian calendar began on January 1, 45 B.C.

3·19. The Julian Calendar was of the solar type, and so neglected the moon's phases. Its chief feature was the adoption of 365¼ days as the average length of the calendar year. This was accomplished conveniently by the plan of leap years. Three common years of 365 days were followed by a fourth year containing 366 days; this *leap year* in our era has a number evenly divisible by 4.

In lengthening the calendar year from 355 days of the old lunisolar plan to the common year of 365 days, Caesar distributed the additional 10 days among the months. With further changes made in the reign of Augustus, the months assumed their present lengths. After Caesar's death, in 44 B.C., the month Quintilis was renamed July in honor of the founder of the new calendar. The month Sextilis was later renamed August in honor of Augustus.

Because its average year of $365^d 6^h$ was $11^m 14^s$ longer than the tropical year, the Julian calendar fell behind with respect to the seasons about 3 days in 400 years. When the council of churchmen convened at Nicaea in A.D. 325, the vernal equinox had fallen back to about March 21. It was at this convention that previous confusion about the date of Easter was ended.

3·20. Easter was originally celebrated by some churches on whatever day the Passover began and, by others, on the Sunday included in the Passover week. The Council of Nicaea decided in favor of the Sunday observance and left it to the church at Alexandria to formulate the rule, which is as follows:

Easter is the first Sunday after the 14th day of the ecclesiastical moon (nearly the full moon) that occurs on or immediately after March 21. Thus if the 14th day of the moon occurs on Sunday,

Easter is observed one week later. Unlike Christmas, Easter is a movable feast because it depends on the moon's phases; its date can range from March 22 to April 25.

DATES OF EASTER SUNDAY

1963, Apr. 14	1968, Apr. 14	1973, Apr. 22
1964, Mar. 29	1969, Apr. 6	1974, Apr. 14
1965, Apr. 18	1970, Mar. 29	1975, Mar. 30
1966, Apr. 10	1971, Apr. 11	1976, Apr. 18
1967, Mar. 26	1972, Apr. 2	1977, Apr. 10

The week of 7 days had been introduced in the Roman calendar in the year 321 by the emperor Constantine. The Christian Era for the recording of dates forward and back from about the time of the birth of Christ is said to have been introduced in the 6th century, but did not replace the Roman plan generally until several centuries later.

3·21. The Gregorian Calendar. As the date of the vernal equinox fell back in the calendar, March 21 and Easter, which is reckoned from it, came later and later in the season. Toward the end of the 16th century the equinox had retreated to March 11. Another reform of the calendar was proposed, formally by Pope Gregory XIII.

Two rather obvious corrections were made in the Gregorian reform. First, 10 days were suppressed from the calendar of that year; the day following October 4, 1582, became October 15 for those who wished to adopt the new plan. The date of the vernal equinox was restored in this way to March 21. The second correction made the average length of the calendar year more nearly equal to the tropical year, so that the calendar would not again get seriously out of step with the seasons. Evidently the thing to do was to omit the 3 days in 400 years by which the Julian calendar year was too long. This was done conveniently by making common years of the century years having numbers not evenly divisible by 400.

Thus the years 1700, 1800, and 1900 became common years of 365 days instead of leap years of 366 days, whereas the year 2000 will remain a leap year as in the former calendar. The average year of the new calendar is still too long by 26 seconds, which is hardly enough to be troublesome for a long time to come.

The Gregorian calendar was gradually adopted, until it is now in use, at least for civil purposes, in practically all nations. England and its colonies including America made the change in 1752. By that time there were 11 days to be suppressed, for that century year was a leap year in the old calendar and a common one in the new calendar. September 2 was followed by September 14. The countries of eastern Europe were the latest to make the change, when the difference had become 13 days.

3·22. Suggested Calendar Reform. Irregularities in our present calendar are frequently cited as reason for reforming it further. The calendar year is not evenly divisible into quarters; the months range in length from 28 to 31 days, and their beginnings and endings occur on all days of the week; the weeks are split between months. Some people believe that the irregularities should be corrected. Others are not sure that the improvement would be great enough to offset the confusion in our records that the change might bring.

Recent proposals for calendar reform are based on the period of 364 days, a number evenly divisible by 4, 7, and also 13, and the addition of two stabilizing days. An extra day might be added each year in such a way as not to disturb the sequence of weekdays, and another might be added every four years in the same manner except in the century years not evenly divisible by 400. Two proposed calendars have been the 13-month perpetual calendar and the 12-month perpetual calendar known as the World Calendar.

The first plan divides the year into 13 months of 28 days each. In this plan a calendar for one month would serve for every other month forever if it is remembered when to add the two stabilizing days. This proposal met with considerable approval for a time, but lost favor because it seemed too drastic a change from the present calendar.

The second plan divides the 364-day period into 12 months. The four equal quarters of the year remain the same forever. Each quarter begins on Sunday and ends on Saturday. Its first month has 31 days, and its second and third months have 30 days each. One stabilizing day is added each year at the end of the fourth quarter; it is called Year-End Day, December Y, and is an extra Saturday. The second extra day is added every fourth year, with the usual exceptions, at the end of the second quarter; it is called Leap-Year Day, June L, and is also an extra Saturday. This plan is a more moderate change from the present calendar. It was disapproved by the United Nations in 1956.

1. Name the term associated with time that is defined by each of the following:

(a) Hour angle of the vernal equinox.
(b) Hour angle of the mean sun plus 12 hours.
(c) Right ascension of a star that is at upper transit.
(d) Difference between apparent and mean solar time.
(e) Meridians spaced 15° apart, beginning with the meridian of Greenwich.

2. Note in Map 1 that the star β Cassiopeiae is nearly on the hour circle of the vernal equinox. (a) Explain that the line from Polaris to this star in Cassiopeia can serve roughly as the hour hand for denoting sidereal time. (b) What is the sidereal time when this hour hand points to the zenith?

3. If a star rises tonight at 9 o'clock by your watch, at what time will it rise tomorrow night? Explain.

4. Why do different groups of constellations appear in the south at the same hour of the evening at the different seasons?

5. Show that days by the sundial are longer in winter than in summer because of the eccentricity of the earth's orbit.

6. State the difference between the time zones employed on land and at sea, and the reason for the difference.

7. Distinguish between universal time and ephemeris time. Why is the latter more satisfactory for the precise prediction of a celestial event?

8. When the zone time is $21^h\ 00^m$ by the ship's clock in longitude 70° W., the universal time is $2^h\ 00^m$ on the following day. Explain.

9. An airplane flying westward is about to cross the international date line at $9^h\ 30^m$ standard time on Friday. State the time and day 10 minutes later when it has crossed the line.

10. The constellation Orion rises at $23^h\ 30^m$ local mean time on September 21. Explain that it rises on October 21 at about $21^h\ 30^m$ local mean time and $23^h\ 30^m$ sidereal time.

11. State (a) the chief feature of the Julian reform of the calendar; (b) two changes made in the Gregorian reform and the reason for each change.

12. State reasons for further reform of the calendar and an objection to any considerable reform.

REFERENCES

The American Ephemeris and Nautical Almanac, The Nautical Almanac, and *The Air Almanac.* Published yearly. Superintendent of Documents, U.S. Government Printing Office, Washington 25, D. C.

4

LIGHT AND THE TELESCOPE

REFRACTION OF LIGHT – DISPERSION OF LIGHT; THE
SPECTRUM – THE REFRACTING TELESCOPE – THE
REFLECTING TELESCOPE – THE RADIO TELESCOPE

The principal feature of the optical telescope is its objective,
which receives the light of a celestial body and focuses the light
to form an image of the object. The image may be formed either
by refraction of the light by a lens or by its reflection from a curved
mirror. Optical telescopes are accordingly of two general types:
refracting telescopes and reflecting telescopes. In the radio telescopes the radiations in radio wavelengths from a celestial source
are collected by an antenna, from which they are conveyed to receiving and recording apparatus.

This chapter begins with some features of light, particularly its
refraction and dispersion into a spectrum.

REFRACTION OF LIGHT

4·1. Light is propagated in waves which emerge from a source such
as a lamp or the sun in something like the way that ripples spread

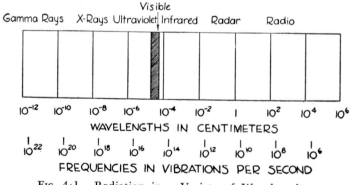

Fig. 4·1. Radiation in a Variety of Wavelengths.

over the surface of a pond when a stone is dropped into the water. When light waves of appropriate lengths enter the eye, they produce the sensation we call light in its different colors from violet to red. The visual effect is caused by a limited range of lengths in the waves that come to us.

Radiation in general emerges from a source in waves of a wide variety of lengths, from gamma rays having billions of wave crests to the inch to radio waves as long as several miles from crest to crest. All radiation has the constant "velocity of light" in empty space.

The *wavelength* of the radiation is the distance between the same phase of successive waves, as from crest to crest. The lengths to which the eye is sensitive range from 4×10^{-5} cm, or about 1/70,000 inch, for extreme violet light to nearly twice that length for the reddest light we can see. The photographic range extends into the ultraviolet and infrared.

The *velocity of light* is about 3×10^{10} cm/sec, or 186,300 miles/ sec. This is the speed in a vacuum. The speed is reduced in a medium such as air or glass, depending on the density of the medium; and in the same medium the reduction is greater for shorter wavelengths than for longer ones.

The *frequency* of the radiation is the number of waves emitted by the source in a second; it equals the velocity of light divided by the wavelength. Thus the frequency of violet light having a wavelength of 4×10^{-5} cm is 7.5×10^{14} cycles/sec.

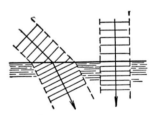

4·2. Refraction of Light. A *ray of light* denotes the direction in which any portion of the wave system is moving. It is often convenient to picture rays of light as radiating in all directions from a source and continuing always in straight lines as long as they remain in the same homogeneous medium. Thus light is said to travel in straight lines.

Fig. 4·2. Refraction of Light. A ray of light passing from a rarer into a denser medium is refracted toward the perpendicular to the boundary between them.

When a ray of light passes from a rarer to a denser medium, as from air into glass, it proceeds through the denser medium with reduced speed. If the ray falls obliquely on the surface of the glass, the part of each wave front on one side of the "ray" enters the glass and has its speed reduced before the other side enters. The front is therefore swung around and the ray changes direction (Fig. 4·2). The parallel lines of the figure represent the progress of the wave after equal intervals of time.

Refraction of light is the change in the direction of a ray of light when it passes from one medium into another of different density. The change is toward the perpendicular to the boundary if the second medium is the denser, and away from the perpendicular if it is the less dense. When the ray enters the second medium at right angles to its surface, there is no refraction, for all parts of the wave front enter and are retarded together.

4·3. Refraction Increases the Altitude of a Star. When a ray of starlight enters the atmosphere, it is refracted downward according

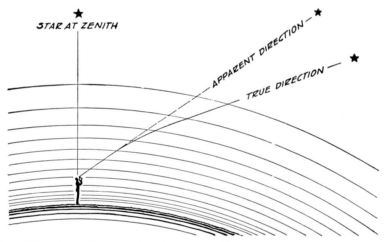

Fig. 4·3. Atmospheric Refraction Increases the Star's Altitude. As the ray of starlight is bent down in passing through the air, the star is apparently elevated. A star in the zenith is not displaced by refraction.

to the rule we have noted; and the bending continues until the earth's surface is reached, because the density of the air increases downward. The point in the sky from which the light appears to come is therefore above the star's true direction. Atmospheric refraction elevates the celestial bodies by amounts which depend on the distance from the zenith. The relations are as follows.

Zenith Distance	Refraction	Zenith Distance	Refraction
0 °	0′00″	85 °	9′45″
20	0 21	86	11 37
40	0 48	87	14 13
60	1 40	88	18 06
70	2 37	89	24 22
80	5 16	90	34 50

These values for average conditions are somewhat altered by varia-tions in the temperature and pressure of the air.

A star directly overhead is not displaced by refraction, because its rays are perpendicular to the atmospheric layers. The amount of the refraction increases as the distance from the zenith increases, but so slowly at first that for considerably more than halfway to the horizon the effect on the star's direction is appreciable only when observed with the telescope. As the horizon is approached, the effect becomes more noticeable. A star at the horizon is raised by refraction more than half a degree, or slightly more than the apparent diameter of the sun, or moon.

4·4. Refraction Effects Near the Horizon. Owing to atmospheric refraction the sun comes fully into view in the morning before any

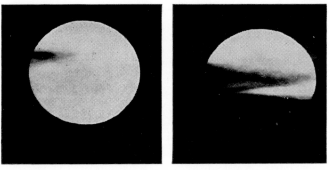

Fig. 4·4.   Apparent Flattening of the Setting Sun by Refraction.   (*Yerkes Observatory photographs*)

part of it would otherwise appear above the horizon, and it remains visible in the evening after it would otherwise have passed below the horizon. Thus refraction lengthens the daily duration of sun-shine. Similarly, the risings of the moon and stars are hastened and their settings are delayed. Refraction also increases by more than half a degree the radius of the region around the north celestial pole where stars never set, and diminishes by the same amount the opposite region where stars never rise (1·15).

Because atmospheric refraction increases with distance from the zenith, the lower edge of the sun's disk is raised more than the upper edge. This apparent vertical contraction becomes noticeable near the horizon, where the amount of the refraction increases most rapidly with increasing zenith distance. Thus the sun near its setting and soon after its rising sometimes appears conspicuously oval.

Another effect near the horizon has no connection with refraction. It is the well-known illusion that the sun, moon, and constellation figures seem magnified there.

4·5. Twinkling of the Stars. The twinkling, or *scintillation,* of the stars, that is, their rapid fluctuations in apparent brightness, results from the turbulence of the atmosphere within a few miles of the earth's surface. Currents differing in temperature and water content cause varying irregularity in the density of the air through which the rays of starlight pass. By variable refraction and especially by reinforcement and interference of different parts of the wave fronts, the starlight comes to us nonuniformly. Alternate fringes of light and shade cross the line of sight with frequencies up to 1000 cycles/sec, according to Geoffrey Keller, and may cause the star to vary by as much as 10 per cent of its average brightness.

The larger planets do not ordinarily twinkle; their steady light distinguishes them from neighboring stars. Similarly, the moon does not twinkle, nor does a street light that is close at hand. Like the moon, these planets are luminous disks, although a telescope is required to show them as such. While each point of the disk may be twinkling, the effects are not synchronized; for the rays take slightly different paths through the air and do not encounter the same irregularities.

Astronomical seeing, referring to the distinctness of the view with the optical telescope, is also affected by the drifting of the recurrent turbulent atmospheric pattern across the incoming beam. If the aperture of the telescope is large relative to the length of the pattern, the image of a celestial object is spread and blurred in "bad seeing," but remains fairly steady. With smaller apertures the image is not greatly enlarged in these conditions, but may shift about somewhat in the field of view.

4·6. Whenever light is refracted, it is separated into its constituent colors. An example is seen in the rainbow, the array of colors from violet to red that is formed when sunlight is refracted by drops of water. Refraction, as we have noted, is caused by the change in the speed of light when it passes from one medium into another of different density. The change in speed is greater as the wavelength of the light is shorter. Thus the amount of the refraction increases with diminishing wavelength. In the visible spectrum

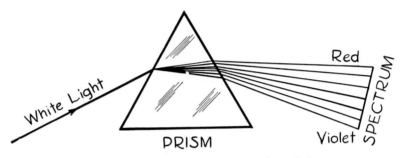

FIG. 4·6. Formation of a Spectrum by a Prism.

violet light is the most changed in direction, red the least, and the other colors intermediate.

Refraction of light is accordingly accompanied by its *dispersion* in order of wavelength into the *spectrum.* The visible spectrum from violet to red comprises only a small part of the whole range of wavelengths radiated by a source such as the sun. The spectrum goes on into the ultraviolet in one direction and into the infrared in the other, where it is recorded by photography and other means.

The *spectroscope* is the instrument with which the spectrum is observed. It is employed in the laboratory and in connection with the telescope.

4·7. The Spectroscope. A familiar type of spectroscope consists of a *prism* of glass, quartz, or other transparent material, toward which a *collimator* and *view telescope* are directed. The light enters the tube of the collimator through a narrow *slit* between the sharpened parallel edges of two metal plates. The slit is at the focus of the collimator lens; after passing through this lens the rays are accordingly parallel as they enter the prism. The light is refracted by the prism and dispersed into a spectrum, which is brought to focus by the objective of the view telescope and magnified by its eyepiece. When the eyepiece is replaced by a plate holder, the view telescope becomes a camera.

If the light is monochromatic, the spectrum is simply the image of the slit in that particular wavelength; if the light is white, that is, composed of all colors, the visible spectrum is a band, violet at one end and red at the other, which is formed by overlapping images of the slit in the different colors. The absence of a certain wavelength in the otherwise continuous spectrum is detected most

FIG. 4·7.   The Spectroscope.   (*Adam Hilger, Ltd.*)

easily when the separate images are so narrow that they overlap as little as possible. This is the reason for the narrow slit.

Thus the spectroscope is an instrument for arraying light in order of wavelength. Bright lines in the spectrum represent the presence of certain wavelengths in the light. Dark lines show the absence of certain wavelengths. Integrated light is like a set of books in many volumes piled in disorder, whereas the spectrum of light is like the set arranged in order on a shelf; if a volume is withdrawn, the vacant space bears witness to the fact.

When the light is bright enough, the scale of the spectrum can be increased by substituting a *grating* for the prism; this is a plate of speculum metal on which many parallel grooves are ruled, perhaps 10,000 or more to the inch. The grating forms spectra by the diffraction of light. Its greatest use in astronomy has been in the study of the sun, where its waste of light as compared with the prism is of no consequence.

4·8. Emission and Absorption Spectra. The spectra of luminous sources are mainly of three types:

The *bright-line spectrum,* or *emission-line spectrum,* is an array of bright lines. The source of the emission is a glowing gas, which radiates in a limited number of wavelengths characteristic of the chemical element of which the gas is composed. Each gaseous element in the same conditions emits its peculiar selection of wave-lengths and can, therefore, be identified by the pattern of lines of its spectrum. The glowing gas of a neon tube, for example, pro-duces a bright-line spectrum.

The *continuous spectrum* is a continuous emission in all wave-lengths. The source is a luminous solid or liquid, or it may be a gas in conditions such that it does not emit selectively. The glow-ing filament of a lamp produces a continuous spectrum. There

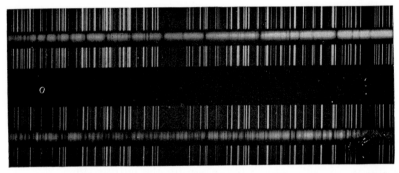

Fig. 4·8. Bright-Line and Dark-Line Spectra. The spectra of Alpha Cygni and Betelgeuse. The bright-line spectrum of luminous iron gas appears for comparison above and below the dark-line spectrum of each star. (*Mount Wilson Observatory photographs*)

may also be emission or absorption continuums (12·7) of limited extent in the spectra of certain gases.

The *dark-line spectrum,* or *absorption-line spectrum,* is a con-tinuous spectrum except where it is interrupted by dark lines. Cooler gas intervenes between the source of the continuous spec-trum and the observer. The intervening gas is opaque to the wave-lengths it emits in the same conditions. The spectrum is therefore the reverse of that of the gas itself; it is a pattern of dark lines, which identifies the composition of the gas. Sunlight, having passed through the atmospheres of both the sun and the earth, produces a dark-line spectrum.

Where the gas consists of molecules such as carbon dioxide or methane, the spectrum shows bands of bright or dark lines charac-teristic of these molecules.

4·9. The Doppler Effect. When the source from which waves are emitted is approaching the observer, the waves are crowded together, so that the wavelengths are diminished. When the source is receding, the waves are spread farther apart, so that their lengths are increased. A familiar example in sound is the lowered pitch of the whistle as a locomotive passes us. The Austrian physicist C. J. Doppler pointed out, in 1842, that a similar effect is required by the wave theory of light.

The wavelengths are shortened when the source of light is approaching the observer and are lengthened when it is receding.

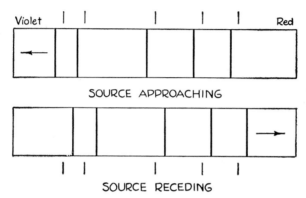

FIG. 4·9. The Doppler Effect. The spectrum lines are displaced to the violet when the source is approaching the observer and to the red when the source is receding from him.

Practically it does not matter whether it is the source or the observer that is moving. The *Doppler effect* as applied to the spectral lines is as follows:

When the source of light is relatively approaching or receding from the observer, the lines in its spectrum are displaced respectively to shorter or longer wavelengths by an amount proportional to the speed of approach or recession.

The amount of displacement of a line in the spectrum is related to the relative speed of approach or recession by the formula:

$$\frac{\text{Change of wavelength}}{\text{Normal wavelength}} = \frac{\text{relative speed}}{\text{speed of light}}.$$

If, for example, the source and observer are relatively approaching at the rate of 18.63 miles per second, the lines in the spectrum of the source are displaced shortward a ten-thousandth of their normal wavelengths.

4·10. Some Uses of Spectrum Analysis. The spectrum of a luminous celestial body gives information as to the physical state of that body. A bright-line spectrum is produced generally by a tenuous gas, and a dark-line spectrum by a gas intervening in the path of the light. The pattern of lines identifies the chemical composition of the gas producing them.

The selective reflection of sunlight for different parts of the spectrum by the surface of a planet may inform us of the nature of the reflecting surface. If a planet has an atmosphere, any dark bands in the spectrum of the reflected sunlight which do not appear in the spectrum of direct sunlight give evidence of the chemical composition of that atmosphere.

The Doppler effect in the spectrum of a celestial body informs us about its motion in the line of sight, whether it is moving relatively toward or away from the earth and how fast it is moving. Other uses of spectrum analysis in astronomy will be noted later.

THE REFRACTING TELESCOPE

4·11. Refraction by Simple Lenses. Lenses are generally of two kinds: converging lenses, which are thicker at the center than at the edge, and diverging lenses, which are thinner at the center.

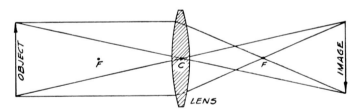

Fig. 4·11. The Convex Lens as an Objective. The lens produces an inverted real image of the object.

An example of the former is the double convex lens, two important uses of which are to form a real image of an object and to serve as a magnifying glass.

The *focal length* of the lens is the distance from the center, *C*, to the *principal focus*, *F* (Fig. 4·11), where rays of light parallel to the optical axis are focused by the lens. When the object is farther from the lens than is the principal focus, the lens produces a real inverted image of the object, which may be shown on a screen or photographic plate. As indicated in the figure, rays passing through the center of a thin lens are unchanged in direction.

When the object is nearer the lens than the position of the principal focus, the eye behind the lens sees an erect and enlarged virtual image of the object (Fig. 4·11A). This is the use of the lens as a magnifier. In combination, two double convex lenses can serve as a simple refracting telescope. The first lens is the *objective* of

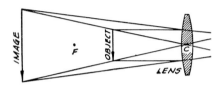

FIG. 4·11A. The Convex Lens as an Eyepiece. It produces an erect and enlarged virtual image.

the telescope, which forms an inverted image of the object. The second lens, the *eyepiece,* placed at the proper distance behind that image, permits the eye to view the object, which now appears magnified and still inverted. Two other lenses may be added at the eye end if it is desired to reinvert the image.

4·12. The Refracting Telescope. The discovery of the principle of the refracting telescope is generally credited to a Dutch spectacle

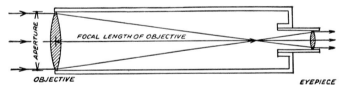

FIG. 4·12. The Simple Refracting Telescope. In its simplest form the refracting telescope consists of two convex lenses separated by a distance equal to the sum of their focal lengths. In modern refracting telescopes both objective and eyepiece are compound lenses.

maker. Galileo, in 1609, was one of the first to apply this principle in the observation of the celestial bodies. Two of his telescopes are preserved intact in the Galileo Museum in Florence, Italy; the larger one, having a paper tube about 4 feet long and less than 2 inches in diameter, magnifies 32 times. The Galilean telescope has a double concave eyepiece. It has the merit of giving an erect image of the object observed, but its field of view is small.

The *simple astronomical telescope,* which is the basis of modern refracting telescopes, contains two double convex lenses at a distance apart equal to the sum of their focal lengths (Fig. 4·12). The objective has the greater *aperture,* or clear diameter, and the longer focal length; it receives the parallel rays from each point of the remote celestial object and forms an inverted image of the object at the principal focus. The eyepiece, set in a sliding tube, serves as a magnifier for viewing the image formed by the objective. As he looks through it, the observer sees an inverted and enlarged image of the celestial object.

The early refracting telescopes proved disappointing, especially when larger ones were constructed. The views of the celestial bodies were blurred. An important cause of the poor definition was the dispersion of light which accompanies its refraction. A single lens focuses the different colors at different distances from the lens, violet light at the least distance and red light farthest away (Fig. 4·13). The image of a star focused in any particular color is confused with out-of-focus images in the other colors. This is *chromatic aberration.*

As long as the telescope contained only single lenses, the only known way to improve the view was to increase the focal length. Toward the end of the 17th century, refracting telescopes as long as 150 and 200 feet were attempted, but they were so unwieldy that not much could be done with them.

4·13. The Achromatic Telescope. The new era of the refracting telescope began, in 1758, with the introduction of the achromatic objective. By an appropriate combination of lenses of different curvatures and compositions it is possible to unite a limited range of wavelengths at the same focus. The objectives of refracting telescopes designed for visual purposes are combinations of two lenses. The upper lens is double convex and of crown glass; the lower lens, either cemented to the upper one or separated by an air space, is likely to be plano-concave and of heavier, flint glass. By the use of two lenses other difficulties inherent in the single spherical lens are compensated as well.

The objective of the visual refracting telescope brings together the yellow and adjacent colors, to which the eye is especially sensitive; but it cannot focus with them the deep red, or the blue and violet light which most strongly affects the ordinary photographic plate. Evidence of this is seen in the purple fringe around the image of the moon. Thus a refracting telescope giving fine definition visually does not by itself produce clear photographs. When the visual refracting telescope is employed as a camera, the plate holder replaces the eyepiece. A correcting lens is introduced before the plate, or else a yellow filter is used to transmit only the sharply focused light to an appropriate type of plate.

The aperture of the objective is usually stated in denoting the size of a telescope. Thus a 12-inch telescope has an objective with

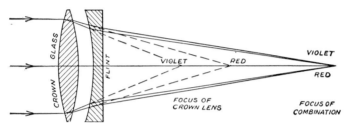

Fig. 4·13. Principle of the Achromatic Objective. The crown lens focuses the different wavelengths at different distances, so that a clear image of a star is not obtained anywhere. The addition of the flint lens increases the focal length and, since it affects the shorter more than the longer wavelengths, brings the different colors to focus more nearly at the same point.

a clear diameter of 12 inches. In ordinary refracting telescopes the ratio of aperture to focal length is about 1 to 15 or more, so that a 12-inch telescope is likely to be about 15 feet long. Refractors designed for photography of large areas of the sky have objectives containing more than two lenses. These permit shorter focal ratios, which increase the diameter of the field and also the speed.

THE REFLECTING TELESCOPE

4·14. Reflection from Curved Mirrors. When a ray of light encounters a polished surface which prevents its further progress in the original direction, the ray bounds back from, or is *reflected* by, the surface. If the mirror is appropriately curved, it forms the image of an object, taking the place of a lens. Consider, for example, a concave spherical mirror (Fig. 4·14), having its center of curvature at C and its principal focus at F. Of an object beyond C the mirror forms an inverted real image, which may be viewed on a screen or with an eyepiece. Thus the mirror can serve as the objective of a telescope.

The mirror has the advantage over the lens of being perfectly achromatic; there is no dispersion when light is reflected. But the spherical mirror, in greater degree than the spherical lens, introduces *spherical aberration;* the focal point is not the same for different zones of the mirror. This effect is seen in the caustic curve formed on the surface of a cup of coffee by light reflected from the sides of the cup. The perfect remedy for spherical aberration is to make the mirror paraboloidal instead of spherical.

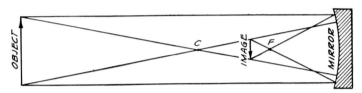

Fig. 4·14. Image Formed by a Concave Mirror. The mirror forms an inverted real image of the object that is beyond the center of curvature.

There are other reasons why the objectives of very large telescopes are mirrors rather than lenses. (1) It is easier to make a disk of glass for a mirror, because the light does not go through the glass. Striae and other defects in the disk, which would render it useless as a lens, do not make it unfit for use as a mirror. (2) The optician has to figure only one surface instead of four. (3) The entire back of the mirror can be supported, whereas the lens is held only at its edge; a large lens may bend slightly under its own weight, affecting its figure and therefore its performance. (4) The focal length of the mirror can conveniently be made shorter than that of the lens (the ratio of aperture to focal length of the mirror is often about 1 to 5 or less), so that the mounting and dome may be smaller, with reduction in the cost of construction.

4·15. The Reflecting Telescope. The objective of the usual type of reflecting telescope is a paraboloidal mirror at the lower end of the tube, which in the largest telescopes is of skeleton construction. The mirror is a circular block of glass having its upper, concave surface coated with a thin film of metal such as aluminum. The light does not pass through the glass, which serves simply to give the required shape to the metal surface. The large mirror reflects the light of the celestial object to focus in the middle of the tube

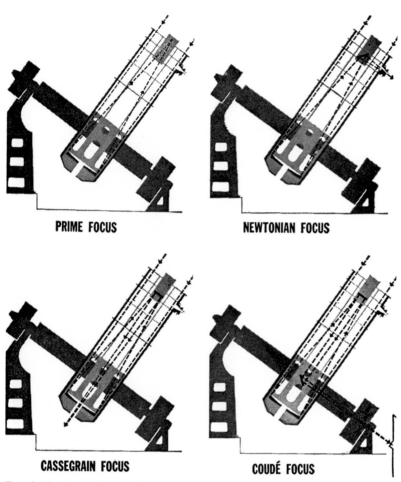

Fig. 4·15.   Four Places of Focus with the Reflecting Telescope.   (1) Prime
Focus.   The focus of the large mirror.   (2) Newtonian Focus.   The converging beam from the large mirror is diverted to the side of the tube by
a small diagonal mirror.   (3) Cassegrain Focus.   The converging beam is
reflected by a small mirror through the central aperture of the large mirror.
(4) Coudé Focus.   The returning beam is diverted by a diagonal mirror
down the polar axis to the spectroscopic room.   (*From* Frontiers in Space
     by permission of Mount Wilson and Palomar Observatories)

near its upper end and may form an image there. Observations
with large telescopes may be made at four different places (Fig. 4·15):

(1) At the *prime focus.* This is generally not easily accessible to
the observer except in the largest telescopes.

(2) At the *Newtonian focus.* A smaller plane mirror at an angle
of 45° near the top of the tube receives the converging beam from

Fig. 4·15A. The Mirror of the 100-inch Telescope of the Mount Wilson
Observatory, After Aluminizing.

the large mirror and reflects it to focus at the side of the tube.
In the visual use the observer looks in at right angles to the direction
of the telescope.

(3) At the *Cassegrain focus.* A small convex hyperboloidal mirror
near the top of the tube reflects the converging beam back through
an opening in the center of the large mirror to focus below it.
The observer then looks in the direction of the star as with the
refracting telescope. The large mirrors of the Mount Wilson telescopes (Fig. 4·15A) have no openings; here the beam returned by
the convex mirror is reflected to focus at the side by a plane mirror
set diagonally in front of the large one.

(4) At the *coudé focus*. The beam returned by the convex mirror is reflected by a small diagonal plane mirror down the polar axis to focus in the laboratory where spectroscopic analysis may be made conveniently.

4·16. The Schmidt Telescope. The type of reflecting telescope described in the preceding section is admirable for viewing and

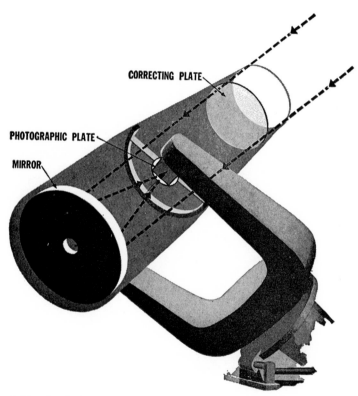

CORRECTING PLATE

PHOTOGRAPHIC PLATE

MIRROR

FIG. 4·16. Optical System of the Schmidt Telescope. The starlight passes through the correcting plate before being reflected by the spherical mirror to focus on the curved photographic plate. (*From* Frontiers in Space *by permission of Mount Wilson and Palomar Observatories*)

photographing limited areas of the heavens. The Schmidt telescope is useful for photographing large areas and is employed only as a camera. It is named after its designer, Bernhard Schmidt, who was an optical worker at the Hamburg Observatory in Germany.

The objective of the Schmidt telescope is a spherical mirror, which is easy to make but is not by itself suitable for a telescope. Parallel light rays reflected by the middle of a spherical mirror are focused

FIG. 4·16A.   The 24-inch Schmidt-Type Telescope, Warner and Swasey Observatory.

farther away from it than are those reflected from its outer zones. The correction is effected by a thin *correcting plate*, set at the center of curvature of the mirror in the upper part of the telescope tube. The correcting plate is so thin in present telescopes that it introduces no appreciable chromatic aberration. It slightly diverges the outer parts of the incoming beam with respect to the middle, so that the entire beam is brought together by the mirror on a somewhat curved focal surface. The photographic plate, suitably curved by springs in the plate holder, faces the mirror between it and the correcting plate. The size of the telescope is denoted by the diameter of the correcting plate.

A large telescope of this kind is the 48-inch Schmidt telescope of the Palomar Observatory. Its 72-inch mirror has a radius of curvature of 20 feet, which is about the length of the tube. The focal length is 10 feet. An initial achievement of this telescope is the National Geographic Society—Palomar Observatory Sky Survey, a photographic atlas of the heavens north of declination 27° S. The atlas consists of 879 pairs of negative prints from blue- and red-sensitive plates, each print 14 inches square and covering an area 7° on a side. The survey reaches stars of the 20th magnitude and exterior galaxies of the 19.5 magnitude.

Other examples of this newer type are the 24-inch Schmidt telescope of the Warner and Swasey Observatory, the similar telescope of the University of Michigan Observatory, the 26-inch telescope of the Astrophysical Observatory of Mexico, the 31½-inch telescope of the Hamburg Observatory, and the 39-inch telescope of the Burakan Observatory in Armenia. The 79-inch reflecting telescope of the German Academy of Sciences, near Jena, has a spherical mirror that can be operated with a 53-inch correcting plate as a Schmidt telescope. Very wide-angle 20-inch Schmidt telescopes having three correcting plates and triaxial mountings have been employed at some stations of the Smithsonian Astrophysical Observatory for tracking space craft.

4·17. The Equatorial Mounting. Most telescopes are mounted so that they can turn on two axes to follow the circles of the equatorial system. The *polar axis* is parallel to the earth's axis and is therefore inclined to the horizontal at an angle equal to the latitude of the place. Around this axis the telescope is turned parallel to the celestial equator, and so along the diurnal circle of the star. The *declination axis* is at right angles to the polar axis; around it the telescope is turned along an hour circle from one declination to another.

Each axis carries a graduated circle. The circle on the polar axis denotes the hour angle of the star toward which the telescope is pointing; and there may be a dial on the pier, from which the right ascension of the star can be read directly. The circle on the declination axis is graduated in degrees of declination. With the aid of these circles the telescope can be quickly pointed toward a celestial object of known right ascension and declination. The telescope is then made to follow that object by driving mechanism, which is operated either mechanically or electrically.

FIG. 4·17.   The 40-inch Refracting Telescope, Yerkes Observatory.

In the standard type of equatorial mounting for refracting telescopes (Fig. 4·17), the polar axis is at the top of a single pier, and the telescope must be reversed frequently from one side of the pier to the other. In the type used for most large reflecting telescopes, the long polar axis is supported by two piers, between which the telescope can swing from the east to the west horizon without reversal. In the fork type the handle of the fork is the polar axis and the two arms of the fork carry the trunnions of the telescope tube.

4·18. Light-Gathering Power. The brightness of the image of a star increases in direct proportion to the area of the telescope objective, or the square of its diameter. This defines the *light-gathering power* of a telescope, aside from loss in the optical parts. Thus a star appears 25 times as bright with the 200-inch telescope as with the 40-inch Yerkes refractor, and a million times as bright as with the naked eye if the aperture of the lens of the eye is taken to be one fifth of an inch.

The telescope shows stars that are too faint to be visible to the eye alone. A larger telescope permits us to see fainter stars than does a smaller one, and extends our view farther into space. Whereas the limit of brightness for the unaided eye is about the 6th magnitude, stars as faint as the 19th magnitude are visible with an eyepiece at the prime focus of the 200-inch telescope; and stars of nearly the 24th magnitude can be detected in photographs made there.

The surface of the daytime sky appears less bright with the telescope than to the eye alone and especially so when higher powers are used. Because the starlight is concentrated by the telescope, the brighter stars and planets are visible with the telescope in the daytime.

4·19. Resolving Power. The image of a star or other point source of radiation is spread by diffraction in the objective of the telescope into a disk surrounded by fainter concentric rings. Two stars which are closer together than the diameter of the brighter part of the diffraction disk cannot be separated by any amount of magnification. This diameter is defined as between points where the intensity of light is one half that at the center of each disk.

The *resolving power* of a telescope, which equals this diameter, is the angular distance between two stars of moderate brightness that can be just separated with the telescope in the best conditions. The least distance, d, in seconds of arc is related to the wavelength, λ, of the light and the aperture, a, of the telescope in the same units by the formula: $d'' = 1.03 \times 206,265'' \times \lambda/a$. For visual telescopes the formula becomes: $d'' = 4''.56/a$, where the wavelength is taken to be about $1/47,000$ inch and the aperture is in inches.

Thus with a 4½-inch telescope the minimum resolvable separation is 1″. It is slightly more than 0″.1 for the large Yerkes and Lick refracting telescopes and is only 0″.023 for the 200-inch telescope on Palomar Mountain. These values are for visual observations. In photographs with all telescopes the least distance for separation of two stars is made greater by the spreading of the images in the photographic emulsions. We note presently how the longer wavelengths employed in radio telescopes affect their resolving power.

Aside from its ability to show fainter objects, a larger telescope has the advantage of better resolving power; it can show finer detail that runs together with the smaller instrument. On the other hand, the blurring of the image by atmospheric turbulence is more pronounced with the larger telescope. In order to profit by its greater resolving power, the site of a large telescope must be chosen carefully with respect to the steadiness of the air at that place.

The correctness of the formula for two stars of equal faintness has been demonstrated by visual observations with telescopes of various apertures. For the eye alone the formula does not hold; it gives the resolving power as about 20″, but the least separation the eye can resolve is several times greater. In fact, the eye is said to be a good one if it can separate the two stars of Epsilon Lyrae, which are 207″ apart. The difference is ascribed to the coarse structure of the retina of the eye.

4·20. The Magnifying Power of a visual telescope is the number of times the telescope increases the apparent diameter of an object as compared with the naked-eye view. It equals the focal length of the objective divided by the focal length of the eyepiece that is used.

The *linear size* of the image of a particular object formed by the objective increases directly with the focal length of the objective. The diameter of the image equals the angular diameter of the object times the focal length of the objective divided by the value of the radian, 57°.3. Thus the diameter of the image of the moon, which has an angular diameter of ½°, formed by an objective of 10-feet focal length is ½° × 120 inches/57°.3, or about 1 inch; this is its size in the photograph when the telescope is used as a camera.

The *angular size* of the image is greater as the eye is nearer it. The least distance of distinct vision for the unaided normal eye is 10 inches. With the eyepiece the eye can be brought closer to the image, which accordingly appears larger. If, for example, the focal length of the objective is 120 inches and that of the eyepiece is ½ inch, the object is magnified 240 times.

A telescope is usually provided with eyepieces of different focal lengths so that the magnification can be varied as desired. There is little gained by using a power greater than 50 times the aperture in inches because of the spreading of the light by magnification; and the higher powers are useful only when the seeing is rather steady. On the other hand, a power less than 3 times the aperture is unsuitable because the beam of light entering the eye is then larger than the widest opening of the lens of the eye at night. Thus with a 10-inch telescope the useful magnifying powers range from 500 down to 30.

Although the sun, moon, and some of the planets appear larger with the telescope, no amount of magnification with most telescopes can show the real disk of a star. This is because the diffraction disk is almost always larger than the angular diameter of the star itself.

4·21. The Telescope as a Camera. Large telescopes and many small ones as well are often employed for photography. The objective becomes the camera lens and the plate holder replaces the eyepiece at the focus. During the time exposure the telescope is turned westward by its driving mechanism to follow the star in the diurnal motion. Any inaccuracies in the following are corrected by slow motion devices, generally operated by the observer, so as to keep a star in the field precisely at the intersection of the cross-wires of the guiding eyepiece.

By cumulative effect of the light during the exposures, the photographs can show features too faint to be visible to the eye at the same telescope. With the addition of a prism or grating they show the spectra of celestial bodies, where there is much information not available in the direct views. The photographs provide permanent records, which the astronomer can observe leisurely and repeatedly so as to increase the accuracy of his results. They are of course valuable to the student of astronomy as well. The reader of this book has before him the prints from many celestial photographs. He can decide for himself as to the correctness of the descriptions and might even find in a photograph a significant feature the astronomer has overlooked.

A limit to the faintness of stars that can be reached by prolonged exposure is set by the light of the night sky. This illumination, caused partly by starlight diffused in the atmosphere and especially by the airglow (10·36), ultimately fogs the photograph seriously. The limiting exposure time for direct photography with fast emulsions with the 200-inch telescope is 30 minutes. The faintest stars

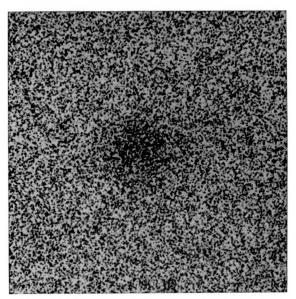

Fig. 4·21. Greatly Magnified Image of a Faint Star. The black specks around the star are grains of the photographic emulsion darkened by the airglow. (*Photograph by William A. Baum, Mount Wilson and Palomar Observatories*)

that can be detected in these photographs are of blue magnitude 23.9, a gain of 5 magnitudes over the visual observations with this telescope.

4·22. Large Optical Telescopes. The 200-inch Hale telescope on Palomar Mountain in California is the largest optical telescope. Next in order of size are the 120-inch telescope of the Lick Observatory on Mount Hamilton, California, the 102-inch telescope of the Crimean Astrophysical Observatory, the 100-inch telescope of the Mount Wilson Observatory in California, the 82-inch telescope of the McDonald Observatory on Mount Locke, Texas, and the 80-inch telescope of the Kitt Peak National Observatory in Arizona.

Half a dozen other telescopes have objectives 6 feet or more in diameter. All are reflecting telescopes.

Refracting telescopes have more moderate apertures. The largest are the 40-inch telescope of the Yerkes Observatory at Williams Bay, Wisconsin, and the 36-inch telescope of the Lick Observatory.

FIG. 4·22. Dome of the 200-inch Telescope, Palomar Observatory. *(Mount Wilson and Palomar Observatories photograph)*

4·23. The 200-inch Telescope on Palomar Mountain is operated by the Mount Wilson and Palomar Observatories. It is named the Hale telescope as a memorial to George E. Hale, who was successively director of the Yerkes and the Mount Wilson Observatory and who had a prominent part in the planning of the Palomar telescope.

The large mirror is a circular disk of Pyrex glass nearly 17 feet in diameter and 27 inches thick, having its concave upper surface coated with aluminum. Its focal length is 55½ feet. The back of the disk is cast in a geometrical rib pattern so that no part of

FIG. 4·23.   The 200-inch Telescope, Palomar Observatory.   (*Drawing by Russell W. Porter*)

the glass is more than 2 inches from the outside air. The telescope tube, 20 feet in diameter, moves in declination within the yoke that forms the polar axis. The skeleton tube, together with the mirror at the lower end and the observer's cage near the upper end, weighs 140 tons. In this cage, 5 feet in diameter, the observer is carried by the telescope as he works at the prime focus—a pioneer feature in telescope construction; the cage obstructs less than 10 per cent of the incoming light. The telescope is housed in a dome 137 feet in diameter.

With the aid of a corrector lens the photographs at the prime focus show in good definition an area of the sky 20′ in diameter, or about 4 inches in diameter on the plate. When the 41-inch convex mirror is set in the converging beam, it reflects the light back through the 40-inch opening in the large mirror to focus below it. The effective focal length is 267 feet at the Cassegrain focus and 510 feet at the coudé focus in the laboratory.

4·24. The 120-inch Telescope of the Lick Observatory resembles the 200-inch telescope in many features of its design. The Pyrex

Fig. 4·24. Dome of the 120-inch Telescope, Lick Observatory.

disk of its mirror also has a ribbed back; it was cast as a trial run for the larger disk and was originally intended for use in testing that mirror. The 120-inch mirror has a focal length of 50 feet; thus the ratio of aperture to focal length is 1 to 5 instead of the ratio of 1 to 3.3 of the Palomar telescope. The scale of the photographs at the prime focus is nearly the same as for the larger telescope, and the light-gathering power is a third as great. There is an observer's cage at the prime focus. The dome is 97 feet in diameter. In both of these domes there is a gallery where visitors may view the telescope through a window without interfering with its operation.

4·25. Possible Improvements in Observing. As long as astronomical observing was almost entirely visual, the long-focus refracting telescope was ideal. Added power was effected by making larger telescopes, culminating in the 40-inch Yerkes refractor. At the beginning of the present century, photography was rapidly replacing visual procedures for many purposes. Photographic refractors were being used with focal ratios around 1 to 5 for added speed and width of field. The new large telescopes were reflectors having about this ratio and operating as well in the infrared as in the ordinary photographic range. The Schmidt telescope with a possible ratio as much as 1 to 1 greatly increased the speed and field.

To increase further the effectiveness of optical observing under our troublesome atmosphere, astronomers are thinking not so much of larger and still more expensive optical telescopes as of ways to improve the reception with present ones. Further improvements may be expected in photographic processes. Photoelectric techniques are developing rapidly. With a successful electronic image converter at its focus, as W. A. Baum has remarked, the 200-inch telescope might reach as far into space as would conventional direct photography with a 2000-inch telescope.

THE RADIO TELESCOPE

Radiations from the Galaxy at radio wavelengths were first detected, in 1932, by K. G. Jansky of the Bell Telephone Laboratories, who was investigating radio noise. In 1936, Grote Reber, an electronic engineer at Wheaton, Illinois, built a paraboloidal antenna 30 feet in diameter for his pioneer radio map of the Milky Way. In England in 1946, radio reception from the sun was announced, the first discrete radio source was discovered, and radar began to be employed extensively in the recording of meteor trails. The only known emission line in the radio spectrum was first observed in America in 1951. By means of this useful line, spiral arms of our galaxy were traced by Dutch astronomers in 1954. These and other results already achieved in this important new branch of astronomy will be noted in later chapters.

4·26. Radio Astronomy is the study of the heavens by use of radio waves. These waves that can come through to the ground range in length from a few millimeters, where they begin to be absorbed by atmospheric molecules, to 20 or 30 meters, where they cannot ordinarily penetrate the ionosphere. Because of their much greater lengths compared with light waves, the radio waves can pass through the clouds of our atmosphere and also through the interstellar dust that conceals all but 5 per cent of the universe from the optical view. Radio reception from the celestial bodies is as effective by day as by night.

Whereas optical spectra of the celestial bodies contain lines, the radio spectrum is almost entirely continuous. The remarkable exception is the line at the wavelength of 21 cm, formed by the neutral hydrogen atom at the ground state. By its Doppler shifts this line provides radio astronomy with means of measuring the velocities of sources in the line of sight.

The observational data in radio astronomy are procured in two ways: (1) from celestial radiations, and (2) by signals transmitted from the earth and reflected back from celestial bodies. An advantage of the second method is that the signals are under the observer's control; a disadvantage is that its application is limited to the nearer bodies of the solar system. The intensity of the reception falls off as the 4th power of the distance of the reflecting body, whereas in the first method it is inversely as the 2nd power of the distance from the source. In addition to echoes of radio signals returned from the moon, reflected beams from Mercury, Venus, Mars, and the sun's corona have been detected, and echoes from meteor trails are frequently recorded.

Cosmic radiations at radio wavelengths arise from two different causes. The first type is *thermal radiation;* its spectrum is that of black-body radiation defined like its optical counterpart by Planck's formula (10·5) for a particular temperature. This kind of radiation is strongest in the centimeter lengths. The second type is *nonthermal radiation,* which may be mainly the sort of radiation emitted by fast-moving particles revolving in the magnetic field of the synchrotron in the radiation laboratory. It is much stronger in the meter wavelengths than in shorter ones, and is separated thereby from the thermal radiation.

4·27. The Radio Telescope is analogous to the optical telescope. Its antenna, like the optical objective, serves to collect the radiations and to concentrate them on the receiver. Instead of an image of the source of radiation, we have here only the strength of the signal collected by the antenna from a particular direction of the sky and recorded by a registering meter. The receiver output may be registered by a moving-chart pen recorder, or else by printed numbers or punches on tape.

An important problem of radio astronomy comes from the low power of the celestial radio source. The total power falling on the entire surface of the earth from the brightest radio source other than the sun is 100 watts, according to F. D. Drake. Of this amount a large radio telescope can collect only about 10^{-14} watts. The problem is to separate the weak radio signal from the noise within the receiver itself, which may be thousands of times greater. An effective solution is by use of a *maser,* for example, a highly refrigerated and magnetized synthetic ruby, to amplify the radio signal relative to the receiver noise.

The antennas of radio telescopes may be either single paraboloids of revolution or else multiple element collectors having a variety of forms.

4·28. The Paraboloidal Type of radio telescope has as its antenna a "dish" of metal sheet or wire mesh, resembling in form the mirror of an optical reflecting telescope. The antenna collects the radio waves from a source and focuses them on a dipole adjusted to the desired wavelength, from which the energy is conveyed to the receiver and meter. The paraboloidal telescope is generally steerable and is usually equatorially mounted. Thus it can be directed to the right ascension and declination of the point of the heavens to be investigated, and it can then be made to follow that point in its diurnal motion.

The University of Manchester in England has a 250-foot telescope at the Jodrell Bank Experimental Station, and the Radiophysics Laboratory in Australia has a 210-foot telescope at a site about 200 miles west of Sydney. Stanford University has a 150-foot telescope with altazimuth mounting. The National Radio Observatory at Green Bank, West Virginia, has a 140-foot steerable telescope and a 300-foot transit-type telescope. The California Institute of Technology operates twin 90-foot paraboloids in Owens Valley about 250 miles north of Pasadena. They are equatorially mounted on flatcars that move on north-south and east-west tracks 1600 feet long from their intersection; these telescopes may be used

FIG. 4·28. The 250-foot Radio Telescope at the Jodrell Bank Experimental Station, University of Manchester. (*Courtesy of A. C. B. Lovell*)

either separately or together as an interferometer giving high resolution. An increasing number of single steerable paraboloids in various parts of the world have diameters between 60 and 90 feet. A 1000-foot fixed bowl designed by Cornell University scientists is being constructed in a natural depression at Areciba, Puerto Rico.

4·29. The Resolving Power of a radio telescope relates to the fineness of detail that can be distinguished. Calculated by the same formula (4·19) as for the optical telescope, it is the angular distance between two radio point sources that can be just separated. This critical distance is directly proportional to the wavelength of the radiation and inversely to the diameter of the antenna in the same units. For this purpose the main beam of the antenna, where its absorption is greatest, is analogous to the diffraction disk of the optical telescope.

Because it works with much longer wavelengths, the paraboloidal radio telescope is far less effective in separating detail than is an optical objective of the same diameter. Thus the critical separation for a 50-foot paraboloid at the wavelength of 21 cm is about 48', compared with the theoretical separation of 0".023 for visual light with the 200-inch Hale telescope. The radio resolution can be improved by employing larger telescopes and shorter wavelengths, or by interferometer methods promoted in a number of different ways.

4·30. Multiple Element Radio Telescopes. Interferometer devices enhance the collecting and resolving powers of radio telescopes at relatively small expense compared with that of increasing the diameters of single paraboloidal antennas. An example of this type is the original radio telescope at the Radio Observatory of Ohio State University, designed and operated by J. D. Kraus and associates (Fig. 4·30). The antenna consists of 96 helices mounted on a steel frame 160 feet long. The frame is pivoted on a horizontal east-west axis so that it may be rotated to face any part of the meridian from the south horizon to the north celestial pole. One accomplishment with this telescope is the radio map of the sky shown in Fig. 17·19.

FIG. 4·30. The 96-Helix Radio Telescope of the Radio Observatory, Ohio State University.

A pioneer example of the multiple element telescope was designed by W. N. Christiansen in Australia for scanning the sun's disk in the centimeter wavelengths. It employs an array of 32 paraboloidal reflectors each 6 feet in diameter, which is spread over a line 713 feet long; the resolution is 1 minute of arc. The classic Mills Cross, designed by B. Y. Mills at Sydney, is a crossed array of dipoles 1500 feet long. The new interferometric telescope of Cambridge University, completed in 1958, has a fixed east-west array of unit parabolas 1450 feet long and a second, moveable aerial at a considerable distance. Multiple element radio telescopes are increasing remarkably in complexity and effectiveness.

REVIEW QUESTIONS

1. Now that we have noted the effect of atmospheric refraction in increasing the altitudes of the stars, it is in order to re-examine some conclusions of Chapter 1. Modify the following statements:

(a) The duration of sunshine is 12 hours on days when the sun is at an equinox.

(b) The polar caps in which the stars never set or never rise have radii equal to the observer's latitude.

(c) The midnight sun is visible only within the arctic and antarctic circles. (State a reason in addition to refraction why this statement is not quite correct.)

(d) As seen from the north pole the celestial equator coincides with the horizon.

2. Describe what occurs when a narrow beam of white light is passed through a glass prism. Suppose that it is monochromatic red light instead.

3. Describe the appearance of: (a) The continuous spectrum; (b) the bright-line spectrum; (c) the dark-line spectrum. What is the nature of the source producing each kind of spectrum?

4. State and explain the effect in the spectrum when the source is approaching or receding from the observer.

5. When two double convex lenses are appropriately separated to form a simple refracting telescope, what does each lens contribute?

6. Why does a single lens as an objective produce a blurred image? How is the definition improved by an achromatic objective?

7. Distinguish between the Schmidt telescope and the ordinary type of reflecting telescope.

8. Why are all very large optical telescopes reflecting telescopes? State the apertures and locations of the three largest optical telescopes.

9. Enumerate some important services of the optical telescope, spectroscope, and photographic plate in studies of the celestial bodies.

10. The following questions are among those asked by visitors in the dome of an observatory. How would you answer them?

(a) How much does this telescope magnify?
(b) Does it magnify stars as well as planets?
(c) How far can you see with the telescope?
(d) How can you point the telescope to a star that is invisible to the naked eye?
(e) Why is this telescope better than a smaller one?

11. Explain that the resolving power of a paraboloidal radio telescope is more limited than that of an optical telescope of equal aperture.

12. Mention some advantages of the radio telescope in studies of the heavens.

PROBLEMS

1. The objective of a 12-inch telescope has a focal length of 15 feet. How much brighter does a star appear through this telescope than to the unaided eye if the aperture of the lens of the eye is one fifth of an inch? Answer: 3600 times.

2. What is the magnifying power of this telescope with an eyepiece of 1-inch focal length? Answer: 180.

3. What is the theoretical resolving power of this telescope? Answer: $0''.38$.

4. What is the diameter of the moon's image as photographed with this telescope? The moon's angular diameter is $0°.5$. Answer: The diameter is slightly more than $1\frac{1}{2}$ inches.

5. A line at the wavelength of 4000 angstroms $(10 \cdot 21)$ in the spectrum of a star is displaced 1 angstrom to the red. Calculate the star's velocity in the line of sight $(11 \cdot 9)$. Answer: 46.6 miles a second, recession.

REFERENCES

Fassero, James S., *Photographic Giants of Palomar*. Drawings by R. W. Porter. Westernlore Press, Los Angeles, 1952.

Ingalls, Albert G., editor, *Amateur Telescope Making, Book 1; Amateur Telescope Making, Advanced; Amateur Telescope Making, Book 3*. Scientific American, New York.

King, Henry C., *The History of the Telescope*. Sky Publishing Corporation, Harvard Observatory, Cambridge, 1955.

Kuiper, Gerard P., and Barbara M. Middlehurst, editors, *Telescopes*. University of Chicago Press, Chicago, 1960.

Miczaika, G. R., and William M. Sinton, *Tools of the Astronomer*. Harvard University Press, Cambridge, 1961.

Mount Wilson and Palomar Observatories, *Frontiers in Space*. The Bookstore, California Institute of Technology, Pasadena.

Wright, Helen, *Palomar*. The Macmillan Company, New York, 1952.

5

THE MOON

MOTIONS OF THE MOON – THE MOON'S SURFACE
FEATURES – THE TIDES

The earth is accompanied in its revolution around the sun by
its single satellite, the moon, which is 2160 miles in diameter, or
a little more than one fourth the earth's diameter. Although it
ranks only sixth in size among the satellites of the solar system,
the moon is larger and more massive in comparison with the earth
than is any other satellite with respect to its primary. The earth-
moon system has more nearly the characteristic of a double planet.

MOTIONS OF THE MOON

5·1. Revolution of the Earth and Moon Around the Sun. The
earth's revolution around the sun has been hitherto described without reference to the influence of the moon. Because the earth and

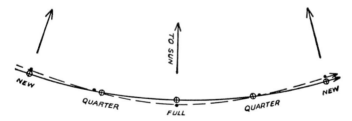

Fig. 5·1. Orbits of the Earth and Moon Around the Sun.

moon mutually revolve around a common center between them
once in nearly a month while they are making the annual journey
around the sun, the orbit of each one relative to the sun is slightly
wavy. What we have called the "earth's orbit" is strictly the orbit
of the center of mass of the earth-moon system. Imagine the earth
and moon joined by a stout rod between their centers; the *center
of mass* is the point of support of the rod for which the two would
balance.

If the earth and moon were equally massive, the center of mass would be halfway between their centers. Very slight shifts in the directions of the nearest planets during the month have revealed that the center of mass is in fact only 2900 miles from the earth's center toward the moon and is, therefore, within the earth. Evidently the moon is much the lighter of the two. A simple calculation shows that its mass is a little less than $\frac{1}{80}$ of the earth's mass.

Astronomical diagrams are often unable to keep the same scale of distances throughout, or of distances and sizes of the celestial bodies. If the distance between the earth and sun in Fig. 5·1 were made equal to the length of the printed page, the distance between the earth and moon on that scale would scarcely exceed the diameter of a period on the page. A drawing exactly to scale would show that the annual orbits of both the earth and moon are always concave to the sun.

5·2. The Moon's Orbit Relative to the Earth. The moon's revolution may be considered in three ways: (1) Its annual motion around the sun, which is disturbed by the attraction of the earth; (2) its monthly motion around the center of mass of the earth and moon, in which the sun is the chief disturbing factor; or what amounts to nearly the same effect in this case: (3) its monthly motion with respect to the earth's center. It is this relative motion with which we are especially concerned. The *orbit of the moon,* for most purposes, is its path around the earth; it is an ellipse of small eccentricity, 0.055, having the earth's center at one focus.

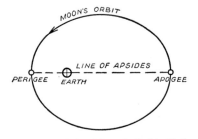

The moon's speed in this orbit averages somewhat more than half a mile a second. By the law of equal areas (3·6), which

Fig. 5·2. The Moon's Orbit Relative to the Earth. The orbit is an ellipse of small eccentricity (much exaggerated in the diagram) with the earth at one focus.

applies to all revolving celestial bodies, the speed is greatest at *perigee,* where the moon is nearest the earth, and is least at *apogee,* farthest from the earth. The major axis, or *line of apsides,* revolves eastward once in about 9 years. This is one of the many variations in the moon's orbit that arise mainly from the influence of the sun. The size of the orbit has been determined by measuring the moon's parallax.

5·3. Parallax; Relation to Distance. *Parallax* is the difference in direction of an object as viewed from two places, or from the two ends of a base line. As an example of the parallax effect we may note the shifting of a nearby object against a distant background

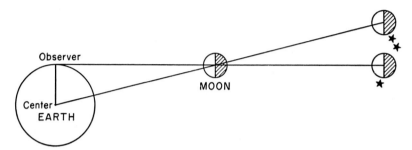

FIG. 5·3. The Moon's Geocentric Parallax. The horizontal parallax is about twice the moon's apparent diameter.

when the eyes are covered alternately. For the same base line the parallax becomes smaller as the distance of the object is increased. When the parallax of an object is measured, its distance may be calculated by the following relation:

$$\text{Distance} = \frac{\text{length of base line}}{\text{sine of parallax}},$$

supposing that the direction of the object is perpendicular to the base line as seen from one end of that line.

Here we have a means of measuring the distances of inaccessible objects such as the celestial bodies. The parallax of the relatively nearby moon can be determined by simultaneous observations of its positions among the stars from two places on the earth a known distance apart. Whatever stations are used, the observed parallax is standardized by calculating from it the parallax that would have resulted if the base line had been the earth's equatorial radius and the moon had been on the horizon. This equatorial horizontal parallax is regarded as the *parallax* of the moon.

5·4. The Moon's Distance. The parallax of the moon at its mean distance from the earth is 57′ 2″.7. By the preceding formula the mean distance between the centers of the earth and moon is 238,857 miles. This value is about 60¼ times the earth's equatorial radius. The distance at any particular time may differ considerably from the average because of the eccentricity of the moon's orbit and of variations in it. The distance at perigee may be as small as 221,463 miles and at apogee may be as great as 252,710 miles.

The moon's distance from us as light travels is 1.28 light seconds; this is the distance in miles divided by 186,300 miles a second, the

Fig. 5·4. Tower of Evans Signal Laboratory, Wall Township, New Jersey. Radar contact with the moon was first made here, in 1946. (*Photograph by U.S. Army Signal Corps Engineering Laboratories*)

speed of light. In 1946, the U.S. Army Signal Corps beamed radar pulses toward the moon (Fig. 5·4) and received the echo of each pulse 2.56 seconds after it was sent out. This pioneer experiment has been repeated frequently. Naval Research Laboratory scientists in 1957 measured the two-way travel times of 60,000 pulses of 10-cm radio waves reflected from the moon. They found for the moon's mean center-to-center distance from the earth 238,-855.95 miles with an uncertainty of 0.75 mile. This value is in close agreement with the distance found by triangulation.

5·5. Aspects of the Moon. In its monthly revolution around us the moon moves continuously eastward relative to the sun's place in the sky. The moon's *elongation* at a particular time is its angular distance from the sun. Special positions receive distinctive names and are known as the *aspects* of the moon.

When the moon overtakes the sun, generally passing it a little to the north or south, the elongation is not far from 0°. The moon is in *conjunction* with the sun when the two bodies have the same celestial longitude. It is in *quadrature* when its elongation is 90° either east or west. The moon is in *opposition* when its celestial longitude differs by 180° from that of the sun, so that its elongation is not far from 180°.

Aspects of the planets relative to the sun are similarly reckoned. For the conjunctions of the planets with the moon and with one another, however, the predictions in the Diary of the *American Ephemeris and Nautical Almanac* are the times to the nearest hour when the two bodies have the same right ascension.

5·6. The Moon's Phases. The changing figures of the waxing and waning moon are among the most conspicuous of celestial phenomena and were among the first to be understood. The moon is a dark globe shining only by reflected light. As it revolves around the earth, its sunlit hemisphere is presented to us in successively increasing or diminishing amounts. These are the *phases* of the moon.

It is the *new moon* that passes between the sun and the earth, and its dark hemisphere is toward us. The moon is invisible at this phase except when it happens to cross directly in front of the sun's disk, causing an eclipse of the sun. On the second evening after the new phase the thin *crescent* moon is likely to be seen in the west after sundown; this was the signal for the beginning of the new month in the early lunar calendars. The crescent becomes thicker night after night, until at the *first quarter* the sunrise line runs straight across the disk. Then comes the *gibbous* phase as the bulging sunrise line gives the moon a lopsided appearance. Finally, a round *full moon* is seen rising in the east at about nightfall.

The phases are repeated thereafter in reverse order as the sunset line moves across the disk; these are gibbous, *last quarter,* and new again. The moon's *age* is the interval at any time since the preceding new moon.

The *terminator* is the line between the bright and dark hemispheres of the moon; it is the line of the sunrise before the time
of the full moon and of the sunset thereafter. Aside from irregularities in its course, which are caused by the mountainous character
of the lunar surface and are often noticed without the telescope,
the terminator generally appears elliptical, because it is a circle
seen in projection. The full circle coincides with the edge of the
moon at the full phase, whereas at the quarter phases it is turned
so that it runs straight across the disk.

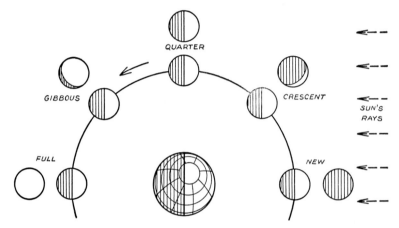

Fig. 5·6. The Phases of the Moon. The outer figures show the phases as
seen from the earth.

The horns, or *cusps,* of the crescent moon point away from the
sun and show nearly the course of the ecliptic in the moon's vicinity.
Thus the positions of the thin crescent near moonset and moonrise
depend on the angle then between the ecliptic and horizon (1·19).
It is left to the reader to explain why the horns are more nearly
vertical after sunset in the spring than in the autumn, as viewed in
our latitudes.

5·7. Earthlight on the Moon. When the moon is in the crescent
phase, the rest of its disk is made visible by sunlight reflected by
the earth. The brighter crescent seems to have a greater diameter
than the earthlit part of the disk and so to be wrapped around it.
This illusion of the difference in scale between the two parts becomes
more striking as the quarter phase is approached, although by this
time the earthlight has faded almost to invisibility.

FIG. 5·7. Earthlight on the Moon. The planet Saturn appears near the moon. (*Yerkes Observatory photograph*)

The earth exhibits the whole cycle of phases in the lunar sky, and these are supplementary to the moon's phases in our skies. "Full earth" occurs there at the time of the new moon. Full earthlight on the moon is many times as bright as is the light of the full moon on the earth. The earth is not only a larger mirror to reflect the sunshine, but it is also a more efficient one because of its atmosphere and clouds.

Earthlight on the moon is bluer than the direct sunlight, for much of the earthlight is selectively reflected by our atmosphere, and in this light the blue of the sky appears.

5·8. The Sidereal and the Synodic Month. Astronomically, the month is the period of the moon's revolution around the earth.

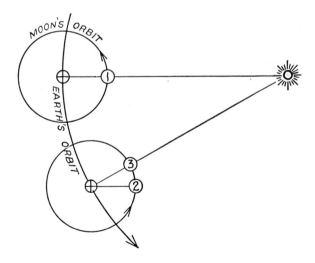

FIG. 5·8. The Synodic Month Is Longer than the Sidereal Month. Between positions 1 and 2 the moon has made one revolution, completing the sidereal month. The synodic month does not end until the moon has reached position 3.

As in the cases of the day and year the different kinds of month depend on the different points in the sky to which the motion is referred. The *sidereal month* is the true period of the moon's revolution; it is the interval between two successive conjunctions of the moon's center with the same star, as seen from the center of the earth. Its length averages $27^d 7^h 43^m 11^s.5$, or nearly $27\frac{1}{3}$ days, and varies as much as 7 hours because of perturbations of the moon's motion.

The *synodic month* is the interval between successive conjunctions of the moon and sun, from new moon to new moon again. This month of the phases is longer than the sidereal month by more than 2 days, the additional time the moon requires to overtake again the slower-moving sun. The length of the synodic month averages $29^d 12^h 44^m 2^s.9$, or a little more than $29\frac{1}{2}$ days, and varies more than half a day.

The moon's eastward progress among the constellations in 1 day averages 360° divided by the length of the sidereal month, which equals 13°.2. The moon's motion in 1 hour is accordingly a little more than half a degree, or slightly more than its own diameter.

5·9. The Moon Rises Later from Day to Day. When the eastward motion is considered, as we have just now done, the moon overtakes the sun at intervals of the synodic month. With respect to the diurnal motion of the heavens, however, the moon keeps falling behind the sun, so that it returns to upper transit 28.5 times in 29.5 solar days. The interval between upper transits is 29.5/28.5 times 24 hours, or about $24^h 50^m$ of mean solar time. Thus the moon crosses the celestial meridian about 50 minutes later from day to day in the average.

The daily retardation of moonrise also averages about 50 minutes, but the actual retardation may differ greatly from this value, especially in high latitudes. In the latitude of New York the greatest possible delay may exceed the least by more than 1 hour. The variation depends mainly on the angle between the moon's path, which is not far from the ecliptic, and the horizon; the smaller the angle at moonrise, the less is the delay in rising from day to day. As we have already noted (1·19), the ecliptic is least inclined to the horizon in our northern latitudes when the vernal equinox rises. When the moon is near that point, its rising is least delayed, a circumstance that is especially conspicuous when the moon is also near the full phase.

5·10. The Harvest Moon is the full moon that occurs nearest the *time* of the autumnal equinox, September 23. Because the sun is then near the autumnal equinox, the full moon is near the position of the vernal equinox and is therefore in that part of its path that is least inclined to the horizon at moonrise. The peculiarity of the harvest moon, as distinguished from other occasions when the moon is near full, is its minimum delay in rising for a few successive nights.

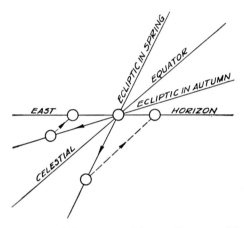

Fɪɢ. 5·10. Explanation of the Harvest Moon. Because of its eastward motion along its path, which nearly coincides with the ecliptic, the moon rises later from night to night. For the nearly full moon, the delay is least in our northern latitudes in autumn, when the ecliptic is least inclined to the horizon at moonrise.

Thus there is bright moonlight in the early evening for an unusual number of evenings in middle and higher northern latitudes. A similar effect is observed in corresponding southern latitudes around March 21.

5·11. The Moon's Apparent Path; Regression of the Nodes. The moon's path on the celestial sphere during a month is nearly a great circle that is inclined about 5° to the ecliptic. The path among the constellations for a particular month may be traced by plotting on a celestial globe the right ascensions and declinations of the moon's center from tables in the *American Ephemeris and Nautical Almanac*. When the plotting is continued through successive months, it is seen that the path shifts westward rather rapidly, keeping about the same angle with the ecliptic.

The *nodes* of the moon's path are the two opposite points where it intersects the ecliptic. The *ascending node* is the point where the moon's center crosses the ecliptic from south to north; the *descending node* is the point where it crosses from north to south. *Regression of the nodes* is their westward displacement along the ecliptic, just as the equinoxes slide westward in their precessional motion, but at a much faster rate; a complete revolution of the nodes is accomplished in 18.6 years. From this and other changes in the moon's orbit, for which the sun's attraction is mainly responsible, the moon's course among the constellations is considerably different from month to month, although it always remains within the confines of the zodiac.

5·12. Ephemeris Time by the Moon. The moon's monthly motion around the heavens is rapid and independent of the earth's variable rotation. It provides an important means of determining time on a uniform basis. Positions of the moon have been observed for a long time on occasions when it transits the meridian or when it

Fig. 5·12. Dual-Rate Moon Position Camera. (*Official U. S. Navy photograph*)

passes over stars (6·13). Because the opportunities for such observations are restricted, astronomers have sought more convenient and accurate means of determining time by the moon-clock.

The dual-rate moon position camera was designed for the purpose by William Markowitz, director of the Time Service of the U.S. Naval Observatory. Attached at the focus of a telescope of moderate size, its plate carriage is driven by a motor to follow the stars in the diurnal motion. A dark filter of glass placed before an opening at the center of the carriage is gradually tilted by a motor, shifting the moon's image optically so as to hold it stationary with respect to the stars during the exposure of about 20 seconds.

The photograph, showing the moon and the stars around it, is observed with a special device where the positions of about 10 stars and 30 to 40 points on the moon's bright edge are measured. Corrections for irregularities of the edge have been determined by C. B. Watts. The final result is the right ascension and declination of the moon's center at the universal time of observation. This time may then be compared with the ephemeris time when the moon is scheduled to reach this observed position.

The operation of the dual-rate camera, which began in 1952 with the 12-inch refractor of the Naval Observatory, is being extended to observatories in other parts of the world. It can supply uniform ephemeris time and its relation to the variable universal time, and it will also improve the understanding of the complex motions of the moon.

5·13. The Moon's Range in Declination. Because the moon's path on the celestial sphere departs only a little from the ecliptic, the moon moves north and south during the month about as much as the sun does in the course of the year. Near the position of the summer solstice the moon rises in the northeast, sets in the northwest, and is high in the sky in our northern latitudes at upper transit. Near the winter solstice about 2 weeks later, the moon rises in the southeast, sets in the southwest, and crosses the meridian at a lower altitude. An example of the many compensations in nature is furnished by the full moon which, being opposite the sun, rides highest in the long winter evenings and lowest in the summer.

When the inclination of the moon's path to the ecliptic is taken into account, we note that the range in declination varies perceptibly as the nodes regress. When the ascending node coincides with the vernal equinox, the moon's path is inclined to the celestial equator

23½° plus 5°, or 28½°; this occurred in 1950. When the ascending node coincides with the autumnal equinox, which occurred in 1959, the inclination to the equator is 23½° minus 5°, or 18½°. Thus the moon's highest and lowest altitudes at upper transits in latitude

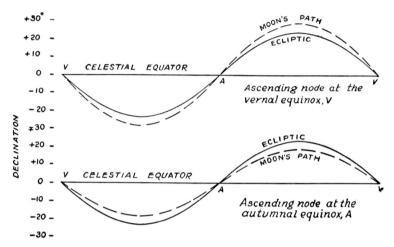

FIG. 5·13.   Effect of Regression of the Nodes of Its Path on the Moon's Range in Declination.

40° north average in the first case 78½° and 21½°, respectively, and in the second case 68½° and 31½°—a decrease in range of about 20°.

The variation of 10° in the moon's maximum declinations north and south in the 18.6-year cycle is chiefly responsible for nutation, the nodding of the earth's axis which accompanies its precessional motion.

5·14. The Moon's Rotation and Librations. The moon rotates on its axis in the same period in which it revolves around the earth, namely, the sidereal month of 27⅓ days. In consequence of the

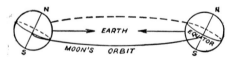

FIG. 5·14.   The Moon's Libration in Latitude. The inclination of the moon's equator to the plane of its orbit causes the moon's poles to be presented alternately to the earth.

equality of the two periods the moon presents about the same
hemisphere toward the earth at all times. It is always the face of
the "man in the moon" that we see near the full phase and never
the back of his head. An examination of the moon's surface
throughout the month, however, shows that features near the edge
of the disk are turned sometimes into view and at other times out

FIG. 5·14A. The Moon's Libration in Longitude. The prominent group
of seas is nearer the edge of the moon's disk in the picture at the right.
(Early photographs at the Observatory of Paris)

of sight. The moon seems to rock slightly; and these apparent oscillations, or *librations,* arise mainly from three causes:

(1) *The libration in latitude* results from the inclination of about
$6\frac{1}{2}°$ between the moon's equator and the plane of its orbit. At
intervals of 2 weeks the lunar poles are tipped alternately toward
and away from us; at times we can see $6\frac{1}{2}°$ beyond the north pole,
at other times the same distance beyond the south pole. The explanation of this libration is analogous to that of the seasons.

(2) *The libration in longitude* is caused by the failure of the
moon's rotation and revolution to keep exactly in step throughout
the month, although they come out together at the end. The rotation is nearly uniform, whereas the revolution in the elliptical orbit

is not uniform (5·2). Thus the moon seems to rock in an east-west direction, allowing us to see as much as 7¾° farther around in longitude at each edge than we could otherwise.

(3) *The diurnal libration* is a consequence of the earth's rotation. Even if the other librations were absent, so that the same hemisphere were turned always toward the center of the earth, we on the surface view the moon from slightly different directions during the day, and therefore see slightly different hemispheres. From the elevated position nearly 4000 miles above the center of the earth the observer can see about 1° farther over the western edge at moonrise and the same amount over the eastern edge at moonset.

In addition to the principal librations, there is a slight physical libration, because the moon's rate of rotation is not quite uniform. Fully 59 per cent of the moon's surface has been visible when the sidereal month is completed. The remaining 41 per cent is never seen from the earth; and throughout this region, of course, the earth would always be invisible to lunar observers.

THE MOON'S SURFACE FEATURES

The unaided eye can discern only the dark areas of the moon's surface, which are known as the lunar seas, and occasional irregularities of the terminator, which suggest that the moon is mountainous. The telescope shows the mountains themselves and other details of the surface. The mountains are clearest near the terminator, either the sunrise or sunset line, where shadows are long and the contrast between mountain and plain is therefore more pronounced.

5·15. Absence of Atmosphere on the Moon. There is no evidence that the moon has any atmosphere. There is no twilight; the sunrise and sunset lines are abrupt divisions between day and night. The effect of twilight in prolonging the cusps of the crescent moon beyond the diameter could be observed if a lunar atmosphere had a density 1/10,000 that of the earth's atmosphere. No perceptible haze dims our view of the moon, even near the edge where an atmosphere would be most effective in this respect. When a star is hidden by the moon, it does not first become fainter and redder, as it would behind a considerable amount of atmosphere. Instead, the star retains its normal brightness and color until it disappears almost instantly at the edge of the moon.

These are indications that the moon has only an extremely rare atmosphere, at the most. The reason is found in the escape of gases from the weak control of the moon's attraction.

5·16. Escape of an Atmosphere. The molecules of a gas are darting swiftly in all directions and are incessantly colliding, so that some are brought momentarily almost to rest while others are propelled to speeds far exceeding the average. The speeds increase as the temperature of the gas is raised, and at the same temperature are greater for lighter gases than for heavier ones.

The *kinetic theory of gases* states that the average squared velocity of the molecules varies directly as the absolute temperature of the gas and inversely as its mean molecular weight. The average speed in miles a second at 0° C is 1.2 for hydrogen, 0.4 for water vapor, and 0.3 for nitrogen and oxygen. These speeds become 17 per cent greater at 100°C.

The ability of a celestial body to retain an atmosphere around it depends on the *velocity of escape* at its surface. This is the initial speed a molecule or any other object must have in order to overcome the pull of gravity and to get away. Calculation suggests that a celestial body will lose half its atmosphere in only a few weeks if the velocity of escape does not exceed 3 times the mean speed of the molecules in that atmosphere. The required time is increased to a few thousand years if the factor is 4, and to a hundred million years if the factor is 5 times the mean speed of the molecules.

The velocity of escape is about 7 miles a second near the earth's surface, without allowance for air resistance, but is only 1½ miles a second near the surface of the moon. We conclude that the earth can retain the chief constituents of its atmosphere for an indefinite period, whereas the moon has been unable to keep any of these gases around it.

5·17. The Character of the Moon's Surface. The surface temperature of the moon varies from more than 100°C when the sun is overhead to −50° at sunset and is reduced to −150° at midnight. These values were determined by Pettit and Nicholson at Mount Wilson Observatory, who also observed a drop of 150°C in the temperature in 1 hour during a lunar eclipse.

Such rapid cooling of the surface when the sunlight is withdrawn is caused partly by the absence of an atmospheric blanket. It is also promoted by the low heat conductivity of the surface material, so that the heat does not penetrate very far into the interior. In this respect the material has been likened to pumice or volcanic ash. Records of radiations from the moon in the radio wavelengths suggest that at only a few yards below the surface the temperature remains constant at about −40°C.

The *albedo,* or reflecting power, of the moon is only 7 per cent, in contrast with the value of 40 per cent for the earth; this refers

FIG. 5·17.   The Full Moon.   (*Lick Observatory photograph*)

to the ratio of the light reflected by the whole illuminated hemisphere of the moon to the light it receives from the sun. There are marked local variations from the average, from the darkest parts of the seas to the very bright floor of the crater Aristarchus. With allowance for shadows, the moon's reflecting power is comparable with that of rather dark brown rock—brown because the moonlight is redder than the direct sunlight.

Presumably it is not entirely bare, unbroken rock that we see. Although the rocks on the moon are not exposed to ordinary weathering by wind and water, their surfaces may have been exfoliated by repeated expansion and contraction with the great range in the temperatures. The accumulation of meteorites and frag-

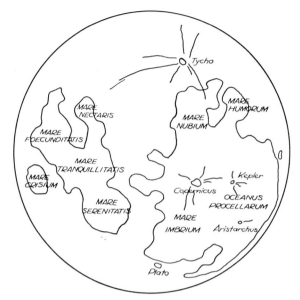

FIG. 5·17A. Key to Photograph of Full Moon.

ments of porous rocks shattered by the fall of meteorites may add
to the rubble.

5·18. Selenography. The mapping of the details of the lunar surface dates from 1610, when Galileo made the first map of the moon
as observed with the telescope. He had recognized the lunar mountains and had called the large dark areas "seas," a misnomer that
persists in the present nomenclature.

J. Hevelius, at Danzig in 1647, published a lunar map showing
250 named formations; the names were after terrestrial features
they may have seemed to resemble. All that survive from this
plan are the names of 10 mountain ranges, including the Apennines and Alps. J. B. Riccioli, at Bologna in 1651, chose the more
enduring plan of naming the lunar craters and some other features in his map after distinguished former scholars; he selected
names such as Copernicus, Tycho, and Plato.

Many lunar maps have since been made, often including more
detail than was contained in previous ones. Especially noteworthy
in the 19th century were the maps by Beer and Mädler, at Berlin in
1837, and by J. Schmidt, at Athens in 1878. The most detailed
recent map, showing at least 90,000 formations, was constructed

by H. P. Wilkins, former director of the Lunar Section of the British Astronomical Association. Some of the later map makers have extended Riccioli's system to smaller features and have assigned them names of contemporary observers. A catalog of about 6000 approved lunar place names, entitled *Named Lunar Formations,* and an accompanying atlas were published in 1935 by the International Astronomical Union.

The principal features of the lunar surface now to be described are the seas, mountains, craters, rays, and rills.

5·19. The Lunar Seas. The large dark areas that form the face of the "man in the moon," the profile of the "girl in the moon," and other products of the lively imagination are the lunar *maria* (seas), so called when they were thought to be seas or the beds of primitive seas. They are also known as *plains.* These areas appear darker because they are more nearly smooth than are most other parts of the moon.

The seas are still designated by the early fantastic names such as Mare Serenitatis (Sea of Serenity) and Mare Nubium (Sea of Clouds). The largest is Oceanus Procellarum (Ocean of Sails). Irregularities in the shorelines are occasionally "bays" and "gulfs"; Sinus Iridum (Bay of Rainbows) is a familiar example. Mostly connected, with the conspicuous exception of the isolated Mare Crisium, the seas cover about half the surface that is visible from the earth, and predominate in the lunar northern hemisphere. The majority are roughly circular.

The first view of the far side of the moon was obtained in photographs from the space probe Lunik III on October 7, 1959; the probe was then passing behind the moon at the distance of about 40,000 miles. The moon was presented to the camera in the gibbous phase, as it appears to us four days before full moon. Two fifths of the moon's surface had not been observed previously, and three fourths of this hitherto unseen portion is shown illuminated by the sunlight in the 1959 photograph. Even with allowance for the somewhat unfavorable phase of the moon and for loss of detail in the processing of the picture, the newly revealed region seems lacking in conspicuous markings; but the kinds of formations are not different from those on the visible hemisphere. Larger dark blotches, as named by Soviet scientists, are Moscow Sea and Sea of Dreams. The crater Tsiolkovsky is prominent and the smaller crater Bruno is the center of a system of bright rays.

5·20. The Lunar Mountains. Among the few formations that have any resemblance to terrestrial mountain ranges are the three that form the western border of Mare Imbrium; they are the Apennines, Caucasus, and Alps. Like others that border the seas, these mountains slope more abruptly on the seaward side and more gradually in the opposite direction. They are surmounted by many

FIG. 5·20. The Moon About Three Days After First Quarter. The moon is inverted and reversed, as it appears ordinarily with the telescope. In the upper part, near the south pole, is the crater Tycho with its long bright rays. The crater Copernicus is near the middle of the terminator. The Bay of Rainbows at the lower edge of Mare Imbrium is near the bottom. (*Lick Observatory photograph*)

peaks, the highest ones rising nearly 20,000 feet above the plain.

Still greater heights are measured in the Leibnitz and Doerfel mountains near the south pole and almost beyond the edge of the moon; some of those peaks have elevations of 26,000 feet, comparable with, but not as high as, Mount Everest. Heights on the moon, however, are less easily compared because they are referred to the neighboring plains; and the plains themselves are at different levels.

The height of a lunar mountain is determined in one way by measuring the length of its shadow and by calculating the sun's altitude above the horizon as seen then from that point on the moon. The height may also be found by measuring the distance of the summit from the terminator as it catches the first rays of the rising sun or the last rays of the setting sun. At those instants the illuminated top of the peak looks like a little star out in the dark beyond the terminator. A sketch of either situation will show that enough data are then known to calculate the height of the mountain by solving a right triangle.

5·21. The Lunar Craters. The most remarkable characteristic of lunar depressions is their preference for nearly circular formations. These *craters* exceed 30,000 in number and range in size from the great walled plains to the smallest craterlets and pits 1000 feet or less across that can be discerned with the larger telescopes. Among the largest walled plains are Clavius, near the moon's south pole, and Grimaldi, near its eastern edge; they measure nearly 150 miles in diameter.

The circumference of a lunar crater is a nearly circular wall, precipitous and often shelving on the inside and more gradually sloping without. Lofty peaks surmount the walls, and lower peaks appear near the centers of many craters. In some cases the crater floor is depressed several thousand feet below the level of the surrounding plain; in a few it is elevated, notably in the crater Wargentin where the floor is raised nearly to the top of the wall. Some craters have rough, bright, saucer-shaped floors; Aristarchus is the brightest. Others, such as Plato, have floors as smooth and dark as the seas.

Copernicus is a fine example of a typical lunar crater. Situated on elevated terrain between Mare Nubium and Mare Imbrium, its floor is 40 miles in diameter and has a group of 7 peaks near its

FIG. 5·21. The Crater Copernicus. (*Lick Observatory photograph*)

center. The wall with average height of 12,000 feet is surmounted by many peaks and broken by great landslips. Around it are rows of hillocks and craterlets.

5·22. The Rays and Rills. The lunar *rays* are bright streaks 5 or 10 miles wide and up to 1500 miles long, which radiate from points near a few of the craters and pass over mountain and plain alike without much regard for the topography. Best seen when the sun is high above them, the rays are prominent features of the full moon. The most conspicuous and longest ray system radiates from Tycho near the south pole. A fine system of shorter, more crooked, and somewhat less brilliant rays centers in the crater Copernicus (Fig. 5·21).

There are many *rills*, or clefts, of the order of half a mile in width and of unknown depth. Some are very tortuous, whereas others are nearly straight for tens of miles. A rather large telescope is needed to show the rills clearly.

FIG. 5·22. Southern Portion of the Moon at Last Quarter. The crater
Tycho is above the center. Above it, halfway to the upper edge, is the
walled plain Clavius. Part of Mare Nubium is at the lower right. The
shadows lengthen as the terminator (sunset line) is approached. (*Mount
Wilson Observatory photograph*)

A fine fault is readily seen near the southwest edge of Mare
Nubium (Fig. 5·22). This is the Straight Wall, 70 miles long and
rising more than 1000 feet above the plain.

5·23. The Origin of the Surface Features of the moon is imperfectly understood and might remain in doubt as long as observers

are confined to the earth. Two very different versions have long been debated. One opinion is that the major features are the result of volcanism. The second attributes them to impacts of bodies falling onto the moon.

The *igneous hypothesis* supposes that the effort of the moon to form a solid crust was resisted repeatedly by upheavals of molten material from below, with resulting local subsidences of the crust. The first permanent features were large ring-mountains, some of them hundreds of miles across. The basins they enclosed were filled much later by lava of extensive fissure flows like those which formed the basaltic plateaus of the earth. The hot lava melted away parts of the original walls and spread outside to join other flows—thus the connecting lunar seas.

The circular formations diminished in size as the moon's crust thickened. The walled plains made their appearance, and later the normal craters such as Tycho and Copernicus developed. Peaks rose in the centers of craters and above their walls; some of the peaks may have been explosive volcanoes. If it could be established that the lunar rays radiate from formerly active volcanoes, such evidence would support the view that the rays are pulverized rock erupted and distributed over the moonscape by the explosions.

The *impact hypothesis* was advanced by the geologist G. K. Gilbert in 1892; it supposes that most of the lunar craters, at least, were produced when meteorites collided with the moon, which itself may never have been molten. There resulted a random distribution of nearly circular formations resembling the meteorite craters of the earth. It is considered significant that when the depths of lunar, terrestrial, and also shell craters are plotted against their diameters the points all lie along the same smooth curve.

This hypothesis has gained an increasing number of adherents. It is believed that the major meteoritic bombardment of the moon, and of the earth as well, occurred three billion years ago. On the airless moon, where ordinary erosion is absent, the original craters remain. On the earth the earlier scars and the remnants of the meteorites that caused them have vanished. Evidence of the existence of the ancient terrestrial craters now seems to be available (9·28). Some of those craters may have been comparable in size with the lunar craters.

5·24. Conditions at the Moon's Surface. Two worlds have grown up in the same neighborhood with equal benefit of the sunlight.

FIG. 5·24.   The Lunar Apennines.   (*Lick Observatory photograph*)

One, the earth, is the scene of activity of many kinds; on the other, the moon, there is absence of activity of any kind. The contrast is caused mainly by difference of surface gravity. With its greater gravity the earth has retained an atmosphere extensive enough to sustain life and to promote by weathering persistent changes in the landscape. With its feebler attraction the moon has not retained sufficient atmosphere to accomplish these things. Because its surface has preserved the records of ancient events, the moon may hold the key to the origin of the solar system.

If anyone should land on the moon, he would find conditions there quite different from those at home. The reduced surface gravity might suggest surprising athletic feats. Absence of considerable atmosphere would produce unfamiliar effects. The glaring sunlight would include dangerous ultraviolet rays. No twilight would intervene between day and night. The sky would be black instead of blue. The bare, lifeless landscape would be that of a perfect desert where practically nothing happens. If the visitor is an astronomer, he might well conclude that for steadiness, clearness, and continuity of view of the celestial bodies the moon would be the perfect site for an observatory.

THE TIDES

The rise and fall of the level of the ocean twice at any place in a little more than a day has been associated with the moon from early times. Newton correctly ascribed the tides in the ocean to the attractions of both the moon and sun and accounted for their general behavior by means of his law of gravitation.

5·25. Lunar Tides. To simplify the explanation of the tides we may imagine, as Newton did, that the whole earth is covered by very deep water. Because the gravitational attraction between two bodies diminishes as their separation is greater, the moon's attraction is greatest for the part of the ocean directly under the moon and is least for the part on the opposite side of the earth. The ocean is accordingly drawn into an ellipsoid of revolution, which in the absence of other effects would have its major axis directed toward the moon. This axis rotates eastward, following the moon in its monthly course around the earth.

Meanwhile, the earth is rotating eastward under the tide figure. The earth makes a complete rotation relative to a particular point in that figure once in a lunar day, which averages about $24^h 50^m$ of solar time. *High tide* occurs at a place of observation at intervals of $12^h 25^m$, and *low tide* at times halfway between them. These are occasions when the ocean level at the place is the highest and lowest, respectively, for that particular cycle.

Thus a succession of tide crests move westward around the earth. They are displaced behind the moon in its diurnal motion by friction with the ocean floor, because the water has not the depth required by the simple static theory, and their progress is interrupted by land masses. High tide and the transit of the moon are generally far from simultaneous. The difference in time between these occurrences varies from place to place and is best determined by observation.

5·26. Spring and Neap Tides.   The sun also causes tides in the
ocean.   It can be shown that the tide-producing force of a body
varies inversely as the cube of the distance of that body and, accordingly, that the sun, despite its far greater mass, is less than half
as effective as the moon in raising tides on the earth.

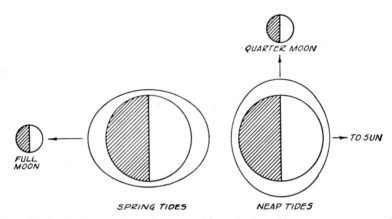

Fig. 5·26.   Spring Tides and Neap Tides.   Spring tides occur at new and
full moon, when lunar and solar tides reinforce each other.   Neap tides
occur at the quarter phases, when one set of tides is partly neutralized by
the other.

The two sets of tides may be considered as operating independently, the relative positions of their crests varying with the moon's
phases.   The *spring tide* occurs when the moon is new or full.
Because the moon and sun are then attracting from the same or
opposite directions, lunar and solar tides reinforce each other.
The *neap tide* occurs when the moon is at either quarter phase.
Then the moon and sun are 90° apart in the sky, so that one set
of tides is partly neutralized by the other.   When the moon is new
or full and also in perigee, the difference in level between low
and high tides is especially great.

The earth itself, like the ocean, is deformed by lunar and solar
tides, but to a much smaller extent.   Consequently, the observed
tides in the ocean represent the differences between ocean and earth
tides.

5·27. Tidal Friction.   The tides in the oceans and in the earth
itself act as a brake on the earth's rotation; they tend to be held
in position by the moon and sun and to impose some restraint on

the daily rotation of the earth. The tides would accordingly be expected to reduce the speed of the rotation and to gradually lengthen the day (2·18). An increase in the period of the earth's rotation at the rate of $0^s.0016$ a century has been derived by comparing the observed times of early eclipses with the times when they would have occurred if the earth's rotation had remained perfectly uniform.

Although the rate of increase might seem negligibly small, the difference in the times has accumulated to a considerable amount within the period in which eclipses have been recorded. The error of a mean solar clock compared with a clock having constant rate is $\frac{1}{2}at^2$ seconds, where in this case $\frac{1}{2}a = 0^s.0008 \times 365\frac{1}{4} \times 100$, or about 29 seconds, and t is the number of centuries intervening. In 20 centuries the error in the earth-clock had amounted to 11,600 seconds, or about $3\frac{1}{4}$ hours. Tidal friction in the shallow seas has been assigned as sufficient reason for this effect. However, the actual rate of increase in the period of the earth's rotation and its cause as well may require further study.

The moon turns one hemisphere toward the earth, and some other satellites do the same with respect to their primaries. The planet Mercury rotates in the period of its revolution around the sun. Such effects have been ascribed to tidal friction within the bodies themselves, which would have been unassisted by ocean tides. These bodies have no oceans and probably never had any.

5·28. Tidal Theory of the Earth-Moon System. Retardation of the earth's rotation by friction of lunar tides would be accompanied by increased speed of the moon's revolution around the earth. The increase of its speed would cause the moon to spiral outward gradually, so that the month would grow longer as well as the day. A possible past and future history of the earth-moon system based on these considerations was traced by G. H. Darwin, son of the naturalist.

The theory begins with the moon about 10,000 miles from the earth. The length of the month was then something like a quarter of its present value, and the day was a still smaller fraction of the present day. Under the action of the tides both month and day slowly increased in length, the month at first faster than the day. Eventually the day will lengthen at a faster rate than the month, until the two become equal to 47 of our present days.

At that remote time in the future, when the moon is much farther away than it is now, the earth-moon system will be internally stable; the earth will turn one hemisphere always toward the moon, just as the moon now presents one hemisphere to the earth. If it happens not to be our hemisphere that is turned moonward, the moon may become one of the sights to see on a trip abroad. At that stage the lunar tides cannot alter the system, but the solar tides will still operate on it and will force the earth and moon out of step again. The history of the system will then be repeated in reverse order, according to the theory, until the moon is brought back close to the earth.

REVIEW QUESTIONS

1. Explain the parallax method of determining the moon's distance and show that the distance may be verified by use of radar pulses.

2. When the moon appears gibbous to us, what is the phase of the earth as seen from the moon?

3. State the aspects of the moon when the phases are new, quarter, and full.

4. Explain why the horns of the thin crescent moon in the west are more nearly vertical in the evenings of spring and more nearly horizontal in the evenings of autumn as viewed in middle northern latitudes. (Refer to Sec. 1·19.)

5. State and explain the characteristic feature of the harvest moon.

6. Why does the full moon pass nearest the zenith around the beginning of winter in middle northern latitudes? What is its least possible distance from your zenith?

7. Give two reasons why more than 50 per cent of the moon's surface is visible in the course of a month.

8. From what observational evidence is it concluded that the moon has little or no atmosphere? Account for the lack of atmosphere.

9. Describe the following features of the moon's surface: the seas, mountains, craters, rays, and rills.

10. If you should make a voyage to the moon, what conditions at its surface and what aspects of the sky would you find different from those at home?

11. Explain the cause of ocean tides. Are there tides in the earth itself as well?

12. Why do high tides recur at a particular place at intervals of 12^h 25^m? Why are they extremely high when the moon is new or full?

REFERENCES

Baldwin, Ralph B., *The Face of the Moon*. University of Chicago Press, Chicago, 1949.

Fielder, Gilbert, *Structure of the Moon's Surface.* Pergamon Press, New
York, 1961.

Kuiper, Gerard P., editor, *Photographic Lunar Atlas.* University of Chicago Press, Chicago, 1960.

Russian *Atlas of the Moon's Far Side.* English translation by R. B. Rod-
man. Published jointly by Interscience Publishers and Sky Publishing
Corporation, 1961.

Wilkins, H. P., and Patrick Moore, *The Moon.* The Macmillan Company, New York, 1955.

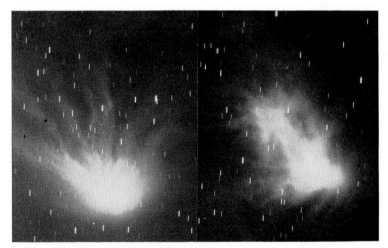

Comet Humason, August 6 and 8, 1962. The comet was then remarkably active structurally. Its tail extended almost directly away from the
earth. Photographs by Elizabeth Roemer with the 40-inch reflector at the
Flagstaff station. (*Official U.S. Navy photographs*)

6

ECLIPSES OF THE MOON AND SUN

Eclipses of the moon occur when the moon, at the full phase, passes through the earth's shadow and is thereby darkened. Eclipses of the sun occur when the moon, then at the new phase, passes between the sun and the earth, so that its shadow falls on the earth; the observer within the shadow sees the sun wholly or partially hidden by the moon.

6·1. Shadows of the Earth and Moon. Because the earth and the moon are globes smaller than the sun, the shadow of each one is a cone having its apex directed away from the sun. This region, from

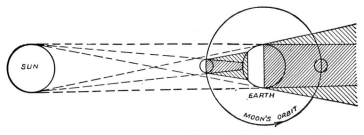

FIG. 6·1. Cause of Lunar and Solar Eclipses. When the moon is opposite the sun's position in the sky, it is eclipsed by the earth's shadow. When the moon is between the sun and the earth, its shadow falls on a portion of the earth; within this region the sun is eclipsed.

which the sunlight is geometrically entirely excluded, is the *umbra* of the shadow and is sometimes called simply the *shadow*. It is surrounded by the larger inverted cone of the *penumbra*, from which the sunlight is partially excluded. There is no way of observing the shadows except as they encounter objects that shine by reflected sunlight.

The average length of the earth's shadow is 859,000 miles, as may be easily calculated from two similar triangles having as their bases the diameters of the earth and sun. By a similar procedure it is found that the length of the moon's shadow averages 232,000 miles when the moon is between the sun and the earth. Because these

152

shadows are more than 100 times as long as their greatest widths, they cannot conveniently be represented in diagrams in their proper proportions.

6·2. The Moon in the Earth's Shadow. If a screen could be placed opposite the sun's direction at the moon's distance from us, the umbra of the earth's shadow falling normally upon the screen

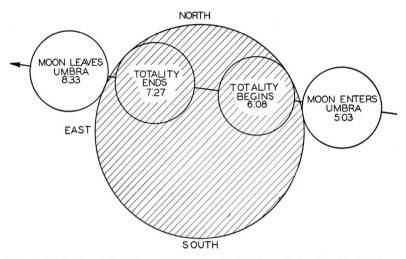

FIG. 6·2. Path of the Moon Through the Umbra of the Earth's Shadow During the Eclipse of November 18, 1956. Universal times are given.

would appear as a dark circle about 5700 miles in diameter. Always opposite the sun, this shadow moves eastward around the ecliptic once in a year. At intervals of a synodic month the faster-moving moon overtakes the shadow and, whenever it then encounters the shadow, enters at the west side and moves through at a rate that is the difference between the speeds of the moon and the shadow; the hourly rate is about 30', or very nearly the moon's apparent diameter.

Umbral eclipses of the moon are total and partial. The longest eclipses occur when the moon passes centrally through the shadow; the duration of the whole eclipse in the umbra is then about $3^h 40^m$, and of the total phase is $1^h 40^m$. Noncentral eclipses are shorter, depending on how nearly the moon's path approaches the center of the shadow. When the least distance from the center exceeds the difference between the radii of the shadow and moon, there is no total phase.

A lunar eclipse is visible, weather permitting, wherever the moon is then above the horizon, that is, from half of the earth and also the part that is rotated into view of the moon while the eclipse is in progress. The times when the moon enters and leaves the penumbra and umbra and of the beginning and end of totality are published in advance in various almanacs.

In the 6-year interval from 1963 to 1968 inclusive there are 8 umbral lunar eclipses scheduled, which are visible from a considerable area of the United States and Canada. Seven of these are total.

UMBRAL LUNAR ECLIPSES VISIBLE IN THE UNITED STATES
AND CANADA

Middle of Eclipse		Duration of Umbral Phase	Duration of Totality
Date	Universal Time		
1963, Dec. 30	11 7	3 34	1 24
1964, June 25	1 7	3 40	1 38
1964, Dec. 19	2 35	3 28	1 4
1965, June 14	1 51	1 40	. . . . .
1967, Apr. 24	12 7	3 34	1 22
1967, Oct. 18	10 16	3 26	0 56
1968, Apr. 13	4 49	3 26	0 56
1968, Oct. 6	11 41	3 28	1 2

6·3. Eclipses of the Moon. The moon is darkened so gradually in its passage through the penumbra of the shadow that this phase of the eclipse is less conspicuous. Soon after the moon enters the umbra, a dark notch appears at the eastern edge and slowly overspreads the disk. So dark in contrast is the shadow that the moon might be expected to vanish in total eclipse. As totality comes on, however, the entire moon is usually plainly visible.

Even when it is totally eclipsed, the moon is still illuminated by sunlight. The light filters through the earth's atmosphere around the base of the shadow and is refracted and diffused into the shadow and onto the moon. Red predominates in this light for the same reason that the setting sun is red. On rare occasions

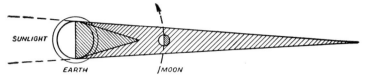

FIG. 6·3. Visibility of the Moon in Total Eclipse. Sunlight is diffused by the earth's atmosphere into the shadow and onto the eclipsed moon.

there is so much cloudiness around the base of the shadow that the eclipsed moon is very dim.

Penumbral eclipses occur when the moon passes through the penumbra of the earth's shadow without entering the umbra. The darkening of the part of the moon in the penumbra is visible to the eye when the least distance of the edge of the moon from the umbra does not exceed 0.35 of the moon's diameter. The darkening is detected in the photographs when the least distance does not exceed 0.65 of the moon's diameter, and by photometric means when the distance is still greater.

FIG. 6·3A. Penumbral Lunar Eclipse of March 23, 1951. The northern (lower) part of the moon is considerably dimmed. (*Photograph by Paul E. Roques, Griffith Observatory*)

The accompanying list of penumbral eclipses, from 1963 to 1977 inclusive, of magnitude great enough to be observed by some means somewhere in the United States and Canada, is taken from an unpublished list by Alexander Pogo, who also supplied the tables of umbral and solar eclipses. The *magnitude* of the penumbral eclipse is the ratio of the least distance of the moon's edge from the umbra to the moon's diameter; it has the minus sign.

Penumbral Lunar Eclipses Observable in the United States and Canada

Date	UT of Closest Approach to Umbra	Magnitude
1963, Jan. 9	23 18	−0.01
1965, Dec. 8	17 11	−0.09
1966, Oct. 29	10 11	−0.14
1973, Jan. 18	21 13	−0.11
1976, Nov. 6	23 5	−0.23
1977, Sept. 27	8 23	−0.14

6·4. The Moon's Shadow on the Earth. In average conditions the umbra of the moon's shadow fails to reach the earth. The average length of this part of the shadow is 232,000 miles, which is almost 3000 miles less than the mean distance of the moon's center from the nearest point of the earth's surface. The fact that the umbra occasionally extends to the earth at solar eclipse results from the eccentricity of the earth's orbit around the sun and of the moon's orbit around the earth. At aphelion the length of the umbra is increased to 236,000 miles, and at perigee the moon's center may be as close as 217,500 miles to the earth's surface. In these extreme conditions the umbra may fall on the earth 18,500 miles inside the umbra's apex.

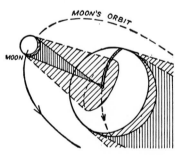

Fig. 6·4. Annular Eclipse of the Sun. The umbra of the moon's shadow does not reach the earth's surface. Within this shadow geometrically produced, a thin ring of the sun's disk remains visible around the moon.

6·5. Total and Annular Solar Eclipses. A *total eclipse* of the sun occurs when the umbra of the moon's shadow falls on the earth. If the observer is then within the umbra, he sees the dark circle of the moon completely hiding the sun's disk. The umbra can never exceed 167 miles in diameter when the sun is overhead.

An *annular eclipse* occurs when the moon is directly between us and the sun, but the umbra of the shadow does not reach the earth. If the observer is within the circle of the umbra produced

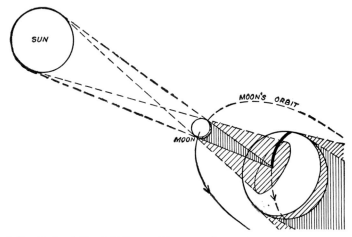

FIG. 6·5.   Path of Total Eclipse. The moon's revolution causes the shadow to move in an easterly direction over the earth's surface. From within the umbra the eclipse is total. Elsewhere within the larger circle of the penumbra the eclipse is partial.

beyond its apex (Fig. 6·4), he sees the moon's disk projected centrally against the sun; the dark disk then appears slightly the smaller of the two, so that a bright ring, or annulus, of the sun remains uneclipsed. Annular eclipses are 20 per cent more frequent than total eclipses.

Around the small area of the earth in which the eclipse appears total or annular at a particular time, there is the larger partly shaded region of the penumbra, from 2000 to 3000 miles in radius. Here the eclipse is *partial;* the moon hides only a fraction of the sun's disk, the fraction diminishing with increasing distance from the center of the shadow. When the axis of the shadow is directed slightly to one side of the earth, only the partial eclipse can be seen.

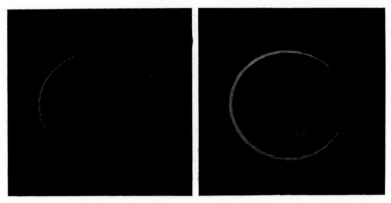

Fig. 6·5A.   Annular Solar Eclipse, September 1, 1951.   Immediately before
(left) and after (right) the beginning of the annular phase.   The sun was
near the horizon.   (*Photographs by Luc Secretan*)

6·6. Path of the Moon's Shadow.   As the moon revolves around us,
its shadow moves generally eastward by the earth at the rate of
about 2100 miles an hour.   Because the earth's rotation at the
equator is at the rate of 1040 miles an hour, also eastward, the
effective speed of the shadow at the equator, when the sun is overhead, is 1060 miles an hour.   In other parts of the earth where the
speed of rotation is less, the effective speed of the shadow is greater.
The speed may reach 5000 miles an hour when the sun is near the
horizon.   Considering the high speed of the shadow and its small
size, it is evident that a total eclipse of the sun cannot last long in
any one place; the maximum possible duration scarcely exceeds
7^m 30^s.   An annular eclipse may last a little longer.   The partial
phase accompanying either type of eclipse may have a duration of
more than 4 hours from beginning to end.

The *path* of total eclipse, or of annular eclipse, is the narrow
track of the central part of the shadow as it sweeps generally eastward over the earth's surface, from the time it first touches the earth
at sunrise until it departs at sunset.   Meanwhile, the penumbra
moves over the larger surrounding region in which the eclipse is
partial.

An eclipse occurs occasionally in which the umbra touches the
earth at the middle of its path, but fails to reach the surface at the
beginning and end of its path.   Such an eclipse begins as annular,
changes to total, and later reverts to the annular type.

Oppolzer's *Canon der Finsternisse* contains the elements of solar and lunar eclipses between 1208 B.C. and A.D. 2163, and also maps showing the approximate paths of total and annular solar eclipses during this interval. More accurate data concerning eclipses are

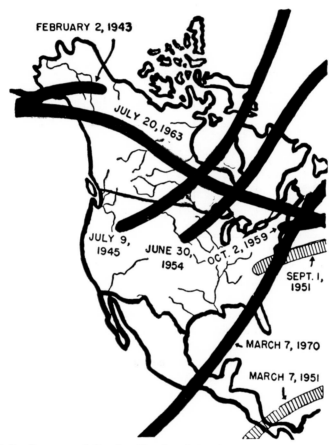

FEBRUARY 2, 1943

JULY 20, 1963

JULY 9, 1945

JUNE 30, 1954

OCT. 2, 1959

SEPT. 1, 1951

MARCH 7, 1970

MARCH 7, 1951

FIG. 6·6. Recent and Coming Total and Annular Solar Eclipses in North America. (*Diagram by Charles H. Smiley, Brown University*)

published in various almanacs for the year in which each occurs. Paths of total eclipses for several years in advance have been published in U.S. Naval Observatory *Circulars*.

The dates, durations at noon, and land areas in which the principal total solar eclipses are visible from 1963 to 1973 inclusive are shown in the accompanying table. The path of the 1965 eclipse touches land near its beginning and end, and is otherwise over the

Pacific Ocean. Eclipses of 1967 November 2 and 1968 September 22, having durations of totality less than 1 minute, are not included in the table; the latter has a short path running nearly south through north central Asia. The paths of recent and coming total and annular eclipses visible in North America through 1970 are shown in Fig. 6·6.

TOTAL SOLAR ECLIPSES

Date	Duration (minutes)	Region
1963, July 20	2	Alaska, Canada, New England
1965, May 30	5	New Zealand, Peru
1966, Nov. 12	2	Central South America
1970, Mar. 7	3	Mexico, Florida, Georgia, Carolinas
1972, July 10	3	NE Asia, Alaska, Canada
1973, June 30	7	South America, Africa

6·7. The Sun in Total Eclipse ranks among the most impressive of celestial phenomena. Although the details vary considerably from one eclipse to another, depending on the diameter of the shadow and other factors, the principal features to be noted are much the same on all these occasions.

The eclipse begins at a particular place with the appearance of a dark notch at the sun's western edge. Thereafter the sun is gradually hidden by the moon. When only a narrow crescent of the sun is left, an unfamiliar pallor overspreads the sky and landscape. Immediately before totality the sky darkens rapidly; shadow bands, like ripples, move across white surfaces; some animals become disturbed and some flowers begin to close. As the umbra of the shadow rushes in on the observer, the remaining sliver of the vanishing sun breaks into bright "Baily's beads" and quickly disappears. With the coming of totality the corona bursts into view; it is brightest close to the eclipsing moon and fades out in streamers. Flame-like prominences sometimes appear; their bases near the west edge of the sun are gradually uncovered, while those around the east edge are hidden as the moon moves across. Some bright stars and planets in the sun's vicinity may become visible to the unaided eye.

FIG. 6·7. Total Eclipse of the Sun, January 24, 1925. From a painting by Howard Russell Butler. (*American Museum of Natural History, New York*)

Totality ends as abruptly as it began. The corona vanishes, and the features of the partial eclipse recur in reverse order.

6·8. Value of Total Solar Eclipses. As spectacles to be long remembered, total eclipses of the sun have a popular appeal that may lead to further interest in astronomy. These brief occasions when the sun's disk is completely hidden by the moon also offer opportunities for observing features near the sun's edge that are ordinarily concealed by the glare of the sunlight. Available then for study are details of the corona, some that cannot be seen at all at

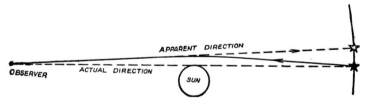

FIG. 6·8. Apparent Displacement of a Star Near the Sun's Edge. By the theory of relativity, starlight passing near the sun is deflected so that the star is apparently displaced outward from the sun's position.

other times and some that can be observed when there is not an eclipse only by use of special devices. The visibility of objects near the sun's place in the sky has permitted the search for a once suspected planet nearer the sun than Mercury's distance, the discovery of certain comets, and a successful test of the theory of relativity.

The theory of relativity requires that stars close to the sun's place be apparently displaced slightly away from the center of the sun; the predicted maximum displacement, for a star at the sun's edge, is 1".75. Such displacements of stars were first observed by English astronomers at an eclipse in 1919 and have been verified at subsequent eclipses. The procedure has been to compare photographs of the region of the sky immediately around the eclipsed sun with other photographs of the same region taken at night at another time of the year. A comparison by G. Van Biesbroeck at the solar eclipse of 1952 February 25 showed an average displacement of 1".70 at the sun's edge.

6·9. Eclipse Seasons. Eclipses of the sun and moon occur respectively when the moon is new and full. Although these phases recur every month, eclipses come less frequently. The reason is that the

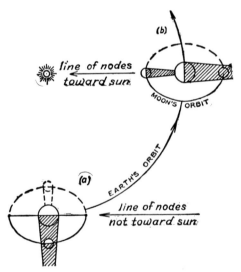

Fig. 6·9. Eclipse Seasons. The inclination of the moon's orbit to the plane of the earth's orbit permits eclipses to occur only at two opposite seasons. These occur, as at *b*, when the sun is near the line of nodes of the moon's path. At other times, as at *a*, the moon cannot pass between the earth and sun or into the earth's shadow.

moon's apparent path on the celestial sphere is inclined 5° to the ecliptic. Each time when the moon overtakes the sun, or the earth's shadow opposite the sun, both sun and shadow have moved eastward on the ecliptic from the previous positions. Traveling in its path inclined to the ecliptic, the moon passes north or south of the sun and shadow, unless the two are near the intersections of the moon's path and the ecliptic. Only then can the moon eclipse the sun or be eclipsed in the shadow.

Eclipse seasons occur around the times when the sun passes one of the nodes of the moon's path. As the nodes regress rapidly westward, the eclipse seasons come more than half a month earlier from year to year. The interval between two successive arrivals of the sun at the same node is the *eclipse year;* its length is 346.620 days. The eclipse seasons in 1960 were around March and September.

6·10. Solar and Lunar Ecliptic Limits. The *solar ecliptic limit* is the angular distance of the sun from the node at which it is grazed by the moon, as seen from some point on the earth. Within this distance the sun will be eclipsed; beyond it an eclipse cannot occur. The value of this limiting angular distance varies with the changing linear distances from us, and therefore the apparent sizes, of the sun and moon, and with fluctuations in the angle between the moon's path and the ecliptic. The extreme values, or major and minor limits, are respectively 18° 31′ and 15° 21′. When the sun's center is beyond the major limit, an eclipse is impossible; when it is within the minor limit, an eclipse is inevitable.

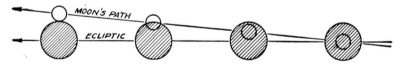

FIG. 6·10. The Lunar Ecliptic Limit. In order to eclipse the moon, the earth's shadow must be near one of the nodes of the moon's path. The greatest distance of the center of the shadow from the node, or of the sun's center from the opposite node, at which an eclipse is possible is the lunar ecliptic limit.

The *lunar ecliptic limit* (Fig. 6·10) is likewise the greatest distance of the sun from the node at which a lunar eclipse is possible. The major and minor limits for umbral eclipses are 12° 15′ and 9° 30′, and for penumbral eclipses are the same as for solar eclipses.

6·11. Frequency of Eclipses. The number of eclipses during each eclipse season is determined by comparing the double ecliptic limits with the distance the sun moves along the ecliptic in a synodic month with respect to the regressing node; this distance is 29.5/346.6 of 360°, or 30°.6. The question is whether the sun, and the earth's shadow opposite it, can possibly pass through the eclipse region without being encountered by the moon. They can do so if the double ecliptic limit is less than 30°.6, although usually they may not escape even then. If the double limit is greater than 30°.6, one eclipse must occur at each node, and two are possible. Because the eclipse year is 18.63 days shorter than the average calendar year, the first eclipse season may return before the end of the calendar year, and in this event one additional eclipse may result.

Two solar eclipses of some kind must occur each year; for twice the minor solar ecliptic limit is 30°.7. Five may occur, and as many as 3 of these may be total or annular. Two lunar eclipses of some kind must occur each year, and 5 are possible; of these no umbral lunar eclipse need occur, but 3 are possible.

The minimum number of eclipses in a year is therefore 4, 2 of the sun and 2 of the moon which may both be penumbral. The maximum number is 7. Thus solar and lunar eclipses are equally frequent for the earth as a whole, although many penumbral lunar eclipses among them cannot be detected. At any one place, lunar eclipses are seen the more often because of the greater area of the earth from which a lunar eclipse is visible.

6·12. Recurrence of Eclipses. The *saros* is the interval of $18^y \ 11\frac{1}{3}^d$ (or a day less or more, depending on the number of leap years included) after which eclipses of the same series are repeated. It is equal to 223 synodic months, which contain 6585.32 days, and is nearly the same in length as 19 eclipse years (6585.78 days). Not only have the sun and moon returned to nearly the same positions relative to each other and to the node, but their distances from us are nearly the same as before, so that the durations of succeeding eclipses in a series also differ very little. Knowledge of the saros, as it applies to cycles of lunar eclipses at least, goes back to very early times.

The effect of the one third of a day in the saros period is to shift the path of the following eclipse 120° west in longitude, and after 3 periods around to nearly the same part of the earth again. At the end of each period the sun is nearly a half-day's journey, or about 28′, west of its former position relative to the node. Thus a gradual change in the character of succeeding eclipses in a series is brought about, together with a progressive shift of their paths in latitude.

Eclipses at intervals of the saros accordingly fall into series, each series of solar eclipses containing about 70 eclipses in a period of about 1200 years. A new series is introduced by a small partial eclipse near one of the poles. After a dozen partial eclipses of increasing magnitude and decreasing latitude of their paths, the series becomes total or annular for 45 eclipses, reverts to about a dozen diminishing partial eclipses, and finally disappears at the opposite pole. Twelve notable series of total solar eclipses are in progress at present; the one that is represented by the eclipses of 1937, 1955, and 1973 is remarkable because the durations of totality are not far from the greatest possible. A series of lunar eclipses runs through about 50 saroses in a period of about 870 years.

6·13. Occultations by the Moon. In its eastward movement around the heavens the moon frequently passes over, or *occults,* a star. Because the moon moves a distance equal to its own diameter in about an hour, this is the longest duration of an occultation. The star disappears at the moon's eastern edge and emerges at the western edge. Observations of the times of such occurrences have been useful for determining the moon's positions at those times for comparison with its predicted positions. These data are now obtained more conveniently and precisely with the dual-rate moon position camera (5·12).

The predicted times of disappearance behind the moon and of subsequent reappearance of the brighter stars and planets, which were formerly published in the American and British Almanacs, have been omitted from these almanacs beginning with the year 1960. The predictions for 12 stations in the United States and Canada are now included annually in a special Occultation Supplement in *Sky and Telescope.*

Occultations by the moon are interesting to watch with the telescope or with the unaided eye when the occulted objects are bright enough. The abruptness of disappearance or of reappearance convinces the observer that the moon has not sufficient atmosphere around it to appreciably dim and redden the objects near the moon's edge and that the apparent diameters of stars are very small. The disks of stars require only a hundredth of a second or less for complete occultation. A. E. Whitford, employing a fast photoelectric system, first demonstrated the difference in the apparent diameters of several stars by observing these intervals.

6·14. Occultations of Planets by the moon are sometimes spectacular. The unusual photographs of Jupiter and its satellites emerging from behind the moon were taken on the morning of January 16, 1947. The moon was then in the crescent phase between last quarter and new. The dark side from which the planet is

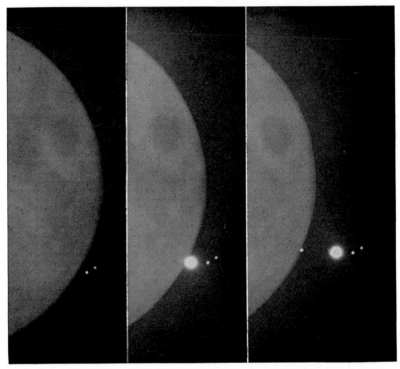

FIG. 6·14. Jupiter and Its Satellites Emerging from Behind the Moon.
(Photographs by Paul E. Roques, Griffith Observatory)

emerging was illuminated by earthlight. The oval dark spot in the upper part of the pictures is Mare Crisium. The times are Pacific standard.

Jupiter disappeared behind the bright edge of the moon at 4 o'clock that morning and reappeared about 50 minutes later at the western edge. The first photograph, taken at 4:50, shows the 4th and 1st satellites already in sight. In the second photograph, taken at 4:54, the planet has just cleared the moon's edge, and in the third picture, taken at 5:03, the 3rd satellite has appeared. The 2nd satellite is readily seen in the original negative but is less clearly shown in the print; it is near the left edge of the planet's disk, having emerged at 3:57 from occultation behind the planet.

REVIEW QUESTIONS

1. Solar eclipses occur at new moon, lunar eclipses at full moon. Why do not eclipses occur every time the moon is new and full?

2. Explain why eclipses occur only at two opposite seasons, and why those seasons come earlier from year to year.

3. There are more eclipses of the sun than umbral eclipses of the moon. Most people can recall having seen a total eclipse of the moon, but the majority have never seen a total solar eclipse. Explain.

4. Why is the totally eclipsed moon visible? What conditions would cause it to be very dim, even in a clear sky?

5. Distinguish between the total and the annular eclipse of the sun, as to cause and appearance. Account for an eclipse which is partly total and partly annular.

6. Describe the appearance of the earth as viewed from the moon when a total solar eclipse is occurring.

7. What information about the sun and its surroundings can be best obtained during a total solar eclipse? Mention a problem that was solved at the time of an eclipse.

8. A particular occultation of a star by the moon occurs for only a limited part of the hemisphere of the earth facing the moon at the time. Explain.

9. During a lunar eclipse may there be an occultation of a star? of Jupiter? of Venus?

PROBLEMS

1. By similar triangles demonstrate the proportion: length of earth's shadow/(length of shadow + earth's distance from sun) = earth's diameter/sun's diameter.

2. Using the proportion of Problem 1 calculate the average length of the earth's shadow. Take ratio of the diameters as 1/109.1 and earth's mean distance from sun as 92,900,000 miles.

Answer: Length of earth's shadow is 859,000 miles.

3. By another proportion calculate the average diameter of earth's shadow where the moon passes through it. Take moon's distance as 239,000 miles and earth's diameter as 7900 miles.

Answer: Diameter of shadow is about 5700 miles.

REFERENCES

Dyson, Frank, and R. V. d. R. Woolley, *Eclipses of the Sun and Moon.* Oxford University Press, New York, 1937.

Mitchell, S. A., *Eclipses of the Sun.* Fifth edition. Columbia University Press, New York, 1951.

7

THE SOLAR SYSTEM

THE PLANETS IN GENERAL — THE PATHS OF THE PLANETS — THE LAW OF GRAVITATION

The *solar system* consists of the sun and the many smaller bodies that revolve around the sun. These include the planets with their satellites, and the comets and meteors. It is a large system; the outermost planet, Pluto, is about 40 times as far from the sun as the earth's distance, and the majority of the comets have the aphelion points of their orbits still more remote. In comparison with the distance of even the nearest star, however, the interplanetary spaces shrink to such insignificance that we look upon the solar system as our own community and the other planets as our neighbors.

THE PLANETS IN GENERAL

7·1. The Principal and Minor Planets. The word *planets* (wanderers) was originally used to distinguish from the multitude of "fixed stars" the celestial bodies, except the comets, that move about among the constellations. Seven of these were known to early observers: the sun, the moon, and the 5 bright planets, Mercury, Venus, Mars, Jupiter, and Saturn, the last of which was believed to be almost as remote as the sphere containing the stars themselves. Thus Omar Khayyám ascended in his meditation "from earth's center through the seventh gate" to the throne of Saturn—from the center of the universe, as he understood it, almost to its limits.

With the acceptance of the Copernican system, the earth was added to the number of planets revolving around the sun, and the moon was recognized as the earth's satellite. Uranus, which is barely visible to the unaided eye, was discovered in 1781. Neptune, which is too faint to be seen without the telescope, was found in 1846. The still fainter Pluto, discovered in 1930, completes the list of the 9 known *principal planets*. In the meantime, in 1801, Ceres, the largest of the *asteroids*, or *minor planets*, was detected.

7·2. The Planets Named and Classified. The planets in order of average distance from the sun are:

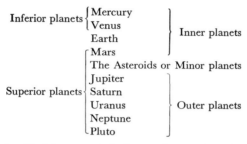

They are classified here as inferior and superior planets and also as *inner* and *outer planets*. The *inferior planets* are nearer the sun than the earth's distance, whereas the *superior planets* have their orbits outside the earth's orbit.

7·3. Planets Distinguished from Stars. Planets are relatively small globes, which revolve around the sun and shine by reflected sunlight. Five of the principal planets look like brilliant stars in our skies, while a sixth is faintly visible to the naked eye. Examined with the telescope, the larger and nearer planets appear as disks. The stars themselves are remote suns shining with their own light; they appear only as points of light even with the largest telescopes.

The bright planets can often be recognized by their steadier light when the stars around them are twinkling. All planets can be distinguished by their motions relative to the stars. The right ascensions and declinations of the principal planets and four asteroids are tabulated in the *American Ephemeris and Nautical Almanac* at convenient intervals during the year; their positions in the constellations can be marked in the star maps for any desired date.

The planet Mercury is occasionally visible to the naked eye in the twilight near the horizon, either in the west after sunset or in the east before sunrise. Venus, the most familiar evening and morning "star" is the brightest starlike object in the heavens. Mars is distinguished by its red color; at closest approaches to the earth it outshines Jupiter, which is generally second in brightness to Venus. Saturn rivals the brightest stars and is the most leisurely of the bright planets in its movement among the stars.

7·4. The Revolutions of the Principal Planets around the sun conform approximately to the following regularities, which seem

to have survived from an orderly origin and evolution of the planetary system (9·29):

(1) The orbits are nearly circular. They are ellipses of small
eccentricity, but with more marked departures from the circular
form in the cases of Pluto and Mercury.

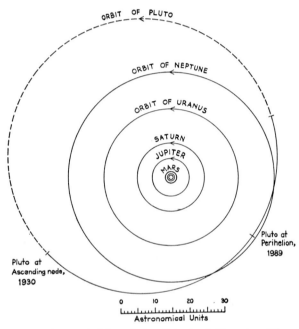

FIG. 7·4. Approximate Orbits of the Principal Planets. The orbits are
in general nearly circles with the sun at the common center and are nearly
in the same plane. The orbit of Pluto departs most conspicuously from
these regularities.

(2) The orbits are nearly in the same plane. With the prominent
exception of Pluto, the inclinations of the orbits to the ecliptic do
not exceed 8°; so that these planets are always near the ecliptic and
are generally within the boundaries of the zodiac.

(3) The revolutions are all *direct,* that is, in the same direction
(west to east) as the earth's revolution. This is the favored direction
of revolution and rotation of all planets and satellites, as compared
with *retrograde* motion (east to west).

(4) The distances of the planets from the sun are given approximately by the "Law" (7·5) employed by J. E. Bode in 1772.

The conspicuous departures from these regularities may be equally significant, as we note later, in showing alterations in the planetary system subsequent to its formation. As an example, it has been shown that Pluto may have been a satellite of Neptune, which escaped from that planet.

7·5. Bode's Law is obtained by writing the numbers 0, 3, 6, 12, 24, . . . , doubling the number each time to obtain the next one, then by adding 4 to each number and dividing the sums by 10. The resulting series of numbers, 0.4, 0.7, 1.0, 1.6, 2.8, . . . , represents the mean distances of the planets from the sun, expressed in astronomical units (Table 7·I). The astronomical unit is the earth's mean distance from the sun.

TABLE 7·I DISTANCES AND PERIODS OF THE PLANETS

Name	Mean Distance from Sun			Period of Revolution	
	Bode's Law	Astron. Units	Million Miles	Sidereal	Mean Synodic
				days	days
Mercury	0.4	0.39	36	88	116
Venus	0.7	0.72	67	225	584
Earth	1.0	1.00	93	365¼	
Mars	1.6	1.52	142	687	780
				years	
Ceres	2.8	2.77	257	5	467
Jupiter	5.2	5.20	483	12	399
Saturn	10.0	9.54	886	29	378
Uranus	19.6	19.18	1783	84	370
Neptune	38.8	30.06	2794	165	367
Pluto		39.52	3670	248	367

There was at the time when Bode called attention to the law, however, one exception to it; the number 2.8 between the numbers for Mars and Jupiter corresponded to the mean distance of no known planet. Bode pointed out that the success of the law in other respects justified a search for the missing planet. The discovery of Uranus, in 1781, at a distance in satisfactory agreement with the series extended one term further, so strengthened his position that a systematic search was undertaken by a group of European astronomers. As it turned out, the asteroid Ceres was discovered accidentally by Piazzi, in 1801, at the expected distance of 2.8 astronomical units. This is very nearly the average distance of the many hundreds of asteroids since discovered.

7·6. Sidereal and Synodic Periods. The *sidereal period* of a planet is the interval between two successive returns of the planet to the same point in the heavens, as seen from the sun. It is the true period of the planet's revolution around the sun. This interval ranges from 88 days for Mercury to 248 years for Pluto.

The *synodic period* is the interval between two successive conjunctions of a planet with the sun, as seen from the earth; for an inferior planet the conjunctions must both be either inferior or superior (Fig. 7·7). It is the interval after which the faster-moving inferior planet again overtakes the earth, or the earth again overtakes the slower superior planet. The relation between the two periods for any planet is:

$$\frac{1}{\text{synodic period}} = \pm \frac{1}{\text{sidereal period}} \mp \frac{1}{\text{earth's sidereal period}},$$

where the upper signs are for an inferior planet and the lower signs are for a superior planet. This is merely the statement of the fact that the rate at which the other planet gains on the earth, or the earth gains on the other planet, is the difference of the angular rates of their revolutions around the sun.

As an example of the use of this relation, let us calculate approximately the synodic period of the planet Mercury from its sidereal period. The relation becomes: 1/synodic period = 1/88 − 1/365¼ days. Mercury's mean synodic period is therefore 365¼ × 88/ (365¼ − 88) days, or about 116 days.

Mars and Venus have the longest synodic periods for the principal planets (Table 7·I) because they run the closest race with the earth. The synodic periods of the outer planets approach the length of the year as their distances from the sun, and therefore their sidereal periods, increase.

7·7. Aspects and Phases of the Inferior Planets. Because the inferior planets, Mercury and Venus, revolve faster than the earth does, they gain on the earth and therefore appear to us to oscillate to the east and west with respect to the sun's place in the sky. Their aspects are unlike those of the moon (5·5), which has all values of elongation up to 180°.

After passing *superior conjunction* beyond the sun, the inferior planet emerges to the east of the sun as an evening star and slowly moves out to *greatest eastern elongation.* Here it turns west and, apparently moving more rapidly, passes between us and the sun at

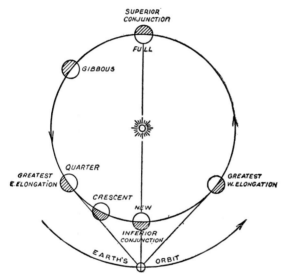

FIG. 7·7. Aspects and Phases of an Inferior Planet. The aspects differ from those of the moon. The phases are the same as the moon's.

inferior conjunction into the morning sky. Turning east again at *greatest western elongation,* it returns to superior conjunction. Greatest elongation does not exceed 28° for Mercury and 48° for Venus.

The phases of the inferior planets resemble those of the moon (5·6). As these planets revolve within the earth's orbit, their sunlit hemispheres are presented to the earth in varying amounts; they show about the full phase at the time of superior conjunction, the quarter phase in the average near the elongations, and about the new phase at inferior conjunction.

7·8. Aspects and Phases of the Superior Planets. Because the superior planets revolve more slowly than the earth does, they move eastward in the sky more slowly than the sun appears to do, so that they are overtaken and passed by it at intervals. With respect to the sun's position they seem to move westward (clockwise in Fig. 7·8), and to attain all values of elongation from 0° to 180°. The aspects of the superior planets are the same as those of the moon.

Jupiter, as an example, emerges from *conjunction* to the west of the sun. It is then visible as a morning star, rising at dawn in the east. Moving westward gradually with respect to the sun, it comes successively to *western quadrature* when it is in the south at sunrise, to *opposition* when it is in the south at midnight, and to *eastern quadrature* when it is in the south at sunset. Setting earlier from night to night as it approaches the next conjunction with the sun, the planet is finally lost in the twilight in the west.

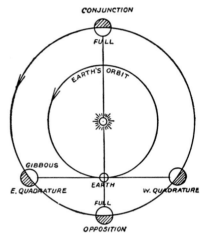

The superior planets do not exhibit the whole cycle of phases that the moon shows. At the conjunctions and oppositions their disks are fully illuminated, and in other positions they do not depart much

FIG. 7·8. Aspects and Phases of a Superior Planet. The aspects are similar to those of the moon. The only phases are full and gibbous.

from the full phase; for the hemisphere turned toward the sun is nearly the same as the one presented to the earth.

The *phase angle* is the angle at the planet between the directions of the earth and sun; divided by 180°, it gives the fraction of the hemisphere turned toward the earth that is in darkness. The phase angle is greatest when the planet is near quadrature; the maximum value is 47° for Mars, 12° for Jupiter, and is successively smaller for the more distant planets. Thus the superior planets show nearly the full phase at all times with the conspicuous exception of Mars, which near quadrature resembles the gibbous moon.

THE PATHS OF THE PLANETS

7·9. Apparent Motions Among the Stars. It is instructive to observe not merely that the planets move among the constellations, but also the complex paths they follow. Mars serves well as an example. Two or three months before the scheduled date of an opposition of Mars, note its position in the sky relative to nearby stars, and mark the place and date on a star map. Repeat the observation about once a week as long as the planet remains in view in the evening sky. A smooth curve through the plotted points, as in Fig. 7·9, represents the apparent path.

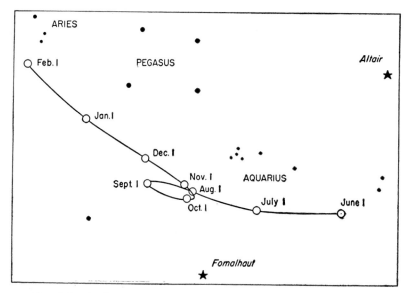

Fig. 7·9. Path of Mars Near the Favorable Opposition of 1956.

Against the background of the stars the motion is generally eastward, or *direct,* the same as the direction of the revolution around the sun. Once during each synodic period the planet turns and moves westward, or *retrogrades,* for a time before resuming the eastward motion. Thus the planets appear to move among the stars in a succession of loops, making progress toward the east and generally not departing far from the ecliptic.

7·10. Retrograde Motions Explained. The earth's eastward movement in its orbit around the sun tends to shift the planets backward, toward the west, among the stars. It is the same effect that one observes as he drives along the highway; objects pass by, and those nearer the road go by more rapidly than do those in the distance.

This effect combines with the planets' real eastward motions to produce the looped paths that are observed.

A superior planet, such as Mars, retrogrades near the time of opposition; for the earth then overtakes the planet and leaves it behind. The direct motion becomes more rapid near conjunction, where the planet's orbital motion and its displacement caused by the earth's revolution are in the same direction.

An inferior planet retrogrades near inferior conjunction. This can be shown by extending the lines in Fig. 7·10 in the reverse

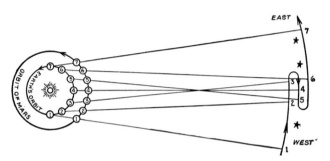

Fig. 7·10. Retrograde Motion of a Superior Planet. Positions of the earth at intervals of a month are numbered on the inner circle. Corresponding positions of Mars in its orbit are similarly numbered on the outer circle. As seen from the faster-moving earth, Mars retrogrades at positions 4 and 5, around the time of opposition.

direction, whereupon it is evident that the earth—an inferior planet relative to Mars, and then near inferior conjunction as viewed from that planet—is retrograding in the Martian sky. Mercury and Venus exhibit this effect to us. In general, a planet retrogrades for us when it is nearest the earth.

As long as the earth was believed to be stationary at the center of the system, the looped paths of the planets had necessarily to be ascribed entirely to the movements of the planets themselves. Complex motions such as these called for a complex explanation. The problem was finally simplified by the acceptance of the earth's revolution around the sun.

7·11. The Earlier Geocentric System. As early as the 6th century B.C., the earth was regarded by the Greek scholars as a stationary globe. Supported on an axis through the earth, the sky was a hollow concentric globe on which the stars were set; it rotated daily from east to west, causing the stars to rise and set. Within the sphere of the stars the sun, moon, and five bright planets shared in the daily rotation. They also revolved eastward around the earth, pausing periodically to retreat toward the west against the turning background of the constellations. The geocentric system remained almost unchallenged for more than 2000 years and was amplified meanwhile in attempts to account for the retrograde movements of the planets.

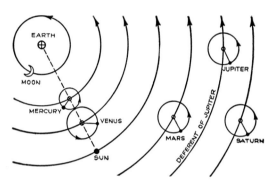

Fig. 7·11.   The Ptolemaic System of Planetary Motions.

The problem of the planetary motions that the early scholars undertook to solve was simply kinematical. By what combination of uniform circular motions centered in the earth could the looped movements be represented? The most enduring solution of the early problem is known as the *Ptolemaic system,* because it is described in detail in Ptolemy's *Almagest.* In the simplest form of the system each planet moved uniformly in a circle, the epicycle, while the center of this circle was in uniform circular motion around the earth.

The working out of the solution consisted in obtaining by trial and error a better fit between the pattern and the apparent paths of the planets among the stars. The undertaking held the attention of astronomers, especially in the Arabian dominions, from Ptolemy's time to the revival of learning in Europe. Eventually the whole construction became cumbersome, but without satisfactory improvement in representing the observed planetary motions.

7·12. The Heliocentric System. Nicolaus Copernicus (1473–1543) inaugurated a new era in astronomy by discarding the ancient theory of the central, motionless earth. In his book, *On the Revolutions* *of the Celestial Bodies,* published shortly before his death, he showed that all these motions could be interpreted more reasonably on the theory of the central sun. He assumed that the earth revolves around the sun once in a year and rotates daily on its axis.

In the *Copernican system* the sun was stationary at the center. Around it the planets revolved uniformly in circles, including the earth and its attendant, the moon. Epicycles were therefore still required, but their number was now smaller. With the additional assumption of the earth's rotation from west to east, the daily circling of all the celestial bodies from east to west became simply the scenery passing by.

No longer required to rotate around the earth, the sphere of the stars could be imagined larger than before. This altered condition and the sun's new status as the dominant member of the system prepared the way for the thought that the stars are remote suns.

It is not surprising that the heliocentric theory met with disapproval on almost every hand; for it was a radical departure from the common-sense view of the world that had persisted from the very beginning of reflections about it. The new theory was supported at the outset by no convincing proof; its greater simplicity in representing celestial motions was the only argument Copernicus could offer in its defense. Moreover, it seemed to be discredited by the evidence of the celestial bodies themselves, as Tycho presently discovered.

7·13. Tycho's Observations. Tycho Brahe (1546–1601), native of the extreme south of Sweden, then a part of Denmark, spent the most fruitful years of his life at the fine observatory that the king of Denmark had financed for him on the island of Hven, about 20 miles northeast of Copenhagen. During the last two years of his life, his observations were made at a castle near Prague.

The instruments of Tycho's observatory were mainly constructed of metal; they had larger and more accurately divided circles than any previously used. His improved methods of observing and his allowance for effects of atmospheric refraction, which observers before him had neglected, made it possible to determine the places of the celestial bodies in the sky with the average error of an observation scarcely exceeding a minute of arc. This was remarkable precision for observations made through the plain sights that preceded the telescope.

Tycho was unable to detect any annual variations in the relative directions of the stars, which he believed would be noticeable if the earth revolved around the sun. Either the nearer stars were so remote (at least 7000 times as far away as the sun) that their very small parallaxes could not be observed with his instruments, or else the earth did not revolve around the sun. Because the first alternative required distances that then seemed impossibly great, Tycho rejected the Copernican assumption of the earth's revolution.

As a substitute for the Copernican system, the *Tychonic system* again placed the earth stationary at the center. In that system the sun and moon circled around the earth, but the other planets revolved around the sun. Aside from slight effects that could not have been detected without a telescope, the Tychonic and Copernican systems were identical for calculations of the positions of the planets.

Tycho's most noteworthy contribution to the improvement of the planetary theory was his long-continued determinations of the places of the planets in the sky, their right ascensions and declinations at different times, especially of the planet Mars. These data provided the material for Kepler's studies, which resulted in his three laws of planetary motions.

7·14. Kepler's Studies. John Kepler (1571—1630), a German, joined Tycho at Prague in 1600 and, as his successor, inherited the records of Tycho's many observations of the places of the planets. Beginning with the recorded places of Mars, Kepler at first undertook to represent them in the traditional way by combinations of epicycles

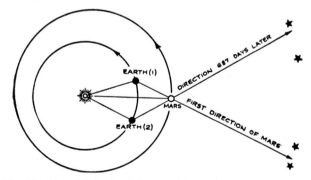

FIG. 7·14. Kepler's Method of Determining the Orbit of Mars. Pairs of apparent places of Mars separated by its sidereal period of 687 days gave the planet's direction and distance in astronomical units from the sun.

and eccentrics, but was unable to fit all the places as closely as their high accuracy seemed to require. Experimenting further with ellipses having the sun at one focus, he was astonished to see the large discrepancies between observation and theory disappear.

Tycho's observations of the planets' right ascensions and declinations gave only their directions from the earth at the various dates. Kepler required for his studies their directions and distances from the sun. This he accomplished by the following device, as Fig. 7·14 is intended to show.

Consider the case of Mars, having a sidereal period of 687 days, and neglect for the present purpose the inclination of its orbit to the ecliptic. Compare two observations of the planet's position made 687 days apart. At the end of this interval Mars has returned to the same place in its orbit, while the earth is 43 days' journey west of its original place. Accordingly, the observed directions of Mars on the two occasions differ widely and, by their intersection, show where the planet is situated in space. By comparing such pairs of observations in different parts of the planet's orbit it is possible to determine the form of the orbit and its size relative to the earth's orbit.

7·15. Kepler's Laws. Kepler's first two laws of the planetary motions were published in 1609, in his book entitled *Commentaries on the Motion of Mars*. The third, or *harmonic law*, the formulation of which gave him greater trouble, appeared in 1618, in his book *The Harmony of the World*. Kepler's laws are as follows:

1. The orbit of each planet is an ellipse with the sun at one of its foci.

2. Each planet revolves so that the line joining it to the sun sweeps over equal areas in equal intervals of time.

3. The squares of the periods of any two planets are in the same proportion as the cubes of their mean distances from the sun.

These laws assert that the planets revolve around the sun, but they do not necessarily include the earth as one of the planets. It was not yet possible to choose between the Copernican and Tychonic systems. The laws bring to an end the practice of representing planetary movements only by combinations of uniform circular motions. The third law determines the mean distances of all the planets from the sun in terms of the distance of one of them, when their sidereal periods of revolution are known. The usual yardstick is the earth's mean distance from the sun, which is accordingly called the *astronomical unit*.

7·16. The Scale of the Solar System. The problem of determining the scale of the solar system as accurately as possible is often called the solar parallax problem, because the sun's geocentric parallax may be regarded as the required constant. The corresponding value of the astronomical unit gives the linear scale. By international agreement the astronomical almanacs since 1896 have adopted 8″.80 as the value of the solar parallax. The earth's mean distance from the sun is accordingly considered to be about 92,900,000 miles.

Because the relative dimensions of planetary orbits are given by Kepler's third law restated to include the masses (7·22), one distance determined in the system provides the scale in miles as well as another distance. The many projects for obtaining the scale of the solar system have employed observed positions of planets that approach the earth nearer than the sun's distance. The optical result believed to have the highest order of precision was derived in 1950 by Eugene Rabe of the Cincinnati Observatory from his studies of the orbit of the asteroid Eros as perturbed by the principal planets. His value of the earth's mean distance from the sun is 92,914,800 miles.

Radio methods of observing the scale of the system are also being employed effectively. The timing of many radar echoes from the planet Venus near its inferior conjunction in April, 1961, gave remarkably consistent results. These programs were reported by Millstone radar, Goldstone radar, and three other radio observatories. The average value of the solar parallax was about 8″.794 and the corresponding value of the earth's mean distance from the sun was about 1.496×10^8 km, or 92,950,000 miles.

7·17. Galileo; the Motions of Bodies. While Kepler was engaged in his studies of planetary orbits, Galileo Galilei (1564–1642), in Italy, was finding evidence with the telescope in favor of the Copernican system.

Galileo's discovery of four bright satellites revolving around the planet Jupiter dispelled the objection that the moon would be left behind if the earth really revolved around the sun. His discovery that Venus shows phases like those of the moon discredited the specification of the Ptolemaic system (Fig. 7·11) that kept the planet always on the earthward side of the sun, where it could never increase beyond the crescent phase. His explanation that the movements of spots across the sun's disk are caused by the sun's rotation provided an argument by analogy for the earth's rotation as well.

Galileo's chief contribution to knowledge of the planetary movements was his pioneer work on the motions of bodies in general. His conclusion that an undisturbed body continues to move uniformly in a straight line, or to remain at rest, and his studies of the rate of change of motion of a body not left to itself prepared the way for a new viewpoint in astronomy. The interest was beginning to shift from the kinematics to the dynamics of the solar system—from the courses of the planets to forces controlling them.

THE LAW OF GRAVITATION

7·18. Force Equals Mass Times Acceleration. The concept of forces acting throughout the universe originates in our own experience with the things around us. If an object at rest, that is free to move, is pulled or pushed, it responds by moving in the direction of the pull or push. We say that force is applied to the object and, with allowance for disturbing factors such as air resistance and surface friction, we estimate the force by the mass of the object that is moved and the acceleration, or the rate at which its motion changes. In general, the acceleration of a body anywhere in any direction implies a force acting on it in that direction. The amount of the force is found by multiplying the mass of the body by its acceleration, or $f = ma$.

Acceleration is defined as the rate of change of velocity. Since *velocity* is directed speed, acceleration may appear either as changing speed or changing direction, or both. A falling stone illustrates the first case; its behavior is represented by the relations:

$$v = v_0 + at; \qquad s = v_0 t + \tfrac{1}{2}at^2,$$

where v_0 is the speed when first observed, a is the acceleration of about 32 feet/sec² toward the earth, and v and s are the speed and the distance the stone has fallen after t seconds. If the stone starts at rest ($v_0 = 0$), it will fall about 16 feet in the first second, 48 feet in the next second, and so on, getting up speed at the rate of 32 feet/sec².

A planet moving in a circular orbit illustrates acceleration in direction only; the speed is constant. If the planet describes an elliptic orbit, the speed also changes in accordance with Kepler's second law.

7·19. The Laws of Motion. The conclusions of Galileo and others concerning the relations between bodies and their motions were consolidated by Isaac Newton (1642–1727), in his *Principia* (1687), into three statements, which are substantially as follows:

1. Every body persists in its state of rest or of uniform motion in a straight line, unless it is compelled to change that state by a force impressed upon it.

2. The acceleration is directly proportional to the force and inversely to the mass of the body, and it takes place in the direction of the straight line in which the force acts.

3. To every action there is always an equal and contrary reaction; or, the mutual actions of any two bodies are equal and oppositely directed.

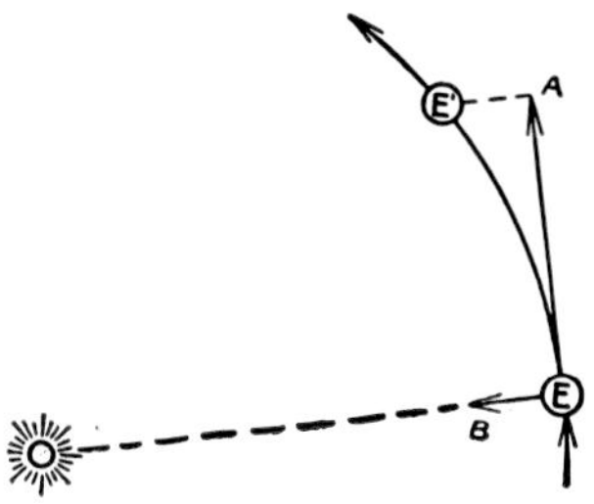

The first law states that a body subject to no external forces moves uniformly in a straight line forever, unless it happens never to have acquired any motion. Up to the time of Galileo, the continued motion of a planet required explanation; since that time, uniform motion is accepted as no more surprising than the existence of matter itself. Changing motion demands an accounting.

Fig. 7·19. The Earth's Revolution Explained by the Laws of Motion. At the position E the earth if undisturbed would continue on to A. It arrives at E' instead, having in the meantime fallen toward the sun the distance EB.

The second law defines force in the usual way. Because nothing is said to the contrary, it implies that the effect of the force is the same whether the body is originally at rest or in motion, and whether or not it is acted on at the same time by other forces.

The third law states that the force between any two bodies is the same in the two directions. The earth attracts the sun just as much as the sun attracts the earth, so that $f_S = f_E$, or $m_S a_S = m_E a_E$. But the effects of the equal forces, that is, the accelerations, are not the same if the masses are unequal; the ratio of the accelerations is the inverse ratio of the masses affected.

7·20. The Law of Gravitation. By means of his laws of motion and by mathematical reasoning, Newton succeeded in reducing Kepler's geometrical description of the planetary system to a single comprehensive physical law. It will serve our present purpose simply to outline the sequence and chief results of Newton's inquiry.

By Kepler's first law, the path of a planet is an ellipse; it is continually curving. Consequently, the planet's motion is continually accelerated and, by the second law of motion, a force is always acting on the planet.

Since the planet moves, by Kepler's second law, so that the line joining it to the sun describes equal areas in equal times, it is easily proved that the force is directed toward the sun. Kepler had suspected that the sun had something to do with the planet's revolution, but he did not understand the connection.

Again from Kepler's first law, since the orbit is an ellipse with the sun at one focus, it can be proved that the force varies inversely as the square of the planet's distance from the sun. An elliptic orbit would also result if the force varied directly as the distance, but in this event the sun would be at the center of the ellipse, not at one focus.

From Kepler's third law and the third law of motion, it can be shown that the attractive force between the sun and any planet varies directly as the product of their masses. In addition, Newton discovered that the moon's revolution is controlled by precisely the same force directed toward the earth. Although his experience did not extend beyond the solar system, he concluded that this force operates everywhere. These were the steps that led to the formulation of the *law of gravitation:*

> Every particle of matter in the universe attracts every other particle with a force that varies directly as the product of their masses, and inversely as the square of the distance between them.

7·21. Examining the Law of Gravitation. The law of gravitation provides the key for the interpretation of celestial motions. It is therefore important to understand the meaning of the law. The statement is

$$f = Gm_1m_2/d^2,$$

where f is the force, m_1 and m_2 are the masses of the two particles, and d is their distance apart.

(1) *The constant of gravitation, G,* is defined as the force of attraction between two unit masses at unit distance apart. If $m_1 = m_2 = 1$ gram, and d is 1 centimeter, then $G = f$. It is believed to be a universal constant, like the speed of light; but it is even more remarkable as a constant, for the speed of light is reduced by an interposing medium such as glass, whereas the force of gravitation is unaffected by anything placed between the attracting bodies.

The value of this constant is best determined in the physical laboratory by the method first employed by the English scientist Henry Cavendish about 1798. It consists in measuring the attractions of metallic balls or cylinders. Heyl's determination at the National Bureau of Standards in 1942 gave the value $G = 6.673 \times 10^{-8}$ in the c.g.s. system. Thus the attraction between gram masses 1 cm apart is only a 15-millionth of a dyne. Although it is very feeble between ordinary bodies, the gravitational force becomes important between the great masses of celestial bodies. The *Gaussian constant of gravitation* is much used in astronomical calculations; it is the acceleration produced by the sun's attraction at the earth's mean distance from the sun.

(2) *The attraction of a sphere is toward its center,* as though the whole mass were concentrated there. Because of their rotations the celestial bodies are not spheres, but the flattening at their poles is often so small and the intervening spaces are so great that the distances between their centers may be used ordinarily in calculating their attractions. The attraction of a spheroid in the direction of its equator is greater than that of a sphere of the same mass, and is smaller in the direction of its poles.

(3) *The acceleration of the attracted body is independent of its mass.* If the force, f_1, on this body is replaced by the equivalent $m_1 a_1$ in the statement of the law of gravitation, the mass, m_1, cancels out, and the acceleration:

$$a_1 = Gm_2/d^2$$

of the attracted body does not depend on its own mass. Galileo is said to have demonstrated this fact by dropping large and small weights from the leaning tower of Pisa. They fell together, thereby discrediting the traditional idea that heavy bodies fall faster than light ones.

The second, or attracting body, as we have chosen to consider it, is itself attracted and has the acceleration $a_2 = Gm_1/d^2$ in the direction of the first. In Galileo's experiment this factor need not be taken into account; it becomes important when the two bodies have comparable masses. The acceleration of one body with respect to the other is the sum:

$$a_1 + a_2 = G(m_1 + m_2)/d^2.$$

Thus the relative acceleration of two bodies varies directly as the sum of their masses.

(4) *Two bodies, such as the earth and sun, mutually revolve around a common center between them.* Imagine the earth and sun joined by a stout rod. The point of support at which the two bodies would balance is the *center of mass;* it is the point around which they revolve in orbits of the same shape. If the masses of the two were equal, this point would be halfway between their centers. Because the sun's mass is 332,000 times as great as the earth's mass, the center of mass is not far from the sun's center. The relation is:

$$\frac{\text{Sun's center to center of mass}}{\text{Earth's center to center of mass}} = \frac{\text{earth's mass}}{\text{sun's mass}}.$$

The distance from the sun's center to the center of mass of the earth-sun system is therefore 92,900,000 miles divided by 332,000, which equals 280 miles.

7·22. Kepler's Third Law Restated. In its original form (7·15), Kepler's harmonic law gave a relation between the periods of revolution and the distances of the planets from the sun. As it is now derived from the law of gravitation, the relation involves the masses of the planets as well; it is as follows:

The squares of the periods of any two planets, each multiplied by the sum of the sun's mass and the planet's mass, are in the same proportion as the cubes of their mean distances from the sun.

Consider two planets, Mars and the earth. Let m represent the mass, P the sidereal period of revolution of the planet, and d its mean distance from the sun. The revised harmonic law is in this case:

$$\frac{(m_S + m_M)P^2{}_{MS}}{(m_S + m_E)P^2{}_{ES}} = \frac{d^3{}_{MS}}{d^3{}_{ES}}.$$

The law in its original form was not far from correct, because the masses of all the planets are so small in comparison with the sun's mass that the ratio of the sums of the masses is nearly unity.

Let the units of mass, time, and distance in the above relation be respectively the sun's mass (neglecting the inconsiderable relative mass of the earth), the sidereal year, and the earth's mean distance from the sun. The denominators then disappear because their terms are all unity. Further, in the place of Mars and the sun take any mutually revolving bodies anywhere, denoting them by the subscripts 1 and 2. They may be the sun and a planet, a planet and its satellite, or a double star. In the more general form Kepler's third law becomes:

$$m_1 + m_2 = d_{12}{}^3/P_{12}{}^2.$$

The sum of the masses of any two mutually revolving bodies, *in terms of the sun's mass,* equals the cube of their mean linear separation, *in astronomical units,* divided by the square of their period of revolution, *in years.*

In this way the masses of the sun and of planets having satellites have been determined, the masses of the second bodies of the pairs being small enough in these cases to be neglected in comparison. The formula does not serve for the solitary planets, such as Mercury and Pluto, nor for the asteroids, the satellites themselves, the comets, and the meteor swarms. Their masses become known only in case they noticeably disturb the orbits of neighboring bodies.

7·23. The Relative Orbit of Two Bodies. We have noted (7·21) that two bodies, such as the earth and sun, mutually revolve around their center of mass, which is nearer the more massive body, so that the less massive component has the larger orbit. It can be shown (1) that the orbits are independent of any motion of the center of mass, that is, of the system as a whole; (2) that the individual orbits are the same in form, and that this is also the form of the *relative orbit* of one body with respect to the other. The relative orbit is often the only one that can be calculated; it is the one understood when one body is said to revolve around another.

Kepler's first law states that the orbits of the planets are ellipses. Newton proved that the orbit of a body revolving around another in accordance with the law of gravitation must be a conic, of which the ellipse is an example.

7·24. The Conics, or conic sections, are the ellipse, parabola, and hyperbola. They are sections cut from a circular cone, which for this purpose is a surface generated by one of two intersecting straight lines when it is turned around the other as an axis, the angle between them remaining the same.

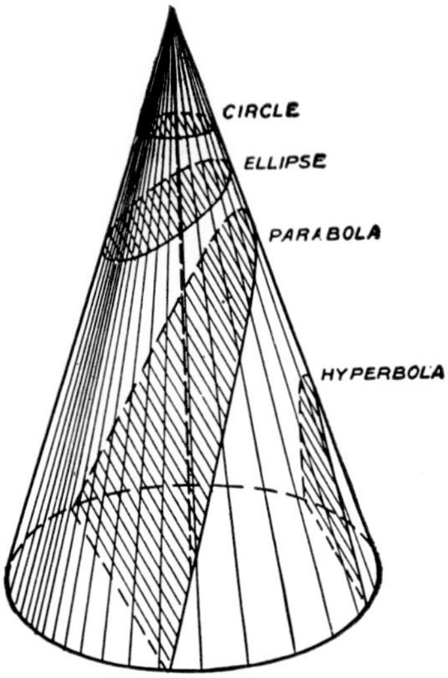

FIG. 7·24. The Conics.

The ellipse (eccentricity 0 to nearly 1) is obtained when the cutting plane passes entirely through the cone, so that the section is closed. When the plane passes at right angles to the axis, the eccentricity of the ellipse is zero, and the section is a circle.

The parabola (eccentricity 1) results when the cutting plane is parallel to an element of the cone. This curve extends an indefinite distance, the two sides approaching parallelism. All parabolas, like all circles, have the same form but not the same size. The orbits of many comets are nearly parabolas.

The hyperbola (eccentricity greater than 1) is obtained when the cone is cut at a still smaller angle with the axis. It is an open curve like the parabola, but the directions of the two sides approach diverging straight lines. If a star passes another and is deflected by attraction from its original course, the orbit is hyperbolic.

7·25. Form of the Relative Orbit. The particular conic in which a celestial body revolves is determined by the central force and the velocity of the body in the orbit; for it is evident that the curvature of the orbit depends on the deflection of the body in the direction of its companion and the distance it has moved forward meanwhile in the orbit. This conclusion, among others, is obtained formally from the *equation of energy*, which is not derived here:

$$V^2 = G(m_1 + m_2)(2/r - 1/a),$$

where V is the velocity of revolution when the two bodies are at the distance r apart, and a is half the major axis of the resulting orbit.

It can be seen from this equation that the semimajor axis lengthens as the velocity is greater. For a moderate speed, the orbit is an ellipse; for increasing speeds the length and eccentricity of the orbit grow greater, until a critical speed is reached at which the orbit becomes a parabola.

If the orbit is a circle, then $a = r$ in the above formula, so that V^2 is proportional to $1/r$. If the orbit is a parabola, a is infinite and V^2 is proportional to $2/r$. There-fore, if the speed of a body revolving in a circular orbit is multiplied by the square root of 2, or about 1.41, the orbit becomes a parabola. Because the earth's orbit is nearly circular, the *parabolic velocity* at our distance from the sun is the earth's velocity, 18½ miles a second, multiplied by 1.41, which equals 26 miles a second. If its velocity should ever become as great as this value, the earth would depart from the sun's vicinity. Many comets and meteors, having their aphelion points far beyond the orbit of Neptune, cross the earth's orbit with speeds of this order.

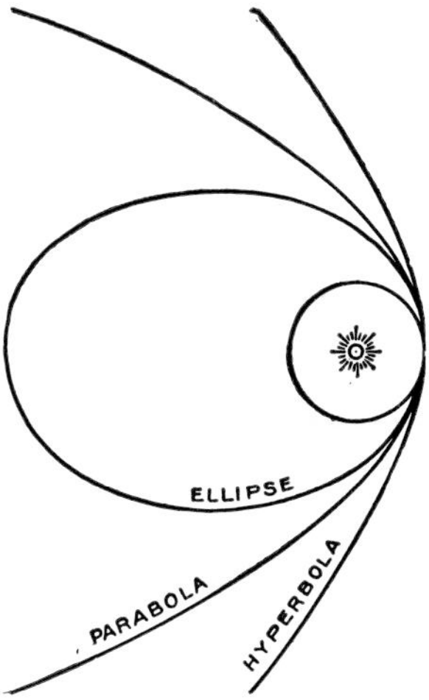

Fig. 7·25. Orbits Having the Same Perihelion Distance. The size and eccentricity of the orbit increase with the speed of the revolving body at perihelion.

7·26. The Elements of the Orbit are the specifications necessary to define it uniquely and to fix the place of the revolving body in the orbit at any time. The elements of the elliptical orbit of a planet, with their symbols, are the following:

(1) *Inclination to ecliptic, i.* If the plane of the orbit is inclined to the ecliptic plane (i denotes the numerical value of the inclination), the line of their intersection is the *line of nodes,* which passes through the sun's position. The *ascending node* is the projection on the ecliptic, from the sun, of the point at which the planet crosses the ecliptic plane going from south to north.

(2) *Longitude of the ascending node,* ☊. It is the celestial longitude of this node as seen from the sun, that is, the angle between the line of nodes and the direction of the vernal equinox. It fixes the orientation of the orbit plane, and, together with the inclination, defines this plane precisely.

(3) *Angle from the ascending node to the perihelion point,* **ω.** It is

measured from the ascending node along the orbit in the direction of the planet's motion, which must be specified; it gives the direction of the major axis of the orbit with respect to the line of nodes, and thus describes the orientation of the orbit in its plane.

(4) *Semimajor axis, a.* This element, which is also known as the planet's *mean distance* from the sun, defines the size of the orbit and, very nearly, the period of revolution; for by Kepler's third law, P^2 is proportional to a^3 regardless of the shape of the ellipse.

(5) *Eccentricity, e.* The eccentricity of the ellipse is the ratio c/a, where c is the sun's distance from the center of the ellipse (one half the distance between the foci). These five elements define the relative orbit uniquely.

(6) *Time of passing perihelion, T.* This element and the value of the period of revolution permit the determination of the planet's position in the orbit at any time.

If the orbit is circular, the longitude of perihelion drops out; if it is a parabola, the semimajor axis, which is then infinite, is replaced as an element by the *perihelion distance, q,* which defines the size of the parabola.

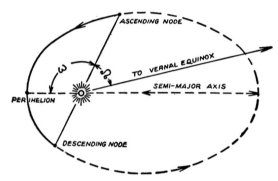

Fig. 7·26. The Orbit of a Planet. The plane of the planet's orbit is inclined to the plane of the earth's orbit, represented by the plane of the paper.

When the elements become known, the position of the planet or comet at any time can be computed; this, combined with the earth's position in its orbit at that time, gives finally the apparent place of the object as seen from the earth, its right ascension and declination. A tabulation of such places at regular intervals, often of a day, is an *ephemeris.* The astronomical almanacs give such tabulations for the sun, moon, principal planets, and certain asteroids for each year in advance.

7·27. Perturbations. Thus far we have dealt with the revolution of a body around the sun generally as though the body were acted on only by the sun's attraction.   This is the *problem of two bodies,* which is solved directly and completely in terms of the law of gravitation.   However, the body is subject to the attractions of other members of the solar system as well, so that it departs in a complex manner from simple elliptic motion.   Thus we have in practice the *problem of three or more bodies,* the solution of which is more troublesome.   It is fortunate for the orderly description of the planetary movements that the masses of the planets are small in comparison with the sun's mass and that their distances apart are very great.   If it were not so, the mutual disturbances of the revolving bodies would introduce so much confusion that simple approximations, such as Kepler's laws, would have been impossible.

Because the sun's mass is dominant in the solar system, it is possible to derive at first the planet's orbit with reference to the sun alone and then to consider the departures from simple elliptic motion that are imposed by the attractions of other members of the system.   *Perturbations* are the alterations so produced.   As examples, the eccentricities and inclinations of planetary orbits fluctuate, perihelia advance, and nodes regress.   All perturbations are oscillatory in the long run, so that they are not likely to alter permanently the general arrangement of the solar system.

7·28. Perturbations of Artificial Satellites.   The orbits of artificial satellites revolving near the earth are strongly perturbed by the oblate earth, effects that are not considerably confused with perturbations by the sun.   These orbits are also perturbed by resistance of the earth's atmosphere, giving information as to the density of the upper atmosphere at different elevations.   As an example, consider the perturbations of satellite 1957-alpha (2·9) as reported by the Smithsonian Astrophysical Observatory from many observed positions of the rocket shell.   The main perturbations of the orbit were:

(1) *Regression of the nodes,* where the orbit crossed the plane of the earth's equator.   The earth's equatorial bulge tended to pull the satellite's orbit into the equator plane, thus decreasing the original 65° inclination of the orbit.   This tendency was resisted by the satellite's revolution.   The result was a gyroscopic westward shifting of the orbit around the earth.   The nodes regressed at the rate of 3°.1 a day, or three complete turns in about a year.   For comparison (5·11) the nodes of the moon's path make a complete turn around the ecliptic in 18.6 years.

(2) *Advance of perigee.* The elliptical orbit of the satellite turned in its plane at the rate of 0°.4 a day, the perigee advancing in the direction of the revolution. The moon's perigee advances much more slowly.

(3) *The effect of air resistance* was to make the satellite spiral toward the earth, revolving faster and in an orbit of decreasing eccentricity. L. G. Jacchia had drawn attention to semiregular fluctuations in the decrease of the revolution periods. These he attributes to corresponding variations in density of the earth's upper atmosphere produced by variability in intensity of short-wave solar radiations.

7·29. Relativity Effects. Events in the heavens and in the laboratory are usually represented practically as well by the formulas of either Newton or Einstein. A few exceptional cases are known where the predictions on the two theories differ widely enough to be subject to the test of observation. These involve the presence of large masses or very high speeds. In such cases the observational evidence supports the theory of relativity.

The first test case was the rate of rotation of the major axis of Mercury's orbit. The perihelion point for this planet advances eastward at the rate of 573″ a century, whereas the rate predicted by the Newtonian theory on the basis of the attractions of other planets is 43″ less. Albert Einstein explained, in 1915, that the whole advance is predicted by the relativity theory; and smaller similar advances in the orbits of Venus and the earth are now known to be more accurately predicted by this theory.

Additional astronomical test cases are the apparent outward displacement of stars from the sun's place in the sky (6·8) and the red-ward displacement of the lines in the spectra of very dense stars (11·30). Another relativity effect is familiar in the operation of the synchrotron; the masses of whirling particles greatly increase as the speeds approach the speed of light.

REVIEW QUESTIONS

1. Mention three ways by which the bright planets are distinguished in the sky from the stars.

2. State the phase of the planet Venus at (a) inferior conjunction; (b) superior conjunction; (c) greatest elongation; (d) greatest brilliancy.

3. Account for the retrograde motion of a planet among the stars.

4. State the chief contribution to knowledge of planetary motions made by each of the following: (a) Copernicus; (b) Tycho; (c) Kepler; (d) Galileo; (e) Newton.

5. Why is the sun's mean distance determined more reliably from the parallaxes of certain planets than directly from the sun's parallax? Describe the more recent radar method of determining this distance.

6. Explain that a planet moving uniformly in a circular orbit is continuously accelerated.

7. Show that Newton's first and second laws of motion contain little more than the definition of force.

8. State the law of gravitation. How is the force between two bodies affected (a) if the original distance between them is doubled? (b) if the distance is unaltered but the mass of each body is doubled?

9. Supposing that Galileo actually made the experiment of dropping objects of different weights from the leaning tower in Pisa, explain by means of the law of gravitation, neglecting air resistance, that they reached the ground at the same instant.

10. Why is it easier to determine the mass of a planet having a satellite than of one without a satellite?

11. It is improbable that the orbit of a body revolving around the sun can be either a circle or a parabola. Explain.

12. Supply the term that is defined by each of the following:

(a) Directed speed.
(b) Rate of change of velocity.
(c) Cross section of a right circular cone.
(d) Earth's mean distance from the sun.
(e) Force of attraction between two 1-gram masses 1 centimeter apart.
(f) Specifications that define the orbit of a planet and the planet's position in the orbit at any particular time.

Problems

1. The sidereal period of Venus is 224.7 days. Calculate (7·6) the synodic period of the planet.

Answer: 583.9 days.

2. A ball near the earth's surface falls from rest 16 feet in the first second, or half the acceleration. The moon's distance from the earth's center is about 60 times the radius of the earth. Show that the moon "falls" toward the earth about $\frac{1}{20}$ inch in 1 second.

3. Employing the 9th satellite of Jupiter and neglecting its mass, calculate the approximate mass of the planet by Kepler's third law in its more general form (7·22). The mean distance of the satellite from Jupiter is about $\frac{1}{6}$ astronomical unit, and its period of revolution is about 2.1 years.

Answer: Jupiter's mass is about $\frac{1}{953}$ of the sun's mass.

4. By analogy with Kepler's original third law, the squares of the periods of two bodies revolving around the earth are in the same proportion as the cubes of their mean distances from the earth. Calculate the approximate period of an artificial satellite revolving close to the earth's surface. Take the moon's sidereal period as $27\frac{1}{3}$ days.

Answer: The period is about 1^h 24^m.

REFERENCES

Blanco, V. M., and S. W. McCuskey, *Basic Physics of the Solar System.* Addison-Wesley Publishing Company, Reading, Mass., 1961.

Brouwer, Dirk, and Gerald M. Clemence, *Methods of Celestial Mechanics.* Academic Press, New York, 1961.

De Vaucouleurs, Gerard, *Discovery of the Universe.* An outline of the history of astronomy from the origins to 1956. The Macmillan Company, New York, 1957.

Dreyer, J. L. E., *History of the Planetary Systems from Thales to Kepler.* Photo-offset of the 1906 edition with title: *A History of Astronomy from Thales to Kepler.* Dover Publications, New York, 1953.

Moulton, F. R., *An Introduction to Celestial Mechanics.* New edition. The Macmillan Company, New York, 1959.

Yerkes Observatory, Williams Bay, Wisconsin.

8

PLANETS AND THEIR SATELLITES

MERCURY – VENUS – MARS, THE RED PLANET – THE
ASTEROIDS – JUPITER, THE GIANT PLANET – SATURN
AND ITS RINGS – URANUS AND NEPTUNE – PLUTO –
TABLES OF THE PLANETS AND SATELLITES

MERCURY

Mercury is the smallest principal planet; its diameter, 2900 miles, does not greatly exceed the moon's diameter. Its surface features seem to resemble those of the moon rather than the earth. The nearest planet to the sun, Mercury revolves around the sun once in 88 days and rotates on its axis in the same period.

8·1. As Evening and Morning Star. Mercury is occasionally visible to the naked eye for a few days near the times of its greatest elongations, which occur about 22 days before and after the inferior conjunctions with the sun. Because the synodic period is only 116 days, three eastern and as many western elongations may come in the course of a year. They are not equally favorable for two reasons. (1) Mercury's apparent distance from the sun at greatest elongations ranges from 28° when the planet is also at aphelion to only 18° at peri-helion. (2) Because the planet is always near the ecliptic, it is highest in the sky at sunrise or

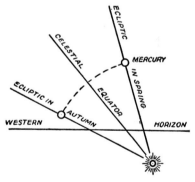

Fig. 8·1. Mercury as Evening Star. It is most conspicuous as evening star near its greatest elongations in the spring.

sunset when the ecliptic is most inclined to the horizon. This con-dition is fulfilled for us in middle northern latitudes (1·19) when the vernal equinox is setting and the autumnal equinox is rising.

195

For the second reason, Mercury is most likely to be visible as evening star near its greatest eastern elongations that occur in March and April, and as morning star near its greatest western elongations in September and October. It then appears in the twilight near the horizon, at times even a little brighter than Sirius, and twinkling like a star because of its small size and low altitude.

The terms *evening star* and *morning star* refer most often to appearances of inferior planets, particularly Venus, in the west after sunset and in the east before sunrise. The terms refer as well to superior planets that are visible in the evening and morning sky, respectively.

8·2. Viewed with the Telescope, Mercury shows phases, as an inferior planet should do (7·7). The phase is full at superior conjunction, quarter near greatest elongation, and new at inferior conjunction. The best views are likely to be obtained in the daytime, when the planet can be observed at higher altitudes. Faint dark blotches on the small disk, which may resemble the lunar seas, have been discerned by experienced observers and are recorded in some photographs. The conclusion that the period of Mercury's rotation is 88 days, the same as that of its revolution around the sun, is confirmed by A. Dollfus in France, who reports that the equator is inclined about 7° to the ecliptic.

Mercury is so near the sun that it has been constrained by powerful sun-raised tides to rotate and revolve in the same period. The same face would always be kept toward the sun if it were not for the considerable eccentricity, 0.2, of the orbit. As it is, the libration in longitude leaves only 30 per cent of the planet's surface in permanent darkness.

8·3. Mercury Resembles the Moon. This planet does not greatly exceed the moon in diameter and mass and, therefore, in surface gravity. Its low velocity of escape suggests scarcely better success than the moon has had in retaining an atmosphere. Its reflecting power is about as low as the moon's, and this small efficiency as a mirror probably has the same cause, namely, the reflection of sunlight from a rough surface having no atmosphere around it. That the planet is at least as mountainous as the moon is shown by the similar great increase in its brightness as the shadows shorten between the quarter and full phases.

The surface of Mercury is subjected to even greater extremes of temperature than that of the moon. Radiometric measures indicate a maximum of 410° C on the sunward side of the planet, which is hotter than the melting points of tin and lead. No radiation at all has been detected from the dark side, where the temperature must be extremely low.

8·4. Transits of Mercury and Venus. The inferior planets usually pass north or south of the sun at inferior conjunction. Occasionally

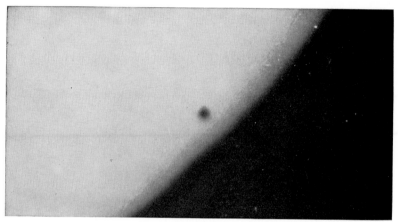

FIG. 8·4. Transit of Mercury, November 14, 1953. Photographed by J. L. Gossner at the Naval Observatory. (*U.S. Navy photograph*)

they *transit,* or cross directly in front of the sun, when they appear as dark dots against its disk. The additional condition necessary for a transit is similar to the requirement for a solar or lunar eclipse; it is that the sun must be near the line of nodes of the planet's orbit.

The sun passes the intersections of Mercury's path with the ecliptic on May 8 and November 10. Transits are possible only within 3 days of the former date and within 5 days of the latter. This difference in the limits, which is caused by the eccentricity of the planet's orbit, makes the November transits twice as numerous as those in May.

About 13 transits of Mercury occur in the course of a century. The latest one, on November 7, 1960, was visible in the United States and Canada. Transits are scheduled for the remainder of the century (Fig 8·4A) on May 9, 1970, November 10, 1973, November 13, 1986, November 6, 1993, and November 15, 1999, which will be a grazing transit. Transits of Mercury can be timed rather accurately and have been useful for improving our knowledge of the planet's motions. They cannot be viewed without a telescope.

Transits of Venus are possible only within about 2 days before or after June 7 and December 9, the dates when the sun passes the nodes of the planet's path. They are less frequent because the limits are narrower and also because conjunctions come less often.

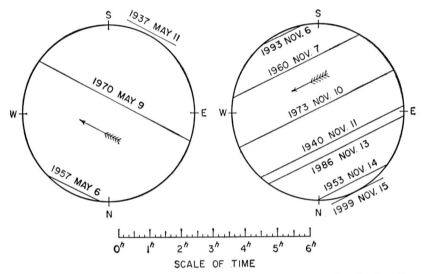

FIG. 8·4A. Transits of Mercury, 1937 to 1999. (*Diagram by Fletcher G. Watson in* Sky *and* Telescope)

Transits of Venus now come in pairs having a separation of 8 years. The latest pair of transits occurred in 1874 and 1882; the next pair is due on June 8, 2004, and June 6, 2012. After a while there will be a long period when they occur singly. These transits are visible without a telescope.

VENUS

Venus, the familiar evening and morning star, is the brightest planet. It outshines all the other celestial bodies except the sun and moon, and near the times of greatest brilliancy it is plainly visible to the naked eye at midday, when the attention is directed to it. The second in order from the sun, this planet revolves next within the earth's orbit at the mean distance of 67 million miles from the sun, completing its revolution once in 225 days. Its orbit is the most nearly circular among the principal planets. Although Venus resembles the earth in size, mass, and distance from the sun, it is quite dissimilar in its higher surface temperature, in the scarcity of free oxygen in its atmosphere, and presumably in its much slower rotation.

8·5. As Evening and Morning Star. Because the orbit of Venus is within the earth's orbit and nearly in the same plane with it, this planet, like Mercury, appears to oscillate to the east and west of the sun's position. At superior conjunction its distance from the

TABLE 8·I   DATES OF CONJUNCTIONS AND ELONGATIONS OF VENUS

Superior Conjunction	Greatest Elongation East (Evening Star)	Inferior Conjunction	Greatest Elongation West (Morning Star)
1962, Jan. 27	1962, Sept. 3	1962, Nov. 12	1963, Jan. 23
1963, Aug. 29	1964, Apr. 10	1964, June 19	1964, Aug. 29
1965, Apr. 12	1965, Nov. 15	1966, Jan. 26	1966, Apr. 6
1966, Nov. 9	1967, June 21	1967, Aug. 30	1967, Nov. 9
1968, June 20	1969, Jan. 27	1969, Apr. 8	1969, June 18
1970, Jan. 25	1970, Sept. 1	1970, Nov. 10	1971, Jan. 21

earth averages 160 million miles, or the sum of the earth's and its own distance from the sun. From this position Venus emerges slowly to the east of the sun as evening star; it comes out a little higher from night to night and sets a little later after sunset, until it reaches greatest eastern elongation 220 days after the time of superior conjunction.

The entire westward movement to greatest western elongation is accomplished in 144 days. Midway, the planet passes nearly between the sun and the earth into the morning sky. At inferior conjunction it averages only 26 million miles from the earth, or the difference between the earth's and its own distance from the sun. This is the closest approach of any principal planet, although some minor planets come at times still closer to the earth. Turning eastward again after greatest western elongation, Venus moves slowly back to superior conjunction, again requiring 220 days for this part of the journey. The synodic period is accordingly 584 days.

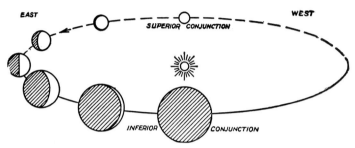

FIG. 8·5. Changing Phase and Apparent Size of Venus.

Greatest brilliancy as evening and morning star occurs about 36 days before and after the time of inferior conjunction. On these occasions Venus is 6 times as bright as the planet Jupiter and 15 times as bright as Sirius, the brightest star.

8·6. Through the Telescope; the Phases. As a visual object with the telescope the conspicuous feature of Venus is its phases, first seen by Galileo, in 1610. The phase is full at superior conjunction, quarter at greatest elongation, and new at inferior conjunction; but a thin extended crescent usually remains at the last-named aspect, because as a rule the planet crosses a little above or below the sun.

Unlike the moon, which is brightest at the full phase, Venus attains greatest brilliancy in our skies when its phase resembles that of the moon 2 days before the first quarter. At the full phase the planet's apparent diameter is 10″; at the new phase it is more than 6 times as great, because the distance from the earth is then reduced to about one sixth the former value. The increasing apparent size more than offsets the diminishing fraction of the disk in the sunlight, until the crescent phase is reached. At greatest brilliancy the crescent sends us 2½ times as much light as does the smaller, fully illuminated disk.

8·7. The Cloudy Atmosphere of Venus, which gives the planet the high reflecting power of 0.76, almost completely conceals its surface. The pale gray markings glimpsed on the silvery disk, aside from

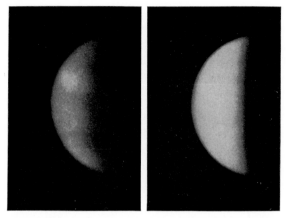

Fig. 8·7. Venus Near the Quarter Phase. In violet light (left) and red light (right). (*Photographs, April 8, 1950, by Gerard P. Kuiper, McDonald Observatory*)

illusory ones, are shadings in the clouds. These are shown much more clearly in the photographs in ultraviolet light. The transitory markings are breaks in the higher cloud layers through which darker drifting lower-level clouds are visible. This interpretation is by Dollfus, who has summarized the extensive visual and photographic studies of the planet at the Pic du Midi Observatory.

Bands of carbon dioxide in the infrared spectrum of Venus indicate that this compound is more abundant above the cloud levels than in the earth's entire atmosphere. Free oxygen has not been detected in the spectrum. A suspected faint band of water vapor in the infrared spectrum photographed from a balloon is not yet confirmed. Water vapor is believed to be scarce in the atmosphere of the planet, and no water at all would be expected on its very hot surface.

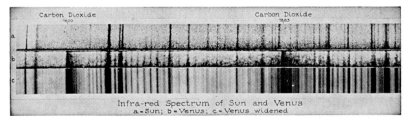

Fig. 8·7A. Infrared Spectra of Sun and Venus Compared. Bands of carbon dioxide are prominent in the spectrum of Venus. (*Mount Wilson Observatory photograph*)

When the spacecraft Mariner II passed in 1962 about 21,650 miles from Venus, it obtained and transmitted to the earth radiometric data that suggested a surprisingly high temperature. A preliminary analysis of the data at the Jet Propulsion Laboratory in Pasadena indicates a surface temperature of 800°F., hot enough to melt lead.

8·8. The Problem of Venus' Rotation. The absence of well-defined markings on the planet's disk and the transitory nature of at least many of them have been responsible for the conflicting views about the rotation period. Some early observers decided on a period of about a day. Schiaparelli, toward the end of the 19th century, concluded that it was 225 days, equal to the revolution period. Later evidence has seemed to require the rejection of both and to place the period somewhere between the two.

Spectroscopic studies of Venus leave no doubt that the rotation is considerably slower than the earth's. If the period were less than two weeks, Doppler slanting of the lines in the spectrum could be detected, which has not been observed. A period as long as 225 days seems dynamically improbable; and there is also no evidence of great difference between the temperatures of two hemispheres, which should be the case if one hemisphere is always turned away from the sun.

F. E. Ross' pioneer ultraviolet photographs of dark markings in the atmosphere of Venus, in 1927, suggested to him that the rotation period might be around a month. More recent photographs of this kind by G. P. Kuiper at McDonald Observatory and R. S. Richardson at Mount Wilson show markings frequently in the form of alternate dark and bright bands. If the bands are parallel to the planet's equator, which would imply a rather short rotation period, they show that the equator is inclined to the ecliptic about as much as are the equators of the earth and Mars.

MARS, THE RED PLANET

Mars is next in order beyond the earth. This red planet revolves around the sun once in 687 days and rotates on its axis once in $24^h 37^m$. Its diameter is about 4200 miles, or slightly more than half the earth's diameter. Viewed with the telescope its surface exhibits a variety of markings. The persistent idea that Mars contains certain forms of life has made this planet an object of special interest, particularly at its closest approaches to the earth.

8·9. Oppositions of Mars. As a superior planet, Mars is best situated for observation when it is opposite the sun's place in the sky; it is then nearer us than usual and is visible through most of the night. Because of the considerable eccentricity, 0.09, of its orbit, Mars varies greatly in its distance from the earth at the different oppositions. The distance exceeds 60 million miles when the planet is near its aphelion, and may be slightly less than 35 million miles at the *favorable oppositions*, when it is also near its perihelion. Oppositions of Mars recur at intervals of the synodic period, which averages 780 days, or about 50 days longer than 2 years. Thus they come in alternate years and each time about 50 days later than before.

Favorable oppositions occur at intervals of 15 or 17 years, usually in August or September, because on August 28 the earth has the same heliocentric longitude as the perihelion of Mars. On these favorable occasions Mars appears brighter in our skies than any other planet except Venus. It may then attain an apparent diameter of 25″, so that a magnification of only 75 times makes it appear

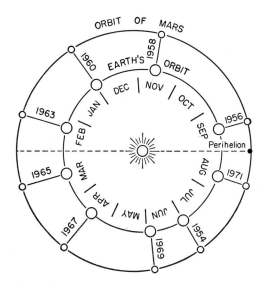

Fig. 8·9. Varying Distances of Mars from the Earth at Oppositions from 1954 to 1971. The latest favorable opposition occurred in 1956. The next will come in 1971.

with the telescope as large as the moon does to the unaided eye. Much of our knowledge of Mars has been gained around the times of the favorable oppositions.

TABLE 8·II   OPPOSITIONS OF MARS

Date of Opposition	Nearest Earth	Distance in Millions of Miles	Magnitude
1956, Sept. 10	Sept. 7	35	−2.6
1958, Nov. 16	Nov. 8	45	−1.9
1960, Dec. 30	Dec. 25	56	−1.3
1963, Feb. 4	Feb. 3	62	−1.0
1965, Mar. 9	Mar. 12	62	−1.0
1967, Apr. 15	Apr. 21	56	−1.3
1969, May 31	June 9	45	−1.0
1971, Aug. 10	Aug. 12	35	−2.6

The dates of oppositions of Mars from the latest favorable opposition of 1956 to the following one of 1971 are given in Table 8·II; these are taken from a more extended table in *Sky and Telescope* for April, 1956, which is reproduced from an earlier one. We note that the oppositions of 1963 and 1965 will be equally unfavorable, although Mars, then in Cancer and Leo respectively, will be superior in brightness to all the stars except Sirius. After the opposition of 1971, a pair about equally favorable will occur in 1986 and 1988.

8·10. Viewed with the Telescope in ordinary conditions, Mars is likely to be disappointing even when it is nearest us. The finer markings of its surface are often blurred by turbulence of our air and are also frequently dimmed by haze in the atmosphere of the planet itself. On rare occasions, when our air is unusually steady and the planet's atmosphere has cleared for a time, the surface features of Mars become surprisingly distinct with telescopes of only moderate size.

The white polar caps are the most conspicuous visual features; they are areas covered with snow to a thickness perhaps not exceeding an inch. Their nature was definitely established by G. P. Kuiper, who observed in the infrared spectrum of the northern

cap an absorption band characteristic of ordinary ice when it occurs in small crystals at very low temperature.

Each snow cap is deposited in a large area around the pole during the winter season of its hemisphere. It shrinks with the approach of summer, and sometimes in its retreat toward the pole it
leaves behind one or more white spots isolated for a time as though
on the summit or colder slope of a hill. A cap normally forms

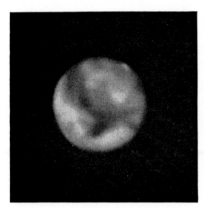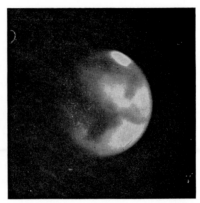

FIG. 8·10. Syrtis Major Region of Mars. Photographed in visual light
October 17, 1941 (left) and August 21, 1956 (right). Changes in the bright
and dark areas are to be noted. (*Photographed by Hamilton M. Jeffers
with the 36-inch refractor, Lick Observatory*)

under an atmospheric veil, but its disappearance can usually be
followed without obstruction by haze or clouds.

Three fifths of the surface of Mars has a reddish hue that accounts for the ruddy glow of the planet in our skies. These
brighter areas are desert expanses, the source of dust storms that
obscure the darker markings. From their effect on the sunlight
they reflect, the red areas are identified by Dollfus with pulverized limonite, the hydrated ferrous oxide. The dark areas, originally supposed to be water areas, have been named seas, lakes,
bogs, canals, and so on; and these designations have survived, like
the lunar "seas."

The nomenclature of Mars was revised by the International
Astronomical Union in 1958. The number of proper names for
the large regions is reduced to 128, which are generally the same
as before. Small details are designated in the revision only by
their approximate Martian longitudes and latitudes. The official

list of names and the maps for identifying the various features are shown in *Sky and Telescope* for November 1958.

8·11. Rotation of Mars. The period of rotation is about 24^h 37^m. The rotation of Mars has the same direction as the earth's rotation, and its period so nearly equals the earth's period that at the same hour from day to day almost the same face of the planet is presented to us, except that everything has stepped backward 10°. Thus the markings pass slowly in review, completing their apparent backward turning in about 38 days.

The inclination of the planet's equator to the plane of its orbit is nearly the same as the angle between the earth's equator and the ecliptic plane. The orientation of the axis differs at present about 90° from that of the earth; its northern end is directed toward the neighborhood of the star Alpha Cephei, not far from the position our own north celestial pole will have 6000 years hence.

8·12. The Seasons of Mars. Mars presents its poles alternately to the sun in the same way that the earth does, because of the similarity of its axial tilt. The seasons resemble ours geometrically, although they are nearly twice as long as ours. The winter solstice of Mars occurs when the planet has the same heliocentric longitude that the earth has about September 10 and not long after the time of its perihelion, when Mars has the same direction from the sun that the earth has on August 28. Summer in its southern hemisphere is therefore warmer than the northern summer, which comes when the planet is near the aphelion point in its orbit, and its southern winters are colder than the northern ones. For the same reason, the earth's southern hemisphere would have the greater seasonal range in temperature if there were no compensating factor (2·33).

Although the whole variation in our distance from the sun is only 3 per cent, Mars in its more eccentric orbit is 20 per cent, or more than 26 million miles, farther from the sun at aphelion than at perihelion. The seasonal difference in the two hemispheres is noticeable. The south polar cap attains an area of the order of 4 million square miles, and the northern cap about 3 million. It is the south polar cap that is toward the earth at the favorable oppositions, and this is accordingly the one that more often appears in the photographs.

8·13. The Surface Features of Mars are recorded with remarkable clearness in the photographs in Fig. 8·13, which were secured at the Pic du Midi Observatory in the early autumn of 1941. The planet is shown inverted, as it generally appears with the telescope. South

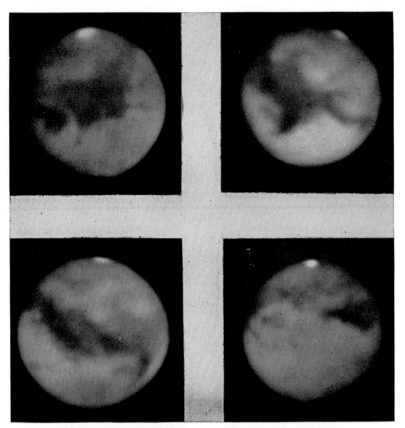

FIG. 8·13.   Mars in 1941.   (*Photographed at Pic du Midi Observatory, France*)

is at the top and east is at the right. In the rotation of Mars the markings move from right to left across the disk.

In the upper left photograph, taken September 23, the prominent dark area near the center of the disk is Mare Erythraeum. At the right the two rather narrow strips Ambrosia and Nectar reach over to the Solis Lacus and a third, the Agathodaemon, sweeps around below the lake. At the left in this picture is the dark Sabaeus Sinus.

In the lower left photograph, taken October 8, the Mare Cimmerium is central. Below and to the right, the triangular Syrtis Major, one of the darkest markings, has come into view. The upper right photograph, taken $3\frac{1}{2}$ hours later on the same night, shows the progress of the rotation after that interval. Here the Syrtis Major is nearly central and the Sabaeus Sinus has reappeared at the right. Just above the center of the disk we see the bright oval area Hellas.

In the lower right photograph, taken October 19, the Solis Lacus appears to the left of the center and the Mare Cimmerium has come around again at the right. Meanwhile, the south polar cap has shrunk to half its diameter in the first view. Summer in that hemisphere began late in August of 1941 by our calendar. Midsummer is approaching there at the time of the fourth photograph. The south polar cap will presently vanish and the northern cap will spread as the depth of winter overtakes its hemisphere.

8·14. Seasonal Changes in the Markings. The seasons of Mars, we have seen, resemble ours except in their greater length. The

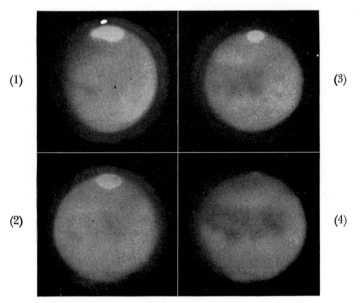

(1)

(3)

(2)

(4)

Fig. 8·14. Seasonal Changes on Mars. Showing, from (1) to (4), the shrinking south polar cap and the gradual darkening of the dark markings as summer comes on in that hemisphere. (*Lowell Observatory photographs*)

cycle of the seasons brings changes in the surface features there as it does on the earth. These effects are not confined to the alternate spreading and shrinking of the snow caps. Seasonal changes in the intensities and outlines of the dark markings have long been recognized by observers of the planet.

With the shrinking of each polar cap the region around the cap darkens, and the darkening gradually extends as far as the equator (Fig. 8·14). The dark areas become more distinct and some of them take on a greenish hue. As summer progresses in that hemisphere, the markings fade. The times of the Martian year when the dark markings change in intensity and color are such as would be expected if the changes are caused by the growth and decline of vegetation. Kuiper's studies of sunlight reflected from the green areas seem to rule out familiar seed plants and ferns. They might be compatible with the presence of something like our lichens and hardy mosses, appearing sporadically in lava basins otherwise like those of the lunar maria.

8·15. The Canals of Mars. The network of very narrow dark lines that are known as the *canals* of Mars was first reported by G. V. Schiaparelli in Italy at the favorable opposition of 1877. He described the canals as resembling "the finest thread of spider's web drawn across the disk." He found them less difficult to see when the snow caps were melting and was tempted to suppose that vege-

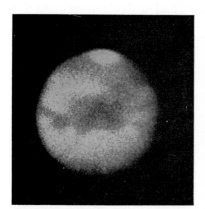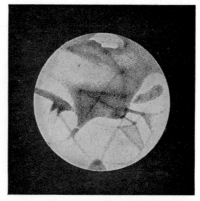

Fig. 8·15. Photograph and Drawing of Mars. The south polar cap is at the top. Mare Erythraeum is in the center. Some canals are represented in the drawing. (*Photograph with red filter and drawing by R. J. Trumpler, Lick Observatory*)

tation in the irrigated regions might add to the width of the narrow strips. These were in addition to the wider strips, which had been recognized before and are now shown clearly in the photographs.

Percival Lowell, who founded the Lowell Observatory at Flagstaff, Arizona, extended Schiaparelli's studies of the canals; he reported several hundred others and drew them all in geometrical pattern. Other experienced observers, such as E. E. Barnard and G. E. Hale in America and E. M. Antoniadi in Europe, saw much fine detail on Mars but were unable to discern a network of straight and narrow canals. The difference of opinion persists today. Many astronomers regard the canals as a partly psychological effect caused by boundaries between areas of different tonality or by small dark features, which cannot be seen separately except in exceptionally good conditions and with large telescopes.

8·16. The Hazy Atmosphere of Mars itself affects the view of the planet's surface. The haze is sometimes so thick that the surface markings become indistinct even in the red photographs. Kuiper concludes that the haze is caused by ice crystals and resembles the cirrus clouds of our own atmosphere. The haze is partly dissipated where the air of the planet is warmer; it is condensed into visible clouds where the air is colder. Thus the blue photographs show white clouds over the polar regions, and they also reveal small clouds forming near the sunset line and disintegrating near the

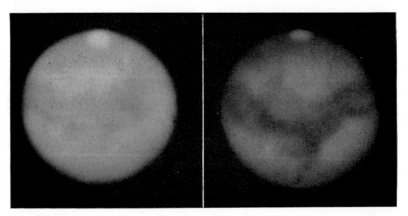

Fɪɢ. 8·16. Mars Through Its Hazy and Clearer Atmosphere. (*Photographs, September 25 and 29, 1909, by E. E. Barnard, Yerkes Observatory*)

sunrise line. Clouds of yellow dust from the deserts sometimes add to the indistinctness of the view.

At times the haze clears rapidly over a large area of the planet; it cleared near the oppositions of 1909, 1924, and 1941, but disappointed the observers by failing to do so at the otherwise favorable opposition of 1956. The 1909 photographs in Fig. 8·16 were both taken in yellow light only 4 days apart. We note the cloud above the polar cap in the veiled view at the left and how much more distinctly the Syrtis Major and other surface markings appear through the clearer atmosphere in the view at the right.

8·17. The Climate of Mars. The atmosphere of Mars is considerably rarer than ours. The low reflecting power, 0.15, of the planet and the relative distinctness of the surface markings lead to this conclusion, while the low velocity of escape, 3 miles a second, gives a reason for it. The chief constituent of the atmosphere is probably nitrogen, which is not expected to show in the spectrum. Kuiper finds that carbon dioxide is twice as abundant as in our atmosphere. He estimates that free oxygen must be less than 1 per cent and water vapor only a tenth of 1 per cent of our supply.

The surface temperature of Mars rises in the tropics at times above the ordinary freezing point of water, as radiometric measures show. The mean temperature for the entire surface is 60° below zero F, compared with 60° above zero for the earth. Mars is generally a cold desert expanse; its average climate might be approached by our bleakest desert if it could be raised into the stratosphere. Nevertheless, scientists have believed that the dark markings with their seasonal changes might be areas of very hardy vegetation.

8·18. The Satellites of Mars were discovered at the favorable opposition of 1877 by Asaph Hall at the Naval Observatory, who named them Phobos and Deimos (Fear and Panic, the companions of Mars). They are very small, probably not exceeding 10 miles in diameter, and are so near the planet as to be invisible except with large telescopes at favorable times. Their color, as measured photoelectrically by Kuiper, is nearly neutral gray, not yellowish like moonlight.

Phobos, the inner satellite, revolves at the distance of 5800 miles from the center of Mars and 3700 miles from its surface. It completes a sidereal revolution in only 7ʰ 39ᵐ, a period less than one third of the period of the planet's rotation in the same direction. As viewed from the planet it rises in the west and sets in the east. No other known satellite in the solar system revolves in a shorter interval than the rotation period of its primary.

FIG. 8·18. The Two Satellites of Mars, September 14, 1956. (*Photograph by Gerard P. Kuiper, McDonald Observatory*)

The distance of Deimos from the center of Mars is 14,600 miles, and its period of revolution is 30^h 18^m. It is smaller than the inner satellite and only a third as bright.

More than 100 years before the discovery of these satellites, Voltaire mentions them in the story of Micromegas; and Swift's Gulliver, in reporting the scientific achievements of the Laputans, refers to their observations of two satellites of Mars, "whereof the innermost is distant from the center of the planet exactly three of his diameters, and the outermost five; the former revolves in the space of ten hours, and the latter in twenty-one and a half."

THE ASTEROIDS

The *asteroids,* or *minor planets,* are the thousands of small bodies which revolve around the sun mainly between the orbits of Mars and Jupiter. The term "asteroid" (starlike) describes the appearance of almost all of them with the telescope. With the single exception of Vesta they are invisible to the naked eye. Ceres, the largest asteroid, is 480 miles in diameter. The majority are less than 50 miles and some are known to be scarcely a mile in diameter. The combined mass of all the asteroids is not greater than 5 per cent of the moon's mass.

Many asteroids have irregular forms, as shown by their periodic fluctuations in brightness in their rotations. This suggests that some smaller asteroids may be fragments of larger ones and that larger ones may have been chipped by collisions.

8·19. Ceres, the First Known Asteroid, was discovered incidentally by G. Piazzi in Sicily, on the first evening of the 19th century, because of its motion among the stars he was observing. It proved to be a minor planet revolving around the sun at the mean distance 2.8 times the earth's distance. This was the planet for which some other astronomers were searching because it seemed to be required by Bode's law (7·5). A second asteroid, Pallas, was found in the following year by an observer who was looking for Ceres; and this discovery promoted the search for others.

The search was visual for nearly a century. The observer at the telescope compared the stars in a region of the sky with a chart

FIG. 8·19. Trails of Three Asteroids. (*Photographed at Königstuhl-Heidelberg*)

previously made of the region. If an uncharted star was seen, it was watched hopefully for movement among the stars that would reveal its planetary character. By this slow procedure, 322 asteroids had been discovered by 1891, when Max Wolf at Heidelberg was the first to apply photography in the search. In this modern method a time exposure of an hour or so is made with a wide-angle telescope. A fast-moving asteroid appears as a trail among the stars in the developed negative.

FIG. 8·19A.   Recovery of the Minor Planet 1322, Coppernicus.   The round image in the center is the minor planet.   The star images are trailed. (*Photograph by Frank K. Edmondson, Goethe Link Observatory*)

Hundreds of asteroids are now picked up each year in celestial photographs, often in the course of other investigations, and most of them are not observed thereafter. F. K. Edmondson and associates at the Goethe Link Observatory, Indiana University, have recovered many asteroids that might otherwise have been lost. Their procedure has been to shift the 10-inch Cooke telescope to follow the expected motion of the object during each exposure. In their photographs the stars appear as short trails and the asteroids as points (Fig. 8·19A), thus permitting the recovery of objects too faint to be detected if they were allowed to trail.

8·20. The Orbits of Asteroids. When its orbit has been reliably determined, an asteroid receives a permanent running number and a name that is less often used unless the object has unusual interest. The numbered asteroids exceed 1600. New asteroids, as their discoveries are reported, are given temporary designations by the central bureau under the direction of Paul Herget at Cincinnati Observatory.

The orbits have more variety than those of the principal planets. Although the majority are not far from circular and only slightly inclined to the ecliptic, some depart considerably from the circular form and are not confined within the bounds of the zodiac. As an extreme case, the orbit of Hidalgo has an eccentricity of 0.66 and is inclined 43° to the ecliptic; its aphelion point is as far away as Saturn. The revolutions of all asteroids are direct. The periods are mainly between $3\frac{1}{2}$ and 6 years.

The asteroid orbits are not distributed at random through the region between the orbits of Mars and Jupiter. There are gaps in the neighborhoods of distances from the sun where the periods of revolution would be simple fractions, particularly one third, two fifths, and one half, of Jupiter's period. The avoidance of these distances, first announced, in 1866, by Kirkwood at Indiana University, is ascribed to frequent recurrences there of the same types of disturbances by Jupiter.

There are accumulations instead of gaps, however, at distances where the fractions are not far from unity. The situation is especially interesting where the period of revolution of asteroids is the same as Jupiter's period.

8·21. The Trojan Asteroids. Long ago, the mathematician J. L. Lagrange discovered a particular solution of the problem of 3 bodies and concluded that when the bodies occupy the vertices of an equilateral triangle the configuration may be stable. Although no celestial example was then known, he took as a hypothetical case a small body moving around the sun in such a way that its distances from Jupiter and the sun remained equal to the distance separating those two bodies. If the small body is disturbed, it will oscillate around its vertex of the triangle.

More than a dozen asteroids are examples of this special case. Achilles was the first of these to be discovered, in 1906. Named after the Homeric heroes of the Trojan War, they are known as the *Trojan group*. In their revolutions around the sun they oscillate about two points east and west of Jupiter, which are equally distant from that planet and the sun.

8·22. Asteroids that Pass Near Us. Several asteroids are known to come within the orbit of Mars and to pass nearer the earth's orbit than does any one of the principal planets. Some of these come in closer to the sun than the earth's distance. They are generally very small and are faint even when they are passing nearest us. The chance of discovering them as they speed by is so slight as to suggest that they are numerous.

Eros, discovered in 1898, is 105 million miles from the sun at its perihelion. Its least distance from the earth's orbit, also near the perihelion point, is less than 14 million miles. The most favorable oppositions of this 15-mile asteroid are infrequent; the latest occurred in 1931, providing data for a re-examination of the value of the astronomical unit (7·16). The next close approach will come in 1975. Eros held the distinction of being the most neighborly of the planets until the discovery of Amor, in 1932. This asteroid comes to perihelion 10 million miles outside the earth's orbit.

Apollo, also discovered in 1932, has its perihelion inside the orbit of Venus and passed within 3 million miles of our orbit. Adonis, discovered in 1936, has its perihelion slightly farther than Mercury's mean distance from the sun; it passed about 1 million miles from the orbits of Venus, the earth, and Mars. Hermes, discovered in 1937, may have come even nearer the earth than did

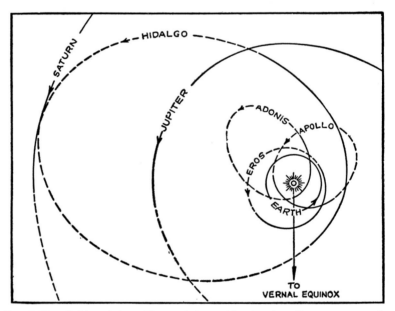

FIG. 8·22. Orbits of Four Unusual Asteroids. Broken lines represent the parts of the orbits south of the plane of the ecliptic. (*Adapted from a diagram by Dirk Brouwer*)

the other two. These three asteroids are about 1 mile in diameter.
They were visible for such short intervals that their orbits were not
very reliably determined. There is small chance of their being
sighted again.

More recently, photographs by C. D. Shane and C. A. Wirtanen
with the 20-inch astrographic camera at Lick Observatory revealed
the long trails of other asteroids near the earth. In 1949, Walter
Baade noticed a long trail in a photograph with the 48-inch
Schmidt telescope; it proved to be the trace of the only known
asteroid that crosses inside Mercury's orbit. Named Icarus, this
object comes at its perihelion less than 20 million miles from the
sun.

8·23. Irregular Shapes of Asteroids. Many asteroids have irregular
shapes, so that they fluctuate periodically in brightness as they rotate and present varying cross sections for the reflection of sunlight to us. Eros is an example. Its brightness alternately increases for 79 minutes and then diminishes during an equal interval. The amplitude of the fluctuation varies conspicuously. At
times the greatest brightness is three times the least; at other times
the difference is slight.

The explanation is that Eros is shaped roughly like a brick 15
miles in length and 5 miles in width and thickness. It rotates on
an axis through the middle of the brick from top to bottom, once
around in 5^h 16^m. When its edge is toward us, the asteroid presents its larger sides and smaller ends in turn, becoming brighter
and fainter in the sunlight twice during each rotation. When
Eros is in another part of its orbit where its top or bottom are
more nearly toward us, its variation in brightness as it rotates is
considerably less.

Photoelectric studies of representative asteroids by G. P. Kuiper
and associates, mainly with the McDonald 82-inch telescope, have
shown that over 90 per cent of the asteroids are variable in brightness. The rotation periods range from 2^h 52^m to 20 hours. The
rotation axes appear to have random orientation. At least one
asteroid, Eunomia, has retrograde rotation with its equator only
slightly inclined to the ecliptic.

Their irregular shapes suggest that the majority of asteroids are
fragments resulting from collisions of larger bodies or have been
nicked by collisions. Many fragments could have been thrown
into orbits of higher eccentricity and inclination to the ecliptic
than those of the bodies before collision. Some might then pass

close to the earth and might even collide with the earth. Thus many meteorites may well be fragments of asteroids.

JUPITER, THE GIANT PLANET

Jupiter is the largest planet and is more massive than all the others combined. It is brighter in our skies than any other planet except Venus and occasionally Mars. At somewhat more than 5 times the earth's distance from the sun, it revolves in a period of nearly 12 years, so that from year to year it moves eastward among the stars through one constellation of the zodiac. Jupiter's banded disk and 4 bright satellites are easily visible with a small telescope. It has 12 known satellites in all, the largest number for any planet.

8·24. Jupiter's Cloud Markings. Viewed with a large telescope, Jupiter exhibits a variety of changing detail and color in its cloudy

Fig. 8·24. Jupiter, October 24, 1952. Showing the Great Red Spot. The 3rd satellite and its shadow appear near the top of the disk. Photographed in blue light at the coudé focus of the Hale telescope. (*Mount Wilson and Palomar Observatories photograph*)

atmosphere. Brown bands parallel to the planet's equator appear on a yellowish background. The banded structure is associated with the rapid rotation. Jupiter's rotation is direct and its period is less than 10 hours, which is the shortest for all the principal planets; the speed of the rotation at the equator exceeds 25,000 miles an hour.

Irregular cloud markings and bright and dark spots break the continuity of the bands. Some are short-lived and change noticeably from day to day, suggesting considerable turmoil beneath the cloud levels. Other spots persist for a very long time. Especially remarkable in this respect is the *Great Red Spot,* which has been visible for at least a century. This elliptical brick-red spot has been as long as 30,000 miles. It drifts about like a solid floating in the near-liquid lower atmosphere.

The positions of many markings vary as well as their forms, so that the rotation periods determined from two spots are not likely to agree precisely. A bright spot in a latitude somewhat south of the Great Spot has a period of rotation 20 seconds the shorter of the two; it drifts by the Spot and gains a lap on it in about 2 years.

8·25. The Constitution of Jupiter. Our understanding of the physical status of the planet is based mainly on observed features at and above the level of the obscuring clouds. The temperature

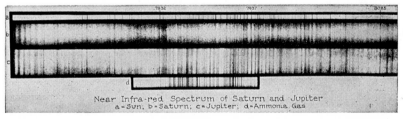

Near Infra-red Spectrum of Saturn and Jupiter
a = Sun; b = Saturn; c = Jupiter; d = Ammonia Gas

FIG. 8·25. Spectra of Saturn and Jupiter Compared with the Spectrum of Ammonia. The dark lines of ammonia are stronger in the spectrum of Jupiter. (*Photograph by Theodore Dunham, Mount Wilson Observatory*)

at this level is −130°C as determined by the radiometric measures. It is about the temperature that would be expected from heating only by radiation from the distant sun.

The light we receive from Jupiter is sunlight that has been reflected by the planet's clouds and has passed through the small amount of its atmosphere above the cloud level. The spectrum of this light is the solar spectrum with additional molecular bands of methane and ammonia, and fine traces of molecular hydrogen. Methane is gaseous at this low temperature; its ordinary boiling point is −162°C. Ammonia freezes at −78°C; this constituent must be present as crystals, which partly sublime in the feeble sunlight. Methane and ammonia are among the impurities in Jupiter's atmosphere, which like the sun must be composed mainly of hydrogen and helium.

Radiation from Jupiter in the radio wavelengths is of three observed types: (1) thermal emission consistent with the temperature already stated; (2) nonthermal emission that issues in short blasts from the planet's ionosphere; (3) nonthermal emission of a different type, which is weak and only at microwave frequencies. It is believed to come from an equivalent of the terrestrial Van Allen belt. This radiation belt is presumably more extensive and the accompanying magnetic field is stronger than are those of the earth (2·7).

Conditions below the cloud level of Jupiter are derived somewhat imperfectly by analysis from observed data about the planet as a whole. Wildt has remarked that the study of the internal structure of a cold planet presents many more difficulties than does the analysis of the interior of a star.

8·26. The Interior of Jupiter. The amount of the bulging of Jupiter's equator provides one clue to conditions in the interior. With

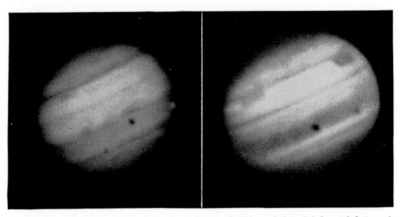

FIG. 8·26. Jupiter in Infrared (left) and Ultraviolet Light (right). A satellite and its shadow are in transit. The Great Red Spot appears near the upper edge of the ultraviolet image. (*Photographs by Gerard P. Kuiper, McDonald Observatory*)

its swift rotation the planet would be even more oblate than is observed if its mass were not highly concentrated toward its center. Other indications of what is hidden beneath the clouds are the low temperature and low average density, about 1.3 times the density of water, of the whole planet, which requires very light material in the outer parts.

Hydrogen is the predominant chemical constituent in recent theoretical models of Jupiter designed by R. Wildt, W. C. De-Marcus, and others. Conditions in the interior are considered highly uncertain. The compression below the cloud levels must eventually reach a critical value where there is no distinction between the gaseous and liquid states. At an undetermined distance below this level even the hydrogen should be converted to a solid state. The conclusion is that Jupiter has little resemblance to the earth.

8·27. The Inner Satellites. Jupiter's 12 known satellites are sharply divided into three groups: the inner satellites and the two groups of outer satellites. The 5 inner satellites have direct revo-

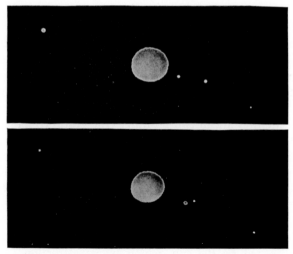

Fig. 8·27. Jupiter's Four Bright Satellites. The lower photograph was taken 3 hours later than the upper one. (*Yerkes Observatory photographs*)

lutions in orbits that are nearly circular and nearly in the plane of the planet's equator. Four of these are bright enough to be readily visible with a small telescope.

The four bright satellites were discovered by Galileo on January 7, 1610. They were independently discovered the following evening by the German astronomer Marius who gave them their names. They are generally designated, however, by numbers in order of their distances from the planet.

The 1st and 2nd satellites are about as large as the moon. The 3rd and 4th are 50 per cent greater in diameter; they are the largest of all satellites and are comparable in size with the planet Mercury. Spectrometer tracings in the infrared suggest that the 2nd and 3rd satellites may be covered with snow. At their greater distance from the sun the combined light of all four upon Jupiter is not more than 30 per cent of the light of the full moon on the earth. Their periods of rotation and revolution are the same. After the four bright ones, the numbering of the other satellites is in order of their discovery. The 5th satellite differs from the others of its group in its small size. Nearest of all to the planet and more difficult to observe on this account, it is the swiftest of all satellites, revolving at the rate of 1000 miles a minute.

8·28. The Outer Satellites have orbits of considerable eccentricity and inclination to the ecliptic. All seven are small and very faint. They were discovered photographically, the latest one by Seth B. Nicholson in 1951; he remarks that the 12th satellite is slightly fainter than the 10th, which itself is not brighter than the light of a candle at the distance of 3000 miles. The 6th satellite is the only outer one that would be visible from Jupiter without a telescope.

These satellites are in two groups. One group contains the 6th, 7th, and 10th satellites, which have direct revolutions at the average distance of a little more than 7 million miles from the planet, and in periods around 260 days. The outer group contains the 8th, 9th, 11th, and 12th satellites. These have retrograde revolutions at the average distance of about 14 million miles and in periods around 700 days; they are the most distant of all satellites from their primaries. Jupiter's control over these remote satellites is disputed by the sun, which by its attraction greatly disturbs their orbits.

The data on the outer satellites in Table 8·V are as given by Nicholson. The order of mean distance of the outermost four from the planet, as he points out, is subject to change in a few years by perturbations by the sun. The diameters of the faint

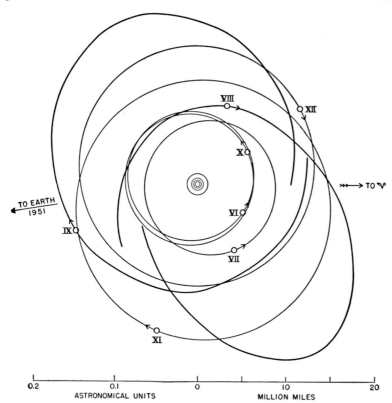

FIG. 8·28. Orbits of Jupiter's Satellites. Showing marked changes in two
  orbits during a single revolution. (*Diagram by Seth B. Nicholson*)

satellites are estimated from their brightness, and the values he
considers perhaps somewhat too great.

8·29. Eclipses and Transits of the Bright Satellites. The orbits of
the four bright satellites are always presented nearly edgewise to us.

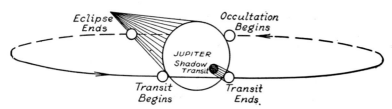

FIG. 8·29. Phenomena of a Satellite of Jupiter. As they appear, not inverted, after the planet's opposition.

As these satellites revolve around Jupiter, they accordingly appear to move back and forth in nearly the same straight line. The forward movement takes them behind the planet and through its shadow, although the 4th satellite often clears both; the backward movement takes them in front of the planet, when their shadows are cast upon its disk. These occultations, eclipses, transits, and shadow transits add interest to observations of Jupiter with the telescope. The times of their frequent occurrences are predicted in some of the astronomical almanacs.

SATURN AND ITS RINGS

Saturn is the most distant of the bright planets from the sun and was the most remote planet known to early astronomers. At nearly twice the distance of Jupiter, it revolves around the sun in a period of 29½ years. This planet ranks second to Jupiter in size, mass, and number of known satellites. Saturn has the least mean density and the greatest oblateness of any principal planet. It is unique in the possession of a system of rings that encircle the planet and make it one of the most impressive of celestial objects viewed with the telescope.

8·30. The Constitution of Saturn resembles that of Jupiter in many respects. The atmospheric markings are likewise arranged in bands, which are here more regular and less distinct. A broad yellowish band overlies the equator, and greenish caps surround the poles. The absorption of ammonia in the spectrum is much weaker, while that of methane is stronger than in Jupiter's spectrum. At the lower temperature of $-150°C$ at the cloud levels of Saturn the ammonia gas is more nearly frozen out, so that the sunlight analyzed in the spectrum has penetrated farther down through the methane of the planet's atmosphere.

Saturn's period of rotation at its equator has been determined spectroscopically as $10^h\ 02^m$. Long-enduring spots, which can show the period more reliably, are rare. A period of about $10^h\ 14^m$ has been derived from several white spots in the equatorial zone, and a second period of about $10^h\ 40^m$ has been found for other spots around latitude 60°. T. A. Cragg at Mount Wilson Observatory concludes that Saturn rotates in these two basic systems instead of having a steady increase of period with increasing latitude. The rapid rotation combined with the large size and low density of the

planet can account for its conspicuous oblateness. Hydrogen is
the main constituent, as in the case of Jupiter.

8·31. Saturn's Rings. Saturn is encircled by three concentric rings
in the plane of its equator. They are designated as the *outer ring*,
the middle or *bright ring*, and the inner or *crape ring*. The rings
are invisble to the unaided eye and were therefore unknown until
after the invention of the telescope. The diameter of the entire

FIG. 8·31.   Saturn in 1943. The rings are widest open. (*Photograph by
George H. Herbig, Lick Observatory*)

ring system is 171,000 miles, or 2.3 times the equatorial diameter
of the planet (74,100 miles). Because they have nearly twice the
diameter of Jupiter and are about twice as far from us, the rings
have about the same apparent diameter as that of Jupiter.

The bright ring is 16,000 miles in width and its outer edge is as
luminous as the brightest parts of the planet. It is separated from
the outer ring by the 3000-mile gap known as *Cassini's division* after
the name of its discoverer. This is the only real division in the
rings, according to Kuiper. There is no gap between the bright
ring and the crape ring.

A surprising feature of the rings is that they are extremely thin;
their appreciable thickness can scarcely exceed 10 miles.

8·32. Saturn's Rings at Different Angles. The rings are inclined
27° to the plane of the planet's orbit and they keep the same direction during the revolution around the sun. Thus their north-

ern and southern faces are presented alternately to the sun and also to the earth; for as viewed from Saturn these two bodies are never more than 6° apart. Twice during the sidereal period of 29½ years the plane of the rings passes through the sun's position.

Fig. 8·32. Saturn in 1952. The rings are nearly edgewise to the earth. (*Mount Wilson and Palomar Observatories photograph*)

It requires nearly a year on each occasion to sweep across the earth's orbit. As the earth revolves in the meantime, the rings become edgewise to us from 1 to 3 times, when they disappear with small telescopes and are only thin bright lines with large ones.

The latest widest opening of the northern face of the rings occurred in 1959, when Saturn was near the position of the winter solstice. The next edgewise presentation will occur late in 1965

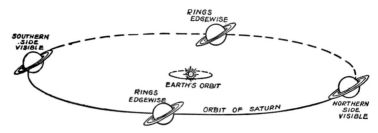

Fig. 8·32A. Cause of the Different Aspects of Saturn's Rings. The plane of the rings is inclined 27° to the plane of Saturn's orbit.

and again in 1966. The following widest opening of the southern face of the rings will come in 1974.

When the rings are widest open, their apparent breadth is 45 per cent of the greatest diameter and one sixth greater than the planet's polar diameter. On these occasions Saturn appears brighter than usual, because the rings at this angle reflect 1.7 times as much sunlight as does the planet alone. When it is also near perihelion and in opposition, Saturn appears twice as bright as Capella.

8·33. Discrete Nature of the Rings. Saturn's rings consist of multitudes of separate particles revolving around the planet in nearly circular orbits in the direction of its rotation. They have the ap-

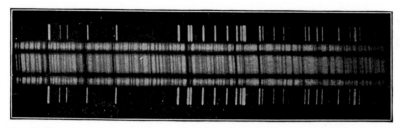

FIG. 8·33. Spectrum of Ball and Rings of Saturn. Wavelengths increase toward the right. In the spectrum of the ball of the planet, in the middle, the lines slant because of the planet's rotation. In the spectrum of the rings, above and below, the lines have the opposite slant. This shows that the inner parts of the rings revolve more rapidly than the outer parts, proving the discrete nature of the rings. The bright lines are the comparison spectrum. (*Lowell Observatory photograph*)

pearance of continuous surfaces because of their great distance from us. G. P. Kuiper's infrared studies with the lead sulfide cell of the sunlight reflected from the rings suggest that they are composed of ice particles.

The Doppler effects (4·9) in the spectrum of Saturn's rings (Fig. 8·33) show that the inner parts of the rings revolve around the planet faster than the outer parts, just as a planet that is nearer the sun revolves around it faster than one that is farther away. The reverse would be the case if the rings were continuous surfaces; for all parts would then go around in the same period, and the outside having farther to go would move the faster. The behavior of the spectrum lines is explained by Fig. 8·33A, where the slit of the spectroscope is placed along Saturn's equator. The upper parts

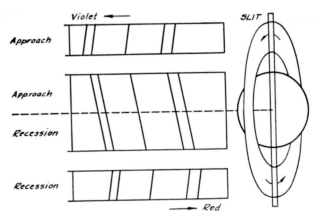

FIG. 8·33A. Doppler Effects in the Spectrum of Saturn and Its Rings. An explanation of Fig. 8·33.

of the planet and the rings are here approaching the observer, and the lower parts are receding from him.

The revolution periods of the outer edge of the outer ring and the inner edge of the bright ring are respectively 14^h 27^m and 7^h 46^m, and the material in the crape ring goes around in still shorter periods. Because Saturn's equator rotates in about 10 hours, it is evident that the outer parts of the ring system move westward across the sky of Saturn. A considerable part of the bright ring, however, and all of the crape ring must rise in the west and set in the east as seen from the surface of the planet, duplicating the behavior of Phobos (8·18) in the sky of Mars.

8·34. The Origin of Saturn's Rings is associated with their nearness to the planet. According to a theory that was invoked in this respect long before the spectroscopic evidence was available, a solid ring so close to the planet would be shattered by the gravitational strain to which it would be subjected, whereas a ring of many small pieces would be reasonably stable. A liquid satellite of the same density as the planet would be broken into small fragments by the tide-raising force of the planet if its distance from the center of the planet is less than 2.4 times the planet's radius.

All parts of Saturn's rings are well within this critical distance, but the nearest satellite is safely outside. Because a stable satellite could not have formed at the distance of the ring, the ring must have formed directly as such. The mass of the ring system is not known from observation but may be similar to that of the innermost satellite of Saturn.

8·35. The Satellites of Saturn. Saturn has nine known satellites. The brightest, Titan, is visible with a small telescope as a star of the 8th magnitude. Five or six other satellites can be seen with telescopes of moderate aperture; they appear as faint stars in the vicinity of the planet and are easily identified by means of convenient tables in some of the astronomical almanacs. Phoebe, the most distant satellite, has retrograde revolution like Jupiter's outer satellites; all the others have direct revolutions.

Two of Saturn's satellites are known to rotate and revolve in the same periods, as is shown by their variations in brightness in the periods of their revolutions. Evidently their surfaces are irregular in form or are uneven in reflecting power. Iapetus is the most remarkable in this respect; it is five times as bright at western as at eastern elongation.

Titan, the largest of Saturn's satellites, is remarkable in three respects. (1) It is the only satellite in the solar system definitely known to have an atmosphere. G. P. Kuiper has recognized methane bands in its spectrum, and he points out another feature probably associated with the atmosphere: (2) The color of Titan is orange. It seems to him likely that the color is caused by action of the atmosphere on the surface material, analogous to the oxidation supposed to be responsible for the orange color of Mars. (3) Lyot and Dollfus have found limb-darkening on Titan's disk, such as is shown by the sun but not by the moon and Jupiter's satellites.

Kuiper also concludes from their very high reflecting power, 0.8, that the inner satellites of Saturn have icy surfaces, and from their low densities that they are probably composed primarily of ice.

8·36. Stability of Atmospheres. Whether a planet or satellite can retain an atmosphere depends on the velocity of escape (5·16) at the surface of the body. It also depends on the mean speed of the molecules in the atmosphere, whether they can become high enough to effect an escape. This speed increases with the temperature of the gas and decreases with increasing weight of the molecules. J. H. Jeans showed that an atmosphere is likely to be retained for astronomical periods of time if the mean speed of its molecules is less than 20 per cent of the velocity of escape. For some gases in our own atmosphere the mean speeds at 20°C are: 2.2 km/sec for H_2, 0.8 for CH_4 and NH_3, 0.6 for N_2, 0.5 for O_2 and CO_2.

TABLE 8·III   CRITICAL VELOCITIES FOR RETENTION OF ATMOSPHERES

Jupiter	18.4 km/sec	Titan	1.0 km/sec
Saturn	12.8	Jupiter's satellite III	0.9
Neptune	11.8	Jupiter's satellite IV	0.7
Uranus	9.0	Jupiter's satellite I	0.7
Earth	2.3	Mercury	0.7
Venus	1.9	Jupiter's satellite II	0.6
Mars	1.1	Moon	0.5

Table 8·III, adapted from data by Kuiper, lists planets and satellites for which the critical velocities are not less than the lowest speed we have given for the gas molecules. These critical velocities are the escape velocities for each body multiplid by the 4th root of its distance in astronomical units from the sun to eliminate the temperature difference, and then reduced to 20 per cent.

Aside from hydrogen, which would be predicted in any considerable amount only around the four giant planets, the dividing line in the table comes below Titan; and this is in fact the division between bodies having known atmospheres and those for which atmospheres have not been detected. Pluto and Triton, where atmospheres are suspected from the strength of their ultraviolet reflections, are not included in the list because of uncertainties in some of the data.

URANUS AND NEPTUNE

8·37. Discoveries of Uranus and Neptune. Uranus was discovered in 1781 by William Herschel in England; he was observing a region in the constellation Gemini when he noticed a greenish object that appeared somewhat larger than a star. The object proved to be a planet more remote than Saturn and was given the name Uranus. An examination of the records showed that Uranus had been seen 20 times in the hundred years preceding its discovery; each time the position had been measured and set down as that of a star.

Because no orbit could be found to fit the older positions satisfactorily, it was necessary to wait for later ones. At length, in 1821, a new orbit was calculated with allowance for the disturbing effects of known planets. It was not long, however, before Uranus began to depart appreciably from the assigned course, until in 1844 the difference between the observed and calculated positions in the sky had increased to more than 2′, an angle not perceptible to the unaided eye but regarded as an intolerable discrepancy by astronomers. There seemed no longer any doubt that the motion of Uranus was being disturbed by a planet as yet unseen.

U. J. Leverrier in France discovered Neptune in 1846. From the discrepancies in the motion of Uranus he was able to calculate the place of the disturber among the stars. All that remained was to observe it. An astronomer at the Berlin Observatory searched with the telescope for the new planet and soon found it within a degree of the specified place in the constellation Aquarius. The discovery was acclaimed as a triumph for the law of gravitation, on which the calculation was based. J. C. Adams in England had successfully completed a similar calculation, but did not obtain effective telescopic cooperation.

8·38. Uranus, the first planet to be discovered, is barely visible to the naked eye. It has direct revolution in a period of 84 years at

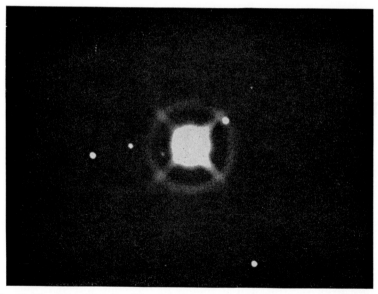

FIG. 8·38. The Five Satellites of Uranus. The fifth satellite appears inside the halation ring to the left of the planet. Ariel is on the ring at the right, Umbriel and Titania are at the left, and Oberon is below the planet. (*Photograph by Gerard P. Kuiper, McDonald Observatory*)

19 times the earth's distance from the sun and rotates once in 10¾ hours, having its equator inclined nearly at right angles to the ecliptic.   Nearly 30,000 miles in diameter, Uranus appears with the telescope as a small disk on which markings are not clearly discernible.   The spectrum shows dark bands of methane and also a broad absorption band in the near infrared, recorded by Kuiper and identified by G. Herzberg with molecular hydrogen.   This was the first direct evidence of the hydrogen molecule in the atmospheres of the major planets.   More recently, C. C. Kiess detected molecular hydrogen in the spectrum of Jupiter.

Uranus has five known satellites.   The 5th, which is fainter and nearer the planet than the others, was discovered by Kuiper in 1948.   The nearly circular orbits of the satellites are presented to the earth at various angles as the planet revolves; they were flatwise to us in 1945 and will appear edgewise in 1966.

8·39. Neptune has nearly the same size as Uranus and seems to resemble it closely in other respects.   Neptune has direct revolu-

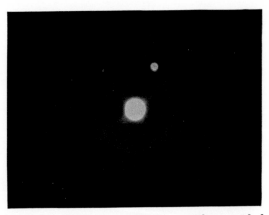

FIG. 8·39.   Neptune and Its Inner Satellite.   (*Photograph by Gerard P. Kuiper, McDonald Observatory*)

tion in a period of 165 years at a distance 30 times the earth's distance from the sun, and it rotates in the same direction once in 15.8 hours, according to the spectroscopic measures.   Always invisible to the naked eye because it is so remote from the sun and earth, Neptune appears with the telescope as a star of the 8th magnitude. Very weak markings have been discerned on its small greenish disk.

Neptune has two known satellites. The first, Triton, is somewhat larger than the moon and is slightly nearer the planet than the moon's distance from the earth. Its mass, as determined by H. L. Alden, is 0.022 times the earth's mass, or nearly twice the mass of the moon, and it may have an atmosphere. Triton has a retrograde revolution around the planet, contrary to the direction of the planet's rotation.

The second satellite, Nereid, discovered by Kuiper in 1949, is much the smaller, fainter, and more distant from the planet; the distance ranges from about 1 to 6 million miles. The satellite has a direct revolution once in nearly a year in an orbit having an eccentricity of 0.75, the greatest for any known satellite.

PLUTO

This most remote planet was discovered, in 1930, by C. W. Tombaugh at the Lowell Observatory as the successful result of a search for a planet beyond Neptune. The first two letters of the planet's name are the initials of Percival Lowell, who had initiated the search a quarter of a century before. From its small size and its unusual orbit for a principal planet, it is believed that Pluto was originally a satellite of Neptune.

8·40. Pluto is visible with the telescope as a star now of visual magnitude 14.9, and 0.8 magnitude fainter in blue light. Its diameter is 3600 miles, as measured by Kuiper with a disk meter on the 200-inch telescope. Unless its density is greater than would be expected, its mass does not exceed a tenth of the earth's mass. Pluto may have a gritty snow-covered surface and perhaps an atmosphere that is considerably rarer than ours.

The period of Pluto's rotation is 6.390 days, as determined by M. F. Walker and Robert Hardie from theirs and Kuiper's photoelectric measures of its periodic fluctuations in brightness. Nonuniformities of its surface cause a variation of 0.1 magnitude in the brightness of the planet in the course of a rotation; the range is great enough to suggest that the axis is more nearly at right angles to than along the line of sight.

FIG. 8·40. Pluto in 1930, Near the Time of Its Discovery. The arrows point to the planet, which appears as a star of the 15th magnitude. The bright star below the planet is Delta Geminorum. (*Lowell Observatory photograph*)

8·41. The Orbit of Pluto.

At its mean distance of 39½ astronomical units, or 3670 million miles, from the sun, Pluto has a direct revolution around the sun once in 248 years. Its orbit is inclined 17° to the ecliptic, the highest inclination for any of the larger planets, so that Pluto ventures at times well beyond the borders of the zodiac. With respect to its origin it might be included among the principal planets only for convenience in the descriptions.

The high eccentricity, 0.25, of Pluto's orbit introduces another feature that is unique among the larger planets. At aphelion Pluto is 1800 million miles beyond Neptune's distance from the sun, whereas at perihelion it comes 35 million miles nearer the sun than the orbit of Neptune. There is no danger of collision in our times, however; in their present orbits the two planets cannot approach each other closer than 240 million miles.

In Fig. 7·4 the plane of the page represents the ecliptic plane. The portion of Pluto's orbit south of this plane is indicated by the broken line in the figure. At the time of its discovery the planet was near the ascending node of its path. It will reach perihelion in 1989.

8·42. Tables of the Planets and Satellites. Some of the data on the planets and satellites in Tables 8·IV and 8·V are taken from the *American Ephemeris and Nautical Almanac.* The adopted length of the astronomical unit is 92,900,000 miles. To express any distance in kilometers, multiply its value in miles by 1.6093. Data on the outer satellites of Jupiter are as given by Nicholson. Dimensions of some planets and satellites are derived by Kuiper from his measures of the apparent diameters with a disk meter, and the magnitudes of the satellites of Uranus are estimates by the same authority.

The diameters of a number of small satellites are uncertain, as is indicated by the question marks after their values in the table. Where the satellites do not show appreciable disks, the diameters are calculated from the observed brightness and assumed albedo.

REVIEW QUESTIONS

1. Name the principal planets in order of distance from the sun. State a unique feature of each.

2. Explain that the greatest elongations of Mercury are not equally favorable for viewing the planet as evening or morning star.

3. Mention some points of resemblance between Mercury and the moon; between Venus and the earth. What conditions on Venus seem to make that planet uninviting to life?

4. Why is the view of Mars most favorable at intervals of 15 or 17 years?

5. Mention some features of Mars that might suggest the presence of life and some conditions that might seem discouraging to life.

6. In what respects does the inner satellite of Mars differ from all other satellites?

7. The periodic fluctuations in the brightness of many asteroids inform us of their irregular shapes and possible origins. Explain.

8. Describe the orbits of asteroids such as Adonis and Hermes; of the Trojan asteroids.

9. Jupiter's satellites are sharply divided into three groups. Explain.

10. Why are Saturn's rings presented to us at different angles? Why are they edgewise to us at intervals of about 15 years?

TABLE 8·IV THE PLANETS

Name		Symbol	Mean Distance from Sun		Period of Revolution		Eccentricity of Orbit	Inclination to Ecliptic
			Astron. Units	Million Miles	Sidereal	Synodic		
Inner	Mercury	☿	0.3871	35.96	days 87.969	days 115.88	0.206	7° 0′
	Venus	♀	0.7233	67.20	224.701	583.92	0.007	3 24
	Earth	⊕	1.0000	92.90	365.256	. . . . .	0.017	0 0
	Mars	♂	1.5237	141.6	686.980	779.94	0.093	1 51
	Ceres	①	2.7673	257.1	years 4.604	466.60	0.077	10 37
Outer	Jupiter	♃	5.2028	483.3	11.862	398.88	0.048	1 18
	Saturn	♄	9.5388	886.2	29.458	378.09	0.056	2 29
	Uranus	♅	19.1820	1783	84.013	369.66	0.047	0 46
	Neptune	♆	30.0577	2794	164.794	367.49	0.009	1 46
	Pluto	♇	39.5177	3670	248.430	366.74	0.249	17 9

Name		Mean Diameter in Miles	Mass ⊕ = 1	Density Water = 1	Period of Rotation	Inclination of Equator to Orbit	Oblateness	Stellar Magnitude at Greatest Brilliancy
Sun	☉	864,000	331,950	1.41	24^d.65	7° 10′	0	−26.8
Moon	☽	2,160	0.012	3.33	27 .32	6 41	0	−12.6
Mercury		2,900	0.05	6.1	88	7?	0	−1.9
Venus		7,600	0.81	5.06	30?	23?	0	−4.4
Earth		7,913	1.00	5.52	23^h 56^m	23 27	1/296	. . . . . .
Mars		4,200	0.11	4.12	24 37	24	1/192	−2.8
Jupiter		86,800	318.4	1.35	9 50	3 7	1/15	−2.5
Saturn		71,500	95.3	0.71	10 14	26 45	1/9.5	−0.4
Uranus		29,400	14.5	1.56	10 45	98	1/14	+5.7
Neptune		28,000	17.2	2.29	15 48?	29	1/40	+7.6

TABLE 8·V THE SATELLITES

Name	Discovery		Mean Distance in Miles	Period of Revolution			Diameter in Miles	Stellar Magnitude at Mean Opposition
Moon			238,857	27^d	7^h	43^m	2160	−12
SATELLITES OF MARS								
Phobos	Hall,	1877	5,800	0	7	39	10?	+12
Deimos	Hall,	1877	14,600	1	6	18	5?	13
SATELLITES OF JUPITER								
Fifth	Barnard,	1892	113,000	0	11	53	150?	13
I Io	Galileo,	1610	262,000	1	18	28	2000	5
II Europa	Galileo,	1610	417,000	3	13	14	1800	6
III Ganymede	Galileo,	1610	666,000	7	3	43	3100	5
IV Callisto	Galileo,	1610	1,170,000	16	16	32	2800	6
Sixth	Perrine,	1904	7,120,000	250	14		100?	14
Seventh	Perrine,	1905	7,290,000	259	14		35?	17
Tenth	Nicholson,	1938	7,300,000	260	12		15?	19
Twelfth	Nicholson,	1951	13,000,000	625			14?	19
Eleventh	Nicholson,	1938	14,000,000	700			19?	18
Eighth	Melotte,	1908	14,600,000	739			35?	17
Ninth	Nicholson,	1914	14,700,000	758			17?	19
SATELLITES OF SATURN								
Mimas	Herschel,	1789	115,000	0	22	37	300?	12
Enceladus	Herschel,	1789	148,000	1	8	53	350	12
Tethys	Cassini,	1684	183,000	1	21	18	500	11
Dione	Cassini,	1684	234,000	2	17	41	500	11
Rhea	Cassini,	1672	327,000	4	12	25	1000	10
Titan	Huygens,	1655	759,000	15	22	41	2850	8
Hyperion	Bond,	1848	920,000	21	6	38	300?	13
Iapetus	Cassini,	1671	2,210,000	79	7	56	800	11
Phoebe	Pickering,	1898	8,034,000	550			200?	14
SATELLITES OF URANUS								
Miranda	Kuiper,	1948	81,000	1	9	56	. . . . .	17
Ariel	Lassell,	1851	119,000	2	12	29	600?	15
Umbriel	Lassell,	1851	166,000	4	3	28	400?	15
Titania	Herschel,	1787	272,000	8	16	56	1000?	14
Oberon	Herschel,	1787	364,000	13	11	7	900?	14
SATELLITES OF NEPTUNE								
Triton	Lassell,	1846	220,000	5	21	3	2350	13
Nereid	Kuiper,	1949	3,440,000	359	10		200?	19

11. Describe the spectroscopic evidence that Saturn's rings are not continuous surfaces.

12. What features of Pluto suggest that it may have been originally a satellite of Neptune?

1. Aspects of Venus recur on nearly the same date at intervals of 8 years (Table 8·I), and transits of Venus now occur in pairs separated by an interval of 8 years. Explain.

Answer: Five times the synodic period equals about 8 years.

2. Although the orbit of Venus is inclined less than $3\frac{1}{2}°$ to the ecliptic, this planet is at times outside the zodiac (more than 8° from the ecliptic). Explain.

Answer: The inclination is the angle at the sun. When Venus is nearest the earth, its observed angular distance from the ecliptic may exceed 8°. This can be shown by a diagram drawn to scale.

3. A planet's distance from the sun at perihelion is $a\,(1 - e)$ and at aphelion is $a\,(1 + e)$, where a is its mean distance and e is the eccentricity of its orbit (Table 8·IV). How much farther from the sun is Mars at aphelion than at perihelion?

Answer: About 26 million miles.

4. The diameter of a satellite of Uranus, which is too small to appear as a disk, is calculated as 1000 miles. Suppose that the satellite's albedo (reflecting power) is actually one half the assumed value. What is the diameter?

Answer: 1400 miles.

5. Jupiter's mass is 318 times the earth's mass and its radius is 11 times the earth's radius. Compare the acceleration of gravity at the surface of Jupiter and of the earth.

Answer: The value for Jupiter is about 2.6 times that for the earth.

6. The plane of Saturn's rings requires about a year to sweep across the earth's orbit. Show by diagrams that the rings may be presented edgewise to us from one to three times in that interval.

REFERENCES

Kuiper, Gerard P., editor, *The Atmospheres of the Earth and Planets.* Revised edition. University of Chicago Press, Chicago, 1952.

Kuiper, Gerard P., and Barbara M. Middlehurst, editors, *Planets and Satellites.* University of Chicago Press, Chicago, 1962.

Richardson, Robert S., *Exploring Mars.* McGraw-Hill Book Company, New York, 1954.

Urey, Harold C., *The Planets.* Their origin and development. Yale University Press, New Haven, 1952.

Whipple, Fred L., *Earth, Moon and Planets.* Revised edition. Grosset and Dunlap, New York, 1958.

9

THE SOLAR SYSTEM (Continued)

COMETS – METEORS AND METEOR STREAMS –
METEORITES AND METEORITE CRATERS – THE
PROBLEM OF THE ORIGIN OF THE SYSTEM

The description of the solar system continues with an account
of the comets and the streams of meteors. Comets revolve around
the sun generally in highly eccentric orbits. Meteor streams are
products of the disintegration of comets. The meteors themselves
make bright trails across the night sky when they chance to plunge
into our atmosphere. Meteorites come through to the ground, and
large ones may have momentum enough to blast out craters in the
earth's surface. Some meteorites are believed to be fragments of
shattered asteroids.

COMETS

Characteristic of all comets, and the only conspicuous feature of
many, is the foggy envelope of the *coma*. The coma surrounds a
rather small *nucleus* of frozen material. A comet's *tail* fans out in
a direction away from the sun.

9·1. Discovery of Comets. Comets are sometimes discovered at the
observatories in examinations of photographs taken for other purposes. They have frequently been found by amateur astronomers
who search for comets. The chief requirements for a comet hunter
are a small telescope, much perseverance, and a catalog of nebulae
and star clusters that could be mistaken for comets, although the
motion of a comet among the stars will soon identify it. The
western sky after nightfall or the eastern sky before dawn are the
most promising regions for the search.

The report of the discovery of a comet, giving the comet's position
and the direction of its motion among the stars, may be made to
the Central Bureau of Astronomical Telegrams at the Copenhagen
Observatory, or to Harvard Observatory, the central station in the
United States for such astronomical news, which forwards the an-

nouncement to other observatories here. As soon as three positions
of the comet have been observed at intervals of a few days, a preliminary orbit is calculated. Then it is usually possible to decide

Fig. 9·1. Comet 1948 1. A composite of two photographs of the comet
from the balcony of the 100-inch dome. (*Photographs by Roscoe F. Sanford, Mount Wilson Observatory*)

whether the comet is a new one or the return of a comet previously
recorded, and what may be expected of it. Further observed positions provide data for the calculation of the definitive orbit.

An average of 5 or 6 comets are picked up each year; about a third of these are returns of comets that have appeared before, and two thirds are new ones. Comets that are bright enough to be visible without a telescope average less than one a year, and only rarely is a comet spectacular enough to attract the attention of those who are not astronomers.

A comet is designated provisionally by the year of its discovery followed by a letter in the order in which the discovery is announced; an example is Comet 1956 h. The permanent designation is the year (not always the year of discovery) followed by a Roman numeral in order of perihelion passage during that year; an example is Comet 1957 II. Many comets, especially the more remarkable ones, are also known by the name of the discoverer, or discoverers, or of the astronomer whose investigations of the comet entitle him by common consent to the distinction; Halley's comet is an example.

9·2. The Orbits of Comets. A comet has no permanent individuality by which it may be distinguished from other comets. The only identification mark is the path it pursues around the sun. The orbits of 566 comets listed in J. G. Porter's catalog of 1961 are known with varying degrees of precision. The comets fall into two groups, with a somewhat indefinite dividing line between them:

(1) Comets having *nearly parabolic orbits*. The orbits of many comets are so nearly parabolas that it is difficult to tell the difference, from the small portions of the orbits near the sun in which the comets can be seen. These orbits extend far out beyond the planetary orbits, and the undetermined periods of revolution are so long that only one appearance of each comet has thus far been recorded. In this sense they are "nonperiodic comets." The orbits are often highly inclined to the ecliptic. The revolutions of half of these comets are direct and of the other half are retrograde.

(2) Comets having *definitely elliptic orbits*. The orbits of "periodic comets," having periods not exceeding a few hundred years, are more closely allied to the organization of the rest of the solar system. Although most of these orbits are also highly eccentric, they are more moderately inclined to the ecliptic, and the revolutions of the comets are mainly direct.

9·3. Some Recently Observed Comets. Tables 9·I and 9·II contain selected lists of recently observed comets prepared in 1957 by Seth B. Nicholson. The first table lists some of the brighter non-

TABLE 9·I   RECENT BRIGHT NONPERIODIC COMETS

Comet	Year	Perihelion Passage	Perihelion Distance (astron. units)	Inclination of Orbit i
Skjellerup	1927 k	1927 Dec.	0.18	85 °
Ryves	1931 c	1931 Aug.	0.06	167
Peltier	1936 a	1936 July	1.10	79
Finsler	1937 f	1937 Aug.	0.86	146
Cunningham	1940 d	1941 Jan.	0.37	52
Paraskevopoulos	1941 c	1941 Jan.	0.79	168
Whipple	1942 f	1943 Feb.	1.36	20
Bester	1947 k	1948 Feb.	0.75	140
	1947 n	1947 Dec.	0.11	138
Honda-Bernosconi	1948 g	1948 May	0.21	23
	1948 l	1948 Oct.	0.14	23
Wilson-Harrington	1951 i	1952 Jan.	0.79	153
Mrkos	1955 e	1955 June	0.54	87
Arend-Roland	1956 h	1957 Apr.	0.32	120
Mrkos	1957 d	1957 Aug.	0.35	94

TABLE 9·II   SOME PERIODIC COMETS RECENTLY OBSERVED

Comet	First Seen	Last Seen	Period (years)	Perihelion Distance (astron. units)
Encke	1786	1957	3.30	0.34
Pons-Brooks	1812	1953	70.88	0.77
Crommelin	1818	1956	27.87	0.74
Pons-Winnecke	1819	1951	6.26	1.23
Faye	1843	1954	7.41	1.65
d'Arrest	1851	1950	6.69	1.38
Temple 2	1873	1956	5.31	1.14
Giacobini-Zinner	1900	(1959)	6.59	1.00
Grigg-Skjellerup	1902	1956	4.90	0.86
Daniel	1909	1950	6.66	1.46
Schaumasse	1911	1951	8.17	1.20
Neujmin	1913	1948	17.93	1.54
Schwassmann-Wachmann	1927	....	16.15	5.52
Oterma	1943	....	7.95	3.41

Fig. 9·3. Comet Mrkos (1957 d). *(Photograph by John Farrell, Fort Worth, Texas)*

periodic comets for which parabolic orbits have been calculated. Note that about half of these comets have direct revolutions (*i* less than 90°) and the others retrograde (*i* greater than 90°). The brightest comets in this list were 1927 k, 1947 n, and 1948 l, which had the small perihelion distances of 0.18, 0.11, and 0.14 astronomical units, respectively. Two rather bright comets, 1956 h and 1957 d, were of considerable public interest. A later bright nonperiodic comet, 1961 d, reached its perihelion in the middle of July of that year.

The second table lists some comets of short period and shows the dates through 1957 when their latest returns were observed. The dates do not appear for the last two entries because these comets, then having orbits of unusually small eccentricity, could be observed at every opposition with the sun.

The Schwassmann-Wachmann comet, 1925 II, revolves entirely between the orbits of Jupiter and Saturn. It was the first comet to be observed near its aphelion. Normally of the 18th magnitude, it is unique in exhibiting large and rapid flare-ups, for which the reason is unknown; an increase of 5 magnitudes or more in brightness has occurred within less than a day. Around the year 1974 the comet's orbit will be made even more nearly circular by close approach to Jupiter.

Oterma's comet had a nearly circular path around the sun between the orbits of Mars and Jupiter from 1943, the year of its discovery, until 1961. By prolonged close approach to Jupiter in the following few years, according to Paul Herget, the eccentricity of the comet's orbit and the revolution period have been drastically increased.

9·4. Jupiter's Family of Comets. Two dozen or more comets of very short period have orbits closely related to the orbit of Jupiter. In each case the aphelion and one of the nodes are near the orbit of Jupiter, so that the comets often pass close to the planet itself.

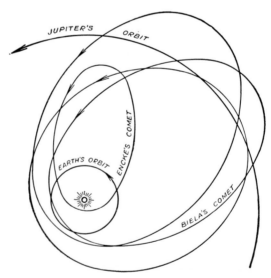

FIG. 9·4. Orbits of Four Comets of Jupiter's Family. Encke's comet has the smallest orbit of all comets.

These are members of *Jupiter's family of comets.* Their close approaches to the giant planet result in such great perturbations of their orbits that the configuration of the family is not stable.

The periods of revolution of these comets around the sun are mostly between 5 and 9 years, averaging a little more than half of Jupiter's period. The orbits are generally not much inclined to the ecliptic and the revolutions are all direct. The comets themselves are never conspicuous objects; a few become faintly visible without the telescope when they pass near the earth.

Encke's comet, discovered in 1786, was the first member of Jupiter's family to be recognized, in 1819. Its period of revolution, 3.3 years, is the shortest of any known comet. Its aphelion point has been drawing in toward the sun and is now a whole astronomical unit inside Jupiter's orbit. Forty-six appearances of this comet have been recorded as observed between 1786 and 1961.

9·5. The Capture of Comets. The relation between Jupiter and its family of comets makes it seem probable that the planet has acquired the family by capturing some of the comets that chanced to be passing by. The low inclinations of the orbits and the direct motions of all comets in the family suggest that the process is selective. Comets having original orbits of sufficiently large perihelion distance and low inclination, so that they moved parallel to Jupiter for a time, are the most likely to be captured; their orbits may be made progressively smaller at successive encounters until they become members of the family.

The capture process was invoked in former times to account for all periodic comets. It was supposed that comets were casual visitors from outside the solar system and that only those captured by planets prolonged their stay with us. It now seems probable that all comets we see are natives of this system.

9·6. Halley's Comet. This famous comet, the first known periodic comet, is named in honor of Edmund Halley, who predicted its return. Halley calculated as a parabola the orbit of the bright comet of 1682 and noted its close resemblance to the orbits that he had similarly calculated for earlier comets of 1531 and 1607 from records of their places in the sky. Concluding that they were appearances of the same comet, which must therefore be moving in an ellipse, Halley predicted that it would return again in 1758. The comet was sighted that year according to prediction; it re-

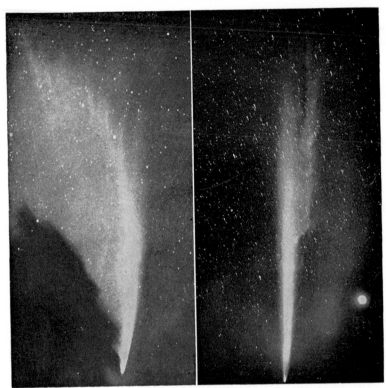

FIG. 9·6. Two Bright Comets of 1910. (Left) Comet 1910 a. (Right)
Halley's Comet, May 13, 1910. The comet was then visible in the east
before dawn. The bright object to the right is the planet Venus. (*Lowell
Observatory photographs*)

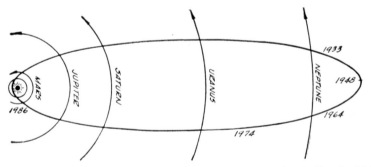

FIG. 9·6A. Orbit of Halley's Comet. The comet passed aphelion in 1948
and will return to perihelion in 1986.

turned again in 1835 and 1910. Halley's comet is the only conspicuous comet having a period less than 100 years. The revolution is retrograde.

Twenty-eight observed returns of this comet have been recorded, as far back as 240 B.C. It was Halley's comet that appeared in 1066, at the time of the Norman conquest of England. The period has varied nearly 5 years meanwhile, because of disturbing effects of planets; the average interval between perihelion passages is 77 years. The comet has now passed its aphelion beyond the orbit of Neptune. It will return to perihelion in 1986.

9·7. A Remarkable Group of Comets includes the great comets of 1668, 1843, 1880, 1882, and 1887. These comets passed unusually close to the sun and their orbits seemed practically identical. They were evidently parts of a single comet, which was disrupted at a previous close approach to the sun. The separate parts were dispersed in orbits of different sizes and, therefore, with periods of different lengths. All the orbits closely resemble the orbit of the original comet in the vicinity of the sun.

Comet 1882 II, the most spectacular of the group, was one of the brightest comets of modern times, plainly visible in full daylight. It passed through the sun's corona, within 300,000 miles of the sun's surface, with a speed exceeding a million miles an hour. Effects of tidal disruption during the close approach were evident soon afterward. The nucleus of the comet divided into four parts, which spread out in the direction of the revolution. These are expected to return as four comets between the 25th and 28th centuries.

9·8. Formation of a Comet's Tail. The tail of a comet is composed of gas and fine dust. It develops as the comet approaches the sun and is likely to become conspicuous if the perihelion is close to

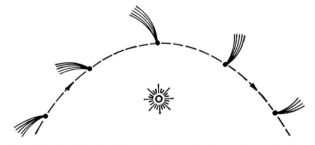

Fig. 9·8. Tail of a Comet Directed Away from the Sun.

the sun. The tail generally points directly away from the sun, being repelled by a force exceeding that of the sun's attraction. The repulsive force is usually ascribed to the pressure of the sun's radiation, perhaps increased irregularly by collision with streams of high-speed particles emerging from the sun. By Kepler's third law the material of the tail revolves around the sun at a slower rate as it moves outward, falling more and more behind the head of the comet. Thus the tail is generally curved, the dusty part the more strongly because this material is likely to be repelled less rapidly than the gases of the tail.

Meanwhile, some heavier meteoric products of the comet's disintegration may fan out behind the comet along the orbit plane, as they did conspicuously from a bright comet in 1957 (9·11).

9·9. The Spectrum of a Comet is characterized by bright bands that are produced by gases set glowing by the sun's radiation. The

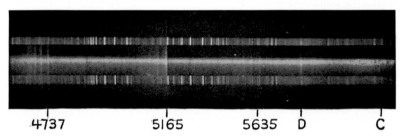

.4737   5165   5635   D   C

FIG. 9·9. Spectrum of Halley's Comet. The spectrum shows bright carbon bands indicated by their wavelengths, the bright D line of sodium, and a few faint dark lines of the reflected sunlight. (*Photograph by V. M. Slipher, Lowell Observatory*)

gases are composed mainly of carbon (C_2), methyne (CH), hydroxyl (OH), ammonia radicals (NH_2 and NH), and cyanogen (CN). These are rather unstable and are soon transformed into more durable molecules, such as carbon monoxide, carbon dioxide, and nitrogen, as they are driven from the coma into the tail. The unstable constituents of the coma are formed by action of sunlight on parent molecules of methane, ammonia, and water in the nucleus. These materials remain frozen there when the comet is far from the sun, and begin to evaporate as it approaches the sun.

Bright lines of sodium may become prominent in the spectrum, and lines of iron and nickel have been seen, when a comet is sufficiently heated by close approach to the sun. A faint replica of the solar spectrum also appears, showing that a comet shines partly by reflected sunlight. This dark-line spectrum is generally the only feature when a comet is more than 3 astronomical units from the sun.

9·10. The Nature of a Comet. A comet's nucleus is a very porous structure of ices having meteoric material embedded in them, according to the theory by F. L. Whipple. The ices are chiefly of methane, ammonia, and water. The meteoric material is generally in small particles and is composed of iron, nickel, calcium, magnesium, silicon, sodium, and other elements. The nucleus of a comet is only a mile or so in diameter.

Some of the ices evaporate at each approach to the sun. The gases issue explosively into the coma, carrying the meteoric fragments with them, and are then swept out through the tail or scattered along the orbit. Whipple estimates that a comet evaporates $\frac{1}{200}$ of its mass around each perihelion passage. That it is not dissipated more rapidly is because the surface of the nucleus becomes increasingly gritty; the meteoric material protects the ices underneath until the structure collapses. After many returns, the comet disappears. The meteoric material originally embedded in the ices continues to revolve around the sun as a meteor stream.

An important feature of the theory accounts for the spiral motions of some comets. The issuing of gas from the sunward side of the comet causes a jet propulsion action on the nucleus in the direction of the sun. If there is delay in setting the evaporation going, the comet's rotation swings a component of the propulsion along the orbit. Where the rotation is in the opposite direction to the revolution, the rotation diminishes the speed in the orbit, so that the comet begins to spiral in toward the sun. This effect seems to explain the hitherto perplexing behavior of Encke's comet (9·4). The opposite effect, where the comet rotates in the same direction as its revolution, is illustrated by d'Arrest's comet.

9·11. Comets Having Sunward Antitails. Comet Arend-Roland (1956 h) was of special interest because it showed a sunward anti-tail in addition to an ordinary tail that became 20° to 30° long to the unaided eye. This nonperiodic comet has a retrograde motion in an orbit inclined 60° to the ecliptic. It reached perihelion on April 8, 1957, at one third of the earth's distance from the sun. On April 25 the earth passed through the plane of the comet's orbit.

FIG. 9·11. Comet Arend-Roland, April 27, 1957. The sunward spike is still conspicuous. (*Photograph by Henry L. Giclas with the 13-inch refractor, Lowell Observatory*)

For a week around that date the antitail was conspicuous; it progressed from a stubby fan to a narrow spike as long as 15° on April 25, then reverted to a short, broad fan, and soon disappeared.

The sunward antitail was produced by meteoric material fanning out in the plane of the comet's orbit. The material in the fan was too diffuse to be easily visible far from the comet's head when presented broadside to us. When the layer was seen nearly on edge, it appeared as a long, narrow spike. Whipple has pointed out that Comet 1862 III similarly spread meteoric material along the orbit plane to produce the stream of the Perseids, or August meteors.

Comet Seki-Lines (1962 c) also showed an antitail. This nonperiodic comet became a bright object to the unaided eye because

Fig. 9·11A. Comet Seki-Lines (1962 *c*). Photograph by Alan McClure, April 9, 1962, from Frazier Mountain, California, with a 5½-inch f/5 Zeiss triplet aerial camera lens and 10-minute exposure on panchromatic film.

its head passed on April 1, 1962 only 2½ million miles from the sun's photosphere. In Alan McClure's photograph on April 9 (Fig. 9·11A) the ordinary tail appears 15°, or 30 million miles, in length and the antitail is a stubby fan.

METEORS AND METEOR STREAMS

Meteors are stony and metallic particles revolving around the sun, which become separately visible only when they plunge into the earth's atmosphere. Melted and vaporized then by impact with the air molecules, they produce luminous trails across the night sky. Unusually bright ones are called *fireballs*. In addition to the sporadic meteors that seem to be moving independently, there are swarms and streams of meteors revolving around the sun, which cause meteor showers when they encounter the earth. A number of streams are identified with the orbits of comets from which they originated.

9·12. The Influx of Meteors. The total number of meteor trails brighter than visual magnitude +5 over all the earth's surface is determined by G. S. Hawkins as 90 million in a 24-hour period. The meteors producing these trails add several tons a day to the

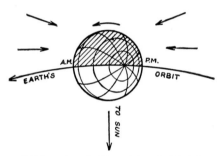

Fig. 9·12.   Meteor Flights Are Swifter After Midnight.   In the morning we are on the forward side of the earth in its revolution.

earth's mass. The number of trails visible to a single observer in this period is usually very small. The recorded hourly rate is likely to increase somewhat through the night. In the evening we are on the following side of the earth in its revolution, where we are protected except for the meteors that overtake the earth. In the morning we are on the forward side, more exposed to the incoming meteors.

The swiftness of the meteor flights across the sky also increases through the night. At our distance from the sun the speeds of the meteors in their eccentric orbits approach the parabolic value of 26 miles a second (7·25). Their speeds relative to the earth accordingly range from 26 minus 18½ miles a second for meteors that overtake us to 26 plus 18½ miles a second for head-on collisions, with some addition for the earth's attraction.

9·13. Meteor Trails and Trains. The *trails* of meteors are the bright streaks they produce in the flights through the air. The faster meteors generally appear in the photographs at a height of about 80 miles and disappear at 60 miles; the slower ones begin at 60 miles and have been followed to a height of 25 miles.

As its flight is resisted by the air molecules, the meteor is heated to incandescence and fused. The brightness of the trail depends on the kinetic energy of the meteor, that is, on its mass and the square of its velocity. The brightness also depends on the density of the air and the compactness of the meteor itself. Many meteors, presumably from the outer parts of comet nuclei, are extremely porous and fragile; these are likely to be shattered in their flights through the air and to collapse with bursts of added brightness.

In addition to their momentary trails, the meteors sometimes leave bright *trains* along their paths. These are cylinders of expanding gases, which remain visible from a few seconds to generally not longer than half an hour, and are often twisted by air currents. A rarer type of meteor train appears in the *noctilucent clouds* recorded especially by Canadian observers. They are dust trains in the wakes of very bright fireballs, and are best seen in the twilight when they are high enough to be illuminated by sunlight.

9·14. Meteors as Members of the Solar System. When the velocity of a meteor as it enters the atmosphere is known, it is possible to calculate its orbit around the sun and to determine among other results whether the meteor was a member of the solar system or came from outside it. Measuring the linear speed and the actual direction of the trail involves a parallax problem requiring positions of the trail among the stars as observed from two stations. The Harvard program, directed by Whipple, employs for this purpose two Baker-Schmidt cameras, having apertures of 12 inches and focal lengths of 8 inches, at stations in New Mexico 22 miles apart. A similar pair is operated north of Edmonton by Canadian observers. The two cameras are directed toward the same point in space 50 miles above the ground. The trail of any bright meteor that passes through this region is recorded by both cameras and is interrupted in the photographs at intervals of a small fraction of a second by rotating shutters in front of the films so as to facilitate the timing.

Several thousand trails have been doubly photographed in New Mexico by such procedure, and many of these have been analyzed for velocities and orbits under the leadership of L. G. Jacchia. Some of the sporadic meteors had orbits of the Jupiter-family comet-type (9·4) with direct motions and low inclinations to the ecliptic.

Some others were of the long-period type with random directions and inclinations. None of these had a reliably determined hyperbolic orbit. Like the meteors in streams the sporadic meteors had elliptical orbits and so were members of the solar system.

The speed by itself is enough to determine the status of the meteor in this respect. If the speed on entering the atmosphere, with allowance for the motions and attraction of the earth, is as great as 26 miles a second, the velocity of escape from the sun at the

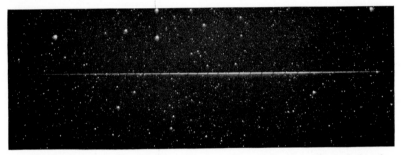

FIG. 9·14. Meteor Trail Interrupted at Intervals of a Twentieth of a Second. The meteor's flight was from left to right. The breaks in the trail are closer together at the left because the meteor was then farther away. (*Photograph from Harvard Observatory Meteor Program*)

earth's distance, the meteor may have come from outside the solar system. If the speed is less than this critical value, the meteor is a member of the system.

The echoes of radio beams returned from the ionized trails of meteors have been observed at Ottawa to determine the speeds of meteors. The beams are emitted either continuously or in pulses, and the echoes are automatically recorded. D. W. R. McKinley's records of more than 10,000 meteors down to the 8th visual magnitude include not one where the original speed was certainly as great as the velocity of escape. Thus the fainter meteors as well as the brighter ones appear to be members of the solar system.

9·15. The Spectra of Meteor Trails have been photographed in considerable numbers in recent years, particularly by P. M. Millman in Canada and J. A. Russell in California. These objective prism and grating spectra give an idea of conditions to which the meteors are subjected in their flights through the air and of the chemical compositions of the meteors themselves.

A meteor spectrum is an array of bright images of the trail in the various wavelengths of the emitted light. The character of the lines depends on the temperature to which the meteor is raised by the air resistance. The spectrum of a swifter meteor is likely to contain prominent H and K lines of ionized calcium. In the spectrum of a very bright Perseid meteor of 1953, Millman's photograph (Fig. 9·15) shows more than 100 bright lines, from which he identified the presence of nine neutral elements: Fe, Mn, Ca, Si, Al,

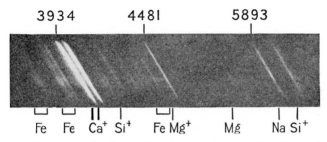

Fig. 9·15. Spectrum of a Perseid Meteor Trail. Showing lines of ionized and neutral atoms. (*Photograph by Peter M. Millman, David Dunlap Observatory*)

Mg, Na, N, and H, and also four ionized elements: Fe, Ca, Si, and Mg. Nitrogen and some oxygen lines are frequently produced in the air that is itself heated by the meteor's flight.

9·16. Meteor Streams and Showers. Multitudes of meteors revolving together around the sun constitute a *meteor swarm*. When the meteors are considerably extended over a similar part of their orbits in the sun's vicinity as is often the case, they form a *meteor stream*.

Because the meteors in a stream are moving in nearly parallel paths when they encounter the earth, their bright trails through the air are nearly parallel. Just as the rails of a track seem to diverge from a distant point, so the trails of meteors in a shower appear to spread from a point or small area in the sky. The *radiant* of a meteor shower is the vanishing point in the perspective of the parallel trails; it is located by extending the trails backward.

Meteor showers and the streams that produce them are generally named after the constellation in which the radiant is situated, or else after the bright star near the radiant at the maximum of the display. Examples are the Perseids and the Beta Taurids. The place of the radiant in the sky drifts from day to day during the progress

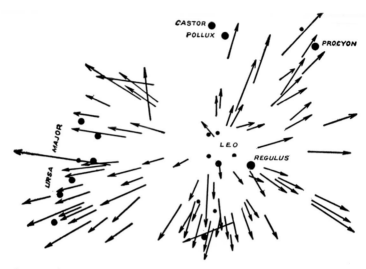

FIG. 9·16. Shower of Leonid Meteors. The trails were observed at Brown University, November 15, 1901, during a watch of 5 hours. With a few exceptions the trails diverged from the radiant in Leo.

of the shower, as the earth keeps changing the direction of its revolution. A stream is sometimes named after the comet with which it is associated. Thus the Draconids are also known as the Giacobinids.

9·17. The Orbits of Shower Meteors. The orbits of a dozen meteors of the Alpha Capricornid stream (Fig. 9·17) show how widely the aphelia of a stream may be scattered in space. These are determined from double-station trails photographed by the Harvard meteor program between July 16 and August 22. This example may be somewhat extreme because there may be more than one stream involved, as the investigators explain. Viewed as a single stream, the shower at maximum display has its radiant northeast of Alpha Capricorni, and it may be associated with Comet 1948 n.

A meteor shower occurs only when the orbit of the swarm intersects or passes near the earth's orbit and when the swarm and the earth arrive together at the intersection. The position of this point on the earth's orbit determines the date of the shower. If the swarm is condensed, the interval between showers depends on the period of revolution of the swarm and its relation to the length of the year. Streams may spend more than a year in crossing the

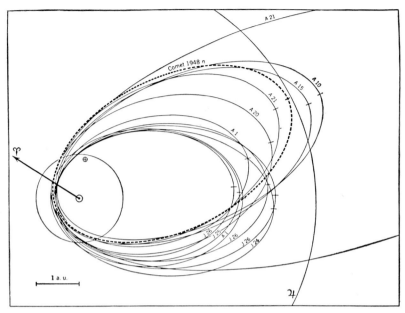

Fig. 9·17. Orbits of Alpha Capricornid Meteors. The trails were photographed on the days in July and August shown on the orbits, which are
projected on the ecliptic plane. (*Diagram by Frances W. Wright, L. G.
Jacchia, and F. L. Whipple, Harvard Observatory Meteor Program*)

earth's orbit, or may be so scattered, as in the case of the Perseids,
that we encounter some of their members every year. Some streams
that formerly produced spectacular showers no longer do so because their orbits have been altered by disturbing effects of planets.

9·18. Some Noteworthy Meteor Showers. The Perseids furnish the
most conspicuous and dependable of the annual showers. Their
trails are visible through 2 or 3 weeks, with the greatest display
about August 12. Their orbit is inclined 65° to the ecliptic plane
and passes near the orbit of no other planet. Next in order of
numbers and annual reliability are the Orionids and the Gem-
inids. Among the less frequent showers, the stream of the Leonids,
revolving around the sun in a period of 33 years, produced in 1833
and 1866–67 the most spectacular showers of modern times. At
later returns, however, the Leonids appeared only in sprinkles.

The Draconids gave the most remarkable showers of the present
century. They revolve in the orbit of the Giacobini-Zinner comet,

FIG. 9·18. Draconid Meteor Trails During the Shower of October 9, 1946. During the 12-minute exposure with a fixed camera the stars moved through small arcs of their daily circles around the celestial pole. The meteor trails were straight and diverged from the radiant in the head of Draco. (*Part of a photograph by Kenneth Spain, Vanderbilt University*)

a member of Jupiter's family (9·4) first noticed in 1900; the comet itself revolves around the sun in a period of 6½ years. The main body of the swarm and the earth have arrived together at the intersection of their paths in October at intervals of 13 years.

After nightfall on October 9, 1933, the skies of western Europe were streaked with meteor trails coming from the head of Draco. Before night began in America, that shower was over. America's turn came on October 9, 1946, 2 weeks after the comet had passed by. For a few hours on that evening there were fine displays wherever the skies were clear. At the height of the shower some observers counted as many as 100 trails a minute despite the bright moonlight, which obscured the fainter ones. A recurrence of the Draconid shower on the night of October 9, 1959, was watched for, but only a few trails were observed. Indeed, an abundant shower was not expected, because a close approach to the planet Jupiter had altered the orbit of the stream.

9·19. Daytime Meteor Showers. Observers at the Jodrell Bank Station of the University of Manchester in England have made systematic surveys of meteor activity by means of radar echoes. With this technique they are unhampered by cloud or daylight. They not only have investigated radiants conforming closely to previous results of evening observers, but also have discovered radiants of showers observable only in the daytime.

The daytime activity they have observed includes a number of showers of very short period. Among the daytime showers of June are the Zeta Perseids, the Arietids, and the Beta Taurids. An unexpected display of Draconids was recorded for 2 hours on the afternoon of October 9, 1952. Evidently an advance contingent of the meteor stream was encountered by the earth half a year before the associated comet was scheduled to reach the intersection with our orbit.

9·20. Association of Meteor Streams and Comets. The Draconids are by no means unique in their association with a comet. When meteoric material is released from the ices of a comet's nucleus (9·10), the material may become a meteor stream extending along the comet's orbit. Table 9·III, which is taken from more extended data by F. L. Whipple and G .S. Hawkins in the *Handbuch der Physik,* volume 52, 1959, lists major meteor showers and the comets associated with them. The table gives in each case the date of maximum display in universal time, the position of the radiant so that it may be located in the star maps, and the name of the parent comet when it is known.

Two meteor showers are associated with Encke's comet. They are the daytime Beta Taurids of June and the Taurids of November; they come from the same extended stream that the earth encounters before and after the perihelion passage of the stream. Two showers are associated less certainly with Halley's comet; they are the Eta Aquarids of May and the Orionids of October. The radiants assigned in the table to the Delta Aquarids and the Taurids are each the means of two radiants several degrees apart.

A remarkable case of the dispersal of a comet into a meteor stream is that of Biela's comet, a member of Jupiter's family having a period of 6½ years. At its return to the sun's vicinity in 1846, the comet had divided into two. The divided comet re-

TABLE 9·III   METEOR SHOWERS AND ASSOCIATED COMETS

Shower	Maximum Display (UT Date)	Radiant at Max. (Equinox of 1950)		Associated Comet (and notes)
		R. A.	Decl.	
Quadrantids	Jan. 3	15^h 20^m	$+48°$	
Lyrids	Apr. 21	18 0	$+33$	1861 I
Eta Aquarids	May 4	22 24	0	Halley(?)
*Arietids	June 8	2 56	$+23$	(= Delta Aquarids)
*Zeta Perseids	June 9	4 8	$+23$	
*Beta Taurids	June 30	5 44	$+19$	Encke
Delta Aquarids	July 30	22 36	-11	(two streams)
Alpha Capricornids	Aug. 1	20 36	-10	1948 n
Perseids	Aug. 12	3 4	$+58$	1862 III
Draconids	Oct. 10	17 36	$+54$	Giacobini-Zinner
Orionids	Oct. 22	6 16	$+16$	Halley(?)
Taurids	Nov. 1	3 28	$+17$	Encke (two streams)
Andromedids	Nov. 14	1 28	$+27$	Biela
Leonids	Nov. 17	10 8	$+22$	Temple
Geminids	Dec. 14	7 32	$+32$	
Ursids (Ursa Minor)	Dec. 22	13 44	$+80$	Tuttle

* Shower in daytime

appeared with greater separation in 1852 and has not since been seen. Traveling in the orbit of the lost comet, the Andromedids, or Bielid meteors, gave fine showers in 1872, 1885, and 1898, and nearly disappeared thereafter. Perturbations by planets have shifted the orbit of the main body of the swarm, according to Hawkins, so that it now passes 2 million miles from the earth's orbit at the closest point.

9·21. The Zodiacal Light and the Gegenschein. The faint triangular glow of the *zodiacal light* in the sky is best seen in middle northern latitudes in the west after nightfall in the spring and in the east before dawn in the autumn. In corresponding southern latitudes it is best seen at the opposite seasons. Broadest near the horizon, where it is then 30° or more from the sun, it tapers upward to a distance of 90° from the sun's place below the horizon. Because the glow is almost symmetrical with respect to the ecliptic, it reaches a higher altitude and is easier to observe at those seasons when the ecliptic is most inclined to the horizon.

In the tropics, where the ecliptic is more nearly perpendicular to the horizon, the zodiacal light is visible throughout the year in both the evening and morning. The glow is said to extend in a

FIG. 9·21. The Zodiacal Light. (*Painting by E. L. Trouvelot*)

narrow band along the ecliptic entirely around the heavens. It also becomes visible at total solar eclipse immediately around the sun, where it blends with the sun's true corona (10·31).

The zodiacal light is attributed to sunlight scattered by a ring of meteoric dust particles that are revolving around the sun near the ecliptic plane. Whipple suggests that the supply of dust may well be continually replenished by disintegrating comets; else it would be depleted as the dust grains fall into the sun or are dispersed by pressure of the sun's radiations.

The *gegenschein,* or *counterglow,* is a very faint, roughly elliptical glow extending about 20° along the ecliptic and 10° in celestial latitude. It is centered 2° or 3° west of the point in the sky opposite the sun and is variable in form and position. This glow is visible to the unaided eye in the most favorable conditions, especially when it is viewed in the fall projected against the dull region of the constellations Pisces and Cetus. It is readily photographed with a very wide-angle camera or recorded with a photoelectric cell. Among the several explanations of the glow, the hypothesis that it is sunlight scattered by a dust-tail of the earth seems plausible at present but is not at all final, according to J. C. Brandt.

METEORITES AND METEORITE CRATERS

A *meteorite* is a mass of stony or metallic material, or both, which survives its flight through the air and falls to the ground. The fall is frequently accompanied by flashes of light and by explosive and roaring sounds, effects that may be magnified in the reports of startled observers. Most meteorites are found on the ground or buried a little way in it. A few very large ones have blasted out the pits we call *meteorite craters.* Many meteorites are believed to be fragments of shattered asteroids.

9·22. The Fall of Meteorites. Meteorites are often found in groups. Either they entered the atmosphere as a compact swarm, or they arrived as single bodies which were shattered in the air by the shock of their reduced speed or when they struck the ground. The individuals of a large group may be distributed over an elliptical area several miles long in the direction of the forward motion. Whenever meteorites are picked up almost immediately after landing, they are likely to be cool enough to be handled comfortably. In their brief flights through the air the heat has not gone far into their cold interiors, and the melted material has been mostly swept away from their surfaces.

Individuals from nearly 1600 falls have been recovered, according to F. C. Leonard's recent catalog of meteoritic falls. The majority of these were not seen to fall, but their features definitely distinguish them from the native rocks. Meteorites are generally named after the locality in which they were found; examples are the Canyon Diablo, Arizona, meteorites, and the Willamette, Oregon, meteorite. Collections are exhibited in the Chicago Natural History Museum, the American Museum of Natural History, New York City, the Arizona State University at Tempe, and many other places.

9·23. External Appearance of Meteorites. Characteristic of most meteorites is the thin, glassy, and usually dark crust. It is formed from the fused material which was not swept away and which hardened quickly near the end of the flight through the air. The surface is often irregular, being depressed in places where softer materials melted faster, and raised in other places where drops of molten spray fell and hardened.

If the meteorite was shattered shortly before reaching the ground, the fragments have irregular shapes. If the individual had a longer flight through the air, it was shaped by the rush of hot air. Some individuals turned over and over as they fell and were rounded. Others kept the same orientation and became conical, a common form.

9·24. Structure and Composition. Meteorites are essentially of two kinds, the stones (aerolites) and the irons (siderites). There

Fig. 9·24. Furnas County, Nebraska, Meteorite. A stony meteorite weighing at least a ton. (*Official photograph of the Institute of Meteoritics, University of New Mexico*)

FIG. 9·24A. Etched Section of Knowles, Oklahoma, Meteorite. The
banded pattern characterizes most iron meteorites. (*American Museum
of Natural History, New York*)

are gradations between them (siderolites) from stones containing
flecks of nickel-iron to sponges of metal with stony fillings. Inside
their varnish-like crusts the *stony meteorites* are often grayish, having a characteristic granular structure that serves to establish their
celestial origin. The rounded granules are crystalline; they are
mainly silicates, of which the most common are iron-magnesium
silicates, such as olivine and enstatite, similar to those in our igneous rocks. Quartz is very rarely a constituent.

The largest known stony meteorite, weighing somewhat more
than a ton, fell on February 18, 1948, in Furnas County, Nebraska
(Fig. 9·24); it is preserved at the University of New Mexico. Another unusually large individual, now in the Chicago Natural History Museum, fell at Paragould, Arkansas, in 1930; it weighs 750
pounds. Stony meteorites do not often have the large dimensions
of many irons, partly because they offer less resistance to fracture
and erosion.

Iron meteorites are silvery under their blackened exteriors; they
are composed mainly of nickel-iron alloys, especially kamacite and
taenite. Where they occur in crystal forms, a characteristic pattern
of intersecting crystal bands (Fig. 9·24A), parallel to the faces of

an octahedron, may be etched with dilute nitric acid on a plane polished section.

Micrometeorites are so minute that they are not greatly altered when they enter the atmosphere. Their presence in interplanetary space is indicated by the scattered sunlight of the zodiacal light (9·21). Meteoritic dust is also produced by the larger meteoritic bodies themselves, when they are either crumbled by collision or are partly melted to form oxidized droplets in the air.

9·25. Large Iron Meteorites.   About 35 known individual meteorites weigh more than a ton (2000 pounds), according to Leonard. Almost all are nickel-iron meteorites. With the exception of the Furnas County stone, two stony-irons, and a 2-ton individual from the 1947 Siberian fall, their falls were not observed. The two largest irons on record are the Hoba meteorite and the Ahnighito meteorite.

The Hoba meteorite lies partly buried in the ground in the Grootfontein district, Southwest Africa. Its rectangular exposed surface measures 9×10 feet, and its greatest thickness is more than 3 feet; its weight is unknown. The Ahnighito meteorite is the largest of three irons that the explorer R. E. Peary found near Cape

Fig. 9·25.   Hoba Meteorite, Grootfontein, Southwest Africa.   **One of the** two largest known meteorites.   The exposed surface measures 9×10 feet.   (*Photograph by W. J. Luyten*)

York in northern Greenland, in 1894, and brought back to New York. It measures about $11 \times 7 \times 6$ feet and weighs a little more than 34 tons (68,085 pounds). This meteorite is exhibited in the American Museum—Hayden Planetarium, New York City, on the scales with which it was first accurately weighed, in 1956.

The Willamette meteorite, also in the Hayden Planetarium, is the largest found in the United States. A conical mass of nickel-

Fig. 9·25A. Ahnighito Meteorite in the American Museum—Hayden Planetarium, New York. The largest known meteorite in America. (*American Museum of Natural History, New York*)

iron, weighing about 15 tons, it was discovered in 1902 south of Portland, Oregon. Large cavities in the base of the cone, which lay uppermost for a long time, were formed by weathering. Three large iron meteorites, each weighing more than 10 tons, were found in Mexico. They are the Bacubirito (29 tons), the Chupaderos (21 tons, in two pieces that fit together), and the Morito (11 tons). The last two may be seen in the School of Mines, Mexico City.

9·26. Two Siberian Falls of large meteorites in the present century have attracted much attention. The first occurred on June 30, 1908, in the forested area of the Tunguska River in central Siberia. The meteorite appeared as a brilliant fireball in full daylight from hundreds of miles away. Its mass is unknown. The trees were felled within a radius of 20 or 30 miles; they lay without bark and branches, and with their tops pointing away from the center of the area. Many craters were blasted out near the center, the largest one 150 feet in diameter. Although larger remnants of the Tunguska meteorite have not been recovered, soil samples from the region are said to contain microscopic chips and spherules of nickel-iron dust.

The second fall occurred on February 12, 1947, over a square mile on the western spurs of the Sikhote-Alin mountain range in southeast Siberia. The original body broke in the atmosphere into many pieces, which came down as an "iron rain" and were further fractured as they struck the ground. The area was pitted with 200 small holes and larger craters, the largest one 90 feet in diameter. The field was strewn with an estimated 100 tons of nickel-iron fragments. An interesting feature of the fall, described by E. L. Krinov, was a wide gray band of dust in the wake of the brilliant meteorite; the dust remained visible for several hours in the daytime sky and gradually settled to earth as microscopic droplets.

9·27. The Barringer Meteorite Crater, near Canyon Diablo in northeast Arizona, is a circular depression in the desert 4200 feet across and 570 feet deep; the depth is measured from the rim, which rises to an average height of about 135 feet above the surrounding plain. Thirty tons of meteoritic iron have been picked up within a distance of 6 miles around the crater. The largest individual, weighing more than 1400 pounds, is exhibited in the museum on the north rim of the crater. Samplings in a survey directed by J. S. Rinehart indicate that the total amount of crushed meteoritic material around the crater is 12,000 tons.

The rocks below the crater floor are crushed to a depth of several hundred feet and give evidence of having been highly heated. Millions of tons of limestone and sandstone were displaced outward to form the crater wall, and loose blocks of rock weighing up to 7000 tons lie around the rim.

The meteorite that produced the Barringer crater is estimated to have had a diameter of 200 feet and to have weighed at least a million tons. When an object of this size encounters the earth, its speed is not greatly reduced by air resistance. When it strikes the

FIG. 9·27. Barringer Meteorite Crater, Arizona. (*Photograph by John Farrell, Fort Worth, Texas*)

ground, at least the outer parts of the meteorite and the ground in contact are intensely heated and fused. The gases expand explosively, blasting out the crater and scattering whatever may be left of the meteorite over the surrounding country.

As fragments of colliding asteroids (8·23), the meteorites would usually revolve around the sun from west to east, as do all asteroids, so that they would be overtaking the earth when they encounter it. Thus the majority of crater-forming meteorites strike the ground with relative speeds not great enough to cause the vaporization of their entire masses. Only an occasional meteorite would be likely to have its orbit so greatly altered that it could land on the earth's advancing hemisphere. Then its higher relative speed might cause an impact of such violence as to leave only microscopic remnants of the intruder for the collectors. The Tunguska fall of 1908 is cited as an example.

9·28. Other Meteorite Craters. More than a dozen other craters or groups of craters in various parts of the world have been definitely considered to be of meteoritic origin. Among the largest is the Wolf Creek crater in West Australia, having a diameter of 2800 feet at the bottom and a depth of 160 feet. These were formed by impacts of meteorites within the last million years. The scars of earlier falls have gradually vanished as readily recognized features of the landscape. Erosion has reduced the heights of their rims, and sedimentation has filled their depressions. A few "fossil craters" scarcely noticeable on the ground have been observed in aerial photographs. Examples are the Brent and Holleford craters in Ontario, described by C. S. Beals. Their diameters are 2 and 1½ miles, respectively, and their ages are estimated as 500 million years.

The geologist Robert S. Dietz has undertaken to increase the list of recognized meteorite craters, where the surface structure itself is inconclusive and where no meteoritic remnants have been reported. He points out in *Scientific American* for August 1961 that the shock generated by the impact of a meteorite in producing a large terrestrial crater transcends that of any volcanic or other earthly explosion. Conclusive evidence of such superintense shock waves are recognized by the unusual fracture pattern in rock fragments known as *shatter cones* and also by a form of silica known as *coesite,* that is produced under extremely high pressure.

An example of a region having shatter cones is the Steinheim Basin in southern Germany, formerly believed to be the site of a great volcanic explosion. Another of several examples mentioned by Dietz is the Vredefort Ring in the Transvaal of South Africa; the entire deformation is 130 miles in diameter, comparable with the largest lunar craters. Coesite, the second shock-wave product, is reported present in the vicinities of the Giant Kettle in southern Germany, the Wabar craters of Arabia, the large Ashanti crater in Ghana, and elsewhere. There is also evidence, according to V. E. Barnes, that the glassy stones known as *tektites* are solidified droplets of molten rock that were splashed into the air by the impact of large meteorites at these and other sites.

THE ORIGIN OF THE SYSTEM

9·29. The Nature of the Problem. Theories of the origin of the solar system are often known as hypotheses in deference to the style set by the distinguished pioneer P. S. de Laplace. These accounts are generally related to the problem of the birth of the sun itself.

By a current theory, which we examine later (16·15), the sun and the other stars evolved from contracting clouds of cosmic gas. How could a planetary system have formed around a youthful sun? The question is specifically about the solar system because this is the only known system of its kind. A successful answer to the question must evidently conform to physical principles and must result in the system as it is known today.

The larger planets, as we have seen (7·4), have direct revolutions around the sun in nearly circular orbits, which are nearly in the same plane; they generally rotate in this direction as well. The larger satellites revolve around their planets and rotate on their axes in a similar manner. The less massive members of the system—the smaller satellites, the asteroids, and the comets and meteor streams—follow these regularities less faithfully, a fact that must be accounted for.

Theories of the origin of the solar system have been devised almost entirely during the past two centuries. The earlier of these theories were concerned with the mechanical features of the system, the later ones with characteristics of individual members as well, such as their compositions and densities. All the theories encounter problems of quantity and distribution of angular momentum.

9·30. The Angular Momentum of a revolving body, such as a planet revolving around the sun or a particle of a rotating globe, is the product of the mass, the square of the distance from the center of motion, and the rate of angular motion. The principle of the conservation of angular momentum asserts that the total angular momentum (the sum of all these products) of an isolated system is always the same.

Consider a rotating globe of gas. The total angular momentum is found by summing the products of mass, square of distance from the axis of rotation, and angular velocity for all molecules of the gas. Suppose now that the globe shrinks, the mass remaining the same. Because the distances of the molecules from the axis are diminishing, the angular velocities must increase to maintain the same angular momentum. Thus the shrinking of the globe increases the speed of its rotation.

A successful theory of the evolution of the solar system must account not only for the present total angular momentum of the system but also for the distribution of the momentum. The sun's rotation contributes only 2 per cent to the total angular momentum of the solar system, whereas Jupiter's revolution accounts for 60 per cent and the four giant planets carry nearly 98 per cent of the total.

Most theories of planetary evolution have begun with a *solar nebula,* a rotating gaseous envelope surrounding the primitive sun in the course of its development. As examples we select the earlier hypothesis of Laplace and the recent accounts of von Weizsäcker and Kuiper.

9·31. The Nebular Hypothesis of Laplace, published by him in 1796, is the most celebrated although not the first of the early attempts. Another hypothesis of the nebular origin of the solar system, proposed by Immanuel Kant in 1755, had not received much attention and was apparently unknown to Laplace.

Laplace's account begins with a gaseous envelope surrounding the primitive sun and having direct rotation around it. As the envelope contracted, it therefore rotated faster and bulged more and more at the equator. When the centrifugal effect of the rotation at the equator became equal to the gravitational attraction toward the center, an equatorial ring of gas was abandoned by the contracting mass. Successively smaller rings were subsequently left behind whenever the critical stage was repeated. Each ring gradually assembled (Fig. 9·31) into a gaseous globe having its circular

FIG. 9·31. Nebular Hypothesis of Laplace. Gaseous rings abandoned by a contracting, rotating solar nebula assembled to form the planets. (*Courtesy of* Scientific American)

orbit around the sun the same as the ring from which it was formed. Many of the globes developed satellites in a similar manner as they condensed into planets.

This process was intended to result in a system having the orderly motions we have noted for the principal members of the solar system, where the rings of Saturn might seem to have remained to demonstrate the correctness of the theory.

9·32. Value of the Nebular Hypothesis. The simplicity of the nebular hypothesis and the weight of its distinguished authorship combined to elevate it to a leading place among astronomical theories throughout the 19th century. It served as a powerful stimulus to scientific thought not only in astronomy but in allied sciences as well; and it led the way to ideas of orderly development in other fields. As its deficiencies were gradually recognized, they gave warning of situations to be avoided in subsequent theories. These are chiefly as follows:

(1) Some of the steps outlined in the hypothesis could scarcely have occurred because of the tendency of gas to disperse. The gaseous rings, for example, would not be expected to assemble into planets.

(2) The hypothetical solar system would not have conformed to the actual one in the amount and distribution of angular momentum. Calculations show that in order to have abandoned the ring from which Neptune was formed the system must have possessed a total angular momentum 200 times as great as the present total. In addition, the hypothesis requires that the greater part of the present angular momentum should appear in the sun's rotation where only 2 per cent is actually found.

(3) The organization of the solar system is more complex than was known in the time of Laplace. Many exceptions have since been discovered, as we have seen, to the regularities that his theory undertook to represent. Moreover, the compositions of the planets and their atmospheres were unknown at that early time.

9·33. Some Later Theories. The failure of Laplace's nebular hypothesis to reproduce the present solar system acceptably suggested eventually the trial of a different process. About the year 1900, the geologist T. C. Chamberlin and the astronomer F. R. Moulton proposed the planetessimal hypothesis. They imagined that another star passed close enough to the sun to cause the emergence from it of much gas by excessive prominence activity. The gaseous envelope thus formed around the sun condensed into small solid particles, called planetessimals, which assembled to produce members of the planetary system. This and an alternate tidal hypothesis were dismissed later as unprofitable. The interest of scientists subsequently reverted to the nebula surrounding the primitive sun as a more promising approach to the evolution of the system.

In 1945 the physicist C. F. von Weizsäcker proposed a revised version of the nebular hypothesis. The nebula was divided for planetary development—not by rotational instability, as in Laplace's theory, but by turbulent vortices caused by its rotation in accordance with Kepler's third law. The nebula was assigned an original mass a tenth of the sun's mass, or 100 times the present combined mass of the planets, and a composition mainly of light chemical elements like the composition of the sun. After their lighter gases had mostly escaped, the planets such as the earth were left with their present increased percentages of heavier elements.

The protoplanet hypothesis, published in 1949 by G. P. Kuiper, is a more recent example of the nebular theory. The following five sections, pertaining particularly to the evolution of the principal planets and their satellites according to this hypothesis, were kindly written by Kuiper for an earlier edition of this book.

9·34. "The Protoplanet Hypothesis of Kuiper avoids the difficulties of the Laplace hypothesis by allowing the solar nebula to contain enough material of solar composition for the present planets with their selective compositions to have formed. This leads to a solar nebula having between 5 and 10 per cent of the sun's mass. This mass is so excessive that the nebula upon further contraction and flattening had to become unstable gravitationally owing to its own attraction. As a result it broke into discrete clouds, or *protoplanets,* which were stable in the tidal field of the sun and which thereafter led an independent existence. In these protoplanets condensation took place, and the solid materials collected near the centers as the result of sedimentation. In this manner cores developed, surrounded by large gaseous envelopes. The envelopes were largely composed of hydrogen, helium, water vapor, ammonia, methane, and neon, as will always be true for gases of solar composition kept at low (planetary) temperatures. The maximum masses which these protoplanets attained depended on the local density of the initial solar nebula. A large density led to a massive protoplanet, which in turn meant a large diameter, given the known tidal field of the sun.

"Since the protoplanets together swept the entire solar nebula clean and since the planetary distances from the sun will have changed very little after the system was formed, one may estimate the maximum dimensions of the original protoplanets and therefore their initial masses. In this manner the theory leads to a mass for proto-Jupiter between 10 and 20 times the present mass, for proto-Saturn about 50 times the present mass, for proto-Uranus and proto-Neptune about 100 times the present masses, and for the earth 1000 times the present mass. An independent determination of the initial protoplanet masses can be made from the present chemical compositions of the planets compared with the sun. The mass-ratios, protoplanet to planet, found in this manner are almost identical with the ratios derived dynamically, which inspires confidence that the theory is basically correct.

"The theory also interprets Bode's law $(7 \cdot 5)$. It is not a fundamental law, but a direct consequence of the radial mass distribution within the solar nebula before its breakup into protoplanets. This follows immediately from the stability conditions mentioned above. A large density leads to large protoplanets and therefore to a comparatively large ratio between the radii of consecutive orbits, and vice versa. Thus the scale factor between consecutive orbits is about 2 in the range Jupiter to Uranus where the large protoplanets occurred, and 1.4 or 1.5 near the earth. It is in fact the discovery of this relation between orbital spacing and mass that led, in 1949, to the formulation of the protoplanet hypothesis, and that still serves as one of its principal supports."

9·35. "The Satellites are explained as having been formed by a repetition of the planet-forming process on a smaller scale. Protoplanets possessing much angular momentum of rotation could not shrink into a single central body, but left behind a flat, rapidly rotating disk like a small-scale solar nebula. Depending on the density distribution within this rotating disk, protosatellites developed by gravitational breakup. The same relation between orbital spacing and mass would be expected as is found in the planetary system; and in fact this is what the present data give if allowance is made in each case for the mass of the gaseous envelope which was subsequently lost.

"The protosatellites were much closer to their primaries, however, than the protoplanets are to the sun if in each case the distances are expressed in terms of the radius of the central body. This procedure is strictly correct only if the densities of the sun and planets were equal; but a correction for the difference is easily made. Therefore, the tidal friction on the protosatellites was in general far greater than on the protoplanets, and will have caused the protosatellites to rotate throughout their development with their orbital periods. As a result these bodies remained very nearly spherical and could not break up once more. This explains the absence of companions to satellites and also the absence of satellites around Mercury and Venus."

9·36. "Orbits and Rotations. The nearly circular orbits and their low inclinations to the ecliptic, for both the planets and the 'regular' satellites, are explained as a natural consequence of the protoplanet hypothesis. If the planets and satellites had been the result of a random capture process, a chaotic system of orbits would have resulted. Only large gaseous masses are able in time to impose on their components the regularity and symmetry shown by the planet and satellite orbits. The planets and the regular satellites must therefore be the product of revolving gaseous disks.

"Yet simple condensation in a single disk would not have produced bodies as large as planets; instead, they might have been less than a mile in diameter. The hypothesis of the breakup into protoplanets is an essential part of the theory. These protoplanets were able to conserve the mass of the cloud until planetary condensation had run its course.

"What caused the protoplanets to rotate from west to east, thus causing the same direct rotation of the planets and the regular satellites? The theory explains this as due to solar tidal friction on the very large protoplanets, which forced them to rotate initially in the direct sense and in the same periods as their revolutions, quite like the present motion of the moon. Later, as the protoplanets contracted and became much smaller, they slipped away from the tidal friction and rotated faster, but always direct.

"There remains the problem of the occasionally high inclinations of planets' equators to their orbits, for Saturn 28° and for Uranus even 97°. The case of Uranus is not fully understood, but the moderately high inclinations are explained by the theory as the combined result of the two effects that will increase the inclina-

tion of a protoplanet's equator: tidal friction exerted by the sun
and evaporation on the sunlit side. If an initial angle of a few
degrees existed, due to random turbulence in the original solar
nebula that also caused the differences in orbital inclination, the
evaporation would be asymmetrical with respect to the planet's
equator and the tilt would increase The total increase by these
effects may easily be 10-fold."

9·37. "The Composition of the Planets depends on the later history of the protoplanets which started out with the same composition as that of the sun. The shrinking sun attained its present
equilibrium size 10^8 years after the solar nebula was left behind.
During that interval the sun, from being large and cold at the surface, became smaller and hot; it began to send out powerful cor-
puscular and ultraviolet radiations. These radiations ionized the
tenuous remnants of the solar nebula and drove them out of the
solar system, in much the same way as comets' tails are repelled
today (9·8). Thereafter, these solar radiations could reach the
protoplanets; their outermost layers became hot and ionized, and
began to evaporate to interplanetary space—just as our upper ionosphere is heated to about 4000°F and evaporates hydrogen and
helium.

"It is this process that caused the enormous mass losses suffered
by the protoplanets, particularly the inner ones; and all this excess material was driven out of the solar system. The evaporation stage probably lasted between 10^8 and 10^9 years, and hardly
anything was left of the inner planets except their solid cores.
Uranus and Neptune were reduced to 1 per cent of their original
masses, Saturn to 2–3 per cent, and Jupiter to 5–10 per cent. As
a result Jupiter and Saturn still have much hydrogen left, but
Uranus and Neptune retain smaller fractions. Thus Uranus and
Neptune are denser than Jupiter and Saturn in spite of their
smaller compression by their own gravity effects."

9·38. "Other Consequences of Mass Loss. If a planet has a satellite and decreases its mass by the factor D, the distance of the satellite will increase by this factor. At the same time the *radius of
action* of the planet, being the limiting distance from its center
to which it can retain satellites in the tidal field of the sun, decreases as the cube root of D. Therefore, even if D were as small
as 8, the satellite's distance measured in terms of the radius of ac-

tion would increase by the factor 16. Such an increase might well move the satellite outside the radius of action. The body will then pursue an independent orbit around the sun similar to that of the parent planet.

"Since the planet was losing mass when the satellite escaped, it still possessed a large gaseous envelope. The 'capture cross section' of the planet was therefore still large, and there was a good chance for the satellite to be recaptured by a later encounter. This could result in either a direct or a retrograde orbit with roughly equal probability. The orbital inclination would not necessarily be low, although very high inclinations would be unlikely, because the planetary envelopes were thin disks and would not offer much resistance to a high inclination impact. These predictions fit the 'irregular' satellites quite well. There are a dozen of these known; they have orbital inclinations greater than 2° or orbital eccentricities greater than 0.02, or both. The revolutions of half of them are direct, and the revolutions of the other half are retrograde.

"Initially a recaptured satellite is likely to have an orbit of high eccentricity; but repeated passages through the shrinking protoplanet's envelope will round off and shrink the orbit, with the satellite gaining mass in the process. A fine illustration of this effect is given by Neptune's satellites, both of which are irregular. Nereid is small, has a large distance from the planet, and a very eccentric orbit; whereas Triton is massive, is close to the planet, and has a nearly circular orbit.

"Some satellites may come close to the planet but miss the disklike envelope, or else they may approach after the envelope has disappeared. Then no capture occurs, and the body is thrown into a very different orbit. This appears to have happened to the asteroid Hidalgo which has its orbit inclined 43° with respect to Jupiter's orbit, but still comes close to that planet at the node (Fig. 8·22). It may also be true of Pluto, at least if it was formed as a satellite of Neptune; its node is not close to Neptune's orbit now but may have been initially.

"Still other escaped satellites could have remained free but have been gradually driven to the triangular points with the planet and the sun (8·21) as a result of continued decrease of the planet's mass. This explanation is offered for the origin of the Trojan asteroids, which in this view are not asteroids at all. The Trojans could not have reached their present positions if the mass of Jupiter had remained constant, regardless of the origin of these bodies. The presence of the Trojans is therefore direct proof that Jupiter's mass has decreased."

1. Supply the names of comets characterized as follows:

(a) The first periodic comet to become known.
(b) The comet having the shortest period of revolution.
(c) A comet that remains visible at aphelion.
(d) A bright comet that is expected to return as four comets.

2. Describe the orbits of Jupiter's family of comets. What is the probable origin of this family?

3. How is it possible to decide whether a recently discovered comet is a new addition to the list or the return of a comet previously recorded?

4. Explain why Halley's comet (Fig. 9·6A) spends much of its time in the small part of its orbit that extends beyond the distance of Neptune.

5. What is the spectroscopic evidence that comets shine partly by their own light and partly by reflected sunlight?

6. State a current theory of the nature of a comet, including the development of the coma, tail, and associated meteor stream.

7. What information about meteors is derived (a) from photographs of their trails from two stations with cameras having rotating shutters? from echoes of radar pulses returned from the trails?

8. Explain the radiant of a meteor shower. What is the method of naming the showers? Name some examples.

9. State some instances of the association of meteor streams and comets.

10. Describe characteristics of stony and of iron meteorites that differ from those of native rocks. Name a large meteorite of each type.

11. Outline Laplace's nebular hypothesis of the origin of the solar system. Mention some features of the system that are inconsistent with or are not explained by this hypothesis.

12. Describe the protoplanet hypothesis.

13. Explain on the basis of the protoplanet hypothesis why some satellites have retrograde revolutions around their planets.

REFERENCES

Leonard, Frederick C., *A Classification Catalog of Meteoritic Falls of the World*. University of California Press, 1956.
Lovell, A. C. B., *Meteor Astronomy*. Oxford University Press, New York, 1954.
McKinley, D. W. R., *Meteor Science and Engineering*. McGraw-Hill Book Company, New York, 1961.
Watson, Fletcher G., *Between the Planets*. Revised edition. Harvard University Press, Cambridge, 1956.

10

THE SUN

THE SUN'S RADIATION AND TEMPERATURE — THE SUN'S
VISIBLE SURFACE; SUNSPOTS — THE CHROMOSPHERE
AND CORONA — ASSOCIATED IONOSPHERIC
DISTURBANCES

The sun is the dominant member and the power plant of the solar system. It is also the only star that is near enough to us to be observed in detail. Our account of the sun is accordingly associated with the descriptions of the planetary system which precede and with those of the stars in the following chapters.

10·1. Structure of the Sun. The sun is a globe of very hot gas having a visible surface 864,000 miles in diameter, or 109 times the earth's diameter. The sun is therefore $1\frac{1}{3}$ million times as large in volume as the earth, and its mass is one third of a million times as great as the earth's mass. Its average density is one fourth the earth's mean density, or 1.4 times the density of water.

The *interior* of the sun, below the visible surface, is known to us only indirectly from theoretical researches. Its temperature increases from 6000°K at the lowest visible level to many million degrees at the center. The outer layers of the sun merge gradually one into another. Conditions in the sun's interior are discussed in Chapter 12, and the problem of the sun's evolution is considered in Chapter 16.

The *photosphere* is the visible surface, the shallow layer from which the continuous background of the solar spectrum is emitted. It is mottled by brighter granulations and faculae and is often marked by darker sunspots. The gases above the photosphere constitute the sun's *atmosphere*.

The *chromosphere* is so named because of its red color, caused mainly by the glow of hydrogen. It extends several thousand miles above the photosphere. Its lowest stratum, sometimes called the reversing layer, is the source of most of the dark lines of the solar spectrum. The *prominences* appear above the chromosphere, at times attaining heights of many hundred thousand miles. They are visible during total solar eclipses and with special apparatus on other occasions.

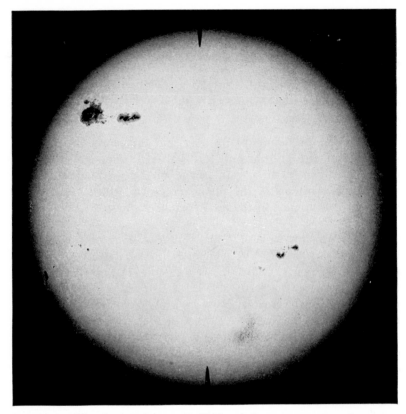

Fig. 10·1. The Sun, February 2, 1946. A large spot group has come around into view. (*Mount Wilson Observatory photograph*)

The *corona* appears around the sun during total eclipses as a filmy halo of intricate structure. Its inner parts can be observed with the coronagraph at other times.

10·2. The Sun's Rotation. The gradual movement of sunspots across the disk of the sun is a well-known effect of the sun's rotation. A spot now near the center of the disk will disappear at the edge in about a week. Two weeks later the spot will reappear at the opposite edge if it lasts that long, and after a week more it will again be seen near the center of the disk. The interval after which a long-lived spot comes around again to the same place on the disk of the sun is about 2 days longer than the actual period of the sun's rotation in that latitude, because of the earth's revolution in the meantime.

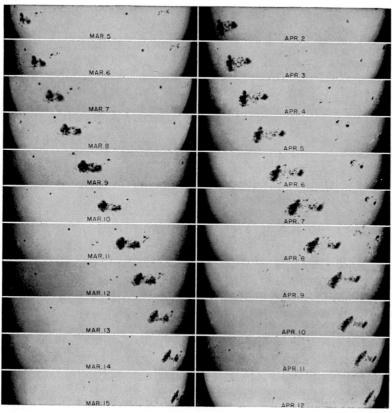

FIG. 10·2. Sunspots Carried Across the Disk by the Sun's Rotation. Showing the large spot group of 1947. (*Mount Wilson Observatory photographs*)

The sun's rotation is in the same sense as the earth's rotation and revolution, from west to east. Thus the spots on the hemisphere which faces us are carried across the disk from east to west with respect to directions in the sky. Because the sun's equator is inclined 7° to the ecliptic plane, the paths of spots are slightly curved. The curvature is greatest in March, when the southern end of the sun's axis is most inclined toward us, and again in September, when its northern end is most inclined toward us. In

June and December the spots move across the disk in lines more nearly straight.

Unlike the earth, where the surface is constrained to rotate all in the same period, the period of the sun's rotation is longer as the distance from its equator is greater. The period at the equator is about 25 days. It has increased to 27 days in latitude 35°, beyond which the spots rarely appear. The further lengthening of the period toward the poles is established by spectroscopic observations.

The speed of the sun's rotation in a particular latitude can be

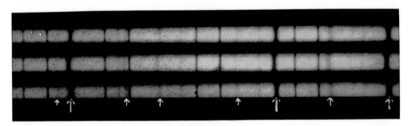

Fig. 10·2A. Effect of the Sun's Rotation on Its Spectrum. In the spectrum of the sun's west edge, shown above and below, the solar lines are displaced to the red (right). In the spectrum of the east edge, in the middle, the lines are displaced to the violet (left). Solar lines are indicated by arrows. Telluric lines, which are not marked, are unaffected by the rotation. Only a small part of the visible spectrum is shown.
(*Mount Wilson Observatory photograph*)

determined by photographing on the same plate the spectra of the west (receding) and the east (approaching) edges, and comparing the two (Fig. 10·2A). The solar lines in the first spectrum are displaced toward the red by the Doppler effect; in the second spectrum they are displaced toward the violet. Half the difference in the positions of the lines represents the apparent speed of the rotation in that latitude, and from it the actual period can be derived. The period of the sun's rotation as determined from the spectra increases progressively from less than 25 days at the equator to as much as 33 days in latitude 75°.

THE SUN'S RADIATION AND TEMPERATURE

10·3. Radiation Received from the Sun; the Solar Constant. The rate at which we receive the sun's radiation is measured by the rate of its heating of a substance that completely absorbs the radiation. The *pyrheliometer* is the instrument that has been employed for this purpose at stations of the Smithsonian Astrophysical Observatory. It contains a thermometer for recording the rate at which the radiation raises the temperature of a blackened silver disk. Allowance is made for the radiation scattered in the earth's atmosphere; this requires the addition of at least 30 per cent to the observed rate of heating, depending on the sun's distance from the zenith.

The *solar constant* is the rate at which the solar radiation is received by a surface exposed at right angles to the sun's direction just outside our atmosphere, when the earth is at its mean distance from the sun. Its value, as determined by R. Tousey, taking into account the results of rocket records, is 2.0 cal/min cm² (calories per minute per square centimeter); this differs from the Smithsonian value, 1.95 cal/min cm² by scarcely more than the probable error. A *calorie* is the quantity of heat required to increase by 1°C the temperature of 1 gram of water at 15°C.

10·4. Energy Radiated by the Sun. The equivalent value of the solar constant is 1.4×10^6 ergs/sec cm². Multiplying by the number of square centimeters in the surface of a sphere having as its radius the earth's mean distance from the sun, we have the rate at which the energy is intercepted by the sphere. This is practically the rate of the sun's total radiation; it equals 4×10^{33} ergs/sec, or about 5×10^{23} horsepower. The rate of the sun's radiation is accordingly 6.5×10^{10} ergs/sec cm², or about 70,000 horsepower per square yard of the sun's surface.

The *erg* is the unit of work, or energy; it is about the impact of a slow-flying mosquito. The *horsepower* is a common unit of the rate of doing work; it equals about 7.5×10^9 ergs/sec.

10·5. Laws of Radiation. The relations between the temperature of a body and the quantity or quality, or both, of the radiation it emits are expressed by the *radiation laws*. These laws apply to a *perfect radiator*, which has the greatest possible efficiency as a radiaator at any particular temperature and is also a perfect absorber of radiation. They also define temperature in the sense that we are here using the term. Despite their ideal character the laws serve reasonably well for the sun, stars, and planets.

Stefan's law (also known as the Stefan-Boltzmann law) states that the total energy, E ergs, emitted in one second by a square centimeter of the radiator is directly proportional to the fourth power of its absolute temperature, T. The relation is $E = aT^4$, where the value of the constant, $a = 5.672 \times 10^{-5}$, is known from laboratory experiments. Thus if the temperature of a body is doubled, its total radiation becomes 16 times as great as before.

Wien's law states that the wavelength, λ_{max} in centimeters, at which the radiation is most intense, is inversely proportional to the absolute temperature of the radiator. The relation is: $\lambda_{max} = 0.2897/T$. If, for example, the temperature is 4000°K, the most intense part of the spectrum has the wavelength of 7242×10^{-8} cm, or 7242 angstroms (10·21), in the red. If the temperature is raised to 8000°, the greatest intensity is shifted to 3621 angstroms, in the ultraviolet. Thus when a piece of metal is heated to incandescence, it first has a dull red glow, which brightens and changes to bluish white as the metal is further heated.

Planck's law is the most general of the radiation laws. By means of this rather complex formula, which may be found in treatises on physics, it is possible to calculate for a perfect radiator at any assigned temperature the rate of radiation in the different wavelengths.

10·6. The Spectral Energy Curve, calculated from the general law for particular temperatures (Fig. 10·6), shows how the intensity of

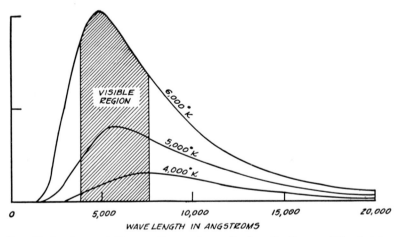

Fig. 10·6. Spectral Energy Curves for a Perfect Radiator. The heights are proportional to the intensity of the radiation. As the temperature is increased, the total radiation represented by the area under the curve increases (Stefan's law), and the peak of the curve is shifted to shorter wavelengths (Wien's law). The curve for each temperature is calculated by Planck's formula. The shaded area indicates the radiation to which the eye is sensitive.

the radiation varies along the spectrum. At a higher temperature the curve is higher at all points; and the increase is greater for shorter wavelengths, so that the peak of the curve is shifted toward the violet end of the spectrum.

Stefan's law and Wien's law refer to special features of the spectral energy curve. The former relates to the area under the curve, which represents the total amount of energy radiated at a particular temperature; the latter gives the wavelength of the most intense radiation at that temperature.

On combining the data of observation with these radiation laws, the sun's *effective temperature* can be determined, that is, the temperature that the sun's surface must have, if it is a perfect radiator, in order to radiate as it does.

10·7. The Sun's Temperature. The effective temperature of the sun's visible surface is about 5750°K. This value is obtained very nearly by substituting the rate of the sun's radiation $(6.5 \times 10^{10}$ ergs/sec cm^2) in the formula of Stefan's law. Since this rate is determined from the solar constant, which is derived from the radiation from all parts of the disk, this effective temperature is the average for the whole disk; it is the value to be used when the temperatures of the sun and stars are to be compared. It will be noted later that the sun's disk is less luminous near the edge than at the center.

The effective temperature at the center of the sun's disk is about 6000°, as determined by three methods:

(1) *By Stefan's law.* The average radiation from all parts of the disk, as calculated from the solar constant, is increased by 16 per cent to represent the radiation from the center of the disk. The corresponding temperature is about 5980°.

(2) *By Wien's law.* The wavelength of the most intense radiation is around 4750 angstroms, in the blue-green of the spectrum. The resulting temperature is something like 6100°. This determination has the least reliability of the three, because of uncertainty in assigning the position of maximum intensity in the spectrum.

(3) *By Planck's law.* The observed intensities of the solar spectrum in the various wavelengths are compared with the energy curves calculated by the formula for different temperatures. A fair general agreement is found between the observed curve and the one calculated for the temperature of 6000°.

Exact agreement in the values obtained from the three laws

would scarcely be expected. Differences between the observed and calculated curves are caused by the thousands of dark lines throughout the solar spectrum, and by general absorption in the sun's atmosphere which is not the same for the different regions of the spectrum.

10·8. Temperatures in Different Parts of the Sun. The sun's effective temperature of 5750°K is the average for all parts of the disk, as we have noted. The apparent surface temperature decreases from 6000° at the center of the disk to 5000° near the edge. The temperatures of sunspot umbras are around 4600°. Below the photosphere the temperatures rise so rapidly with increasing depth that most of the sun's interior is above 1,000,000°. The central temperature is now believed to be of the order of 13,000,000°, a considerable reduction from values formerly assigned it. Throughout the sun the heat is sufficient to keep all the material in the gaseous state.

The temperature diminishes with increasing height above the photosphere; it is 4500° in the lower chromosphere, and it would be 3000° in the corona as measured by the heating of a perfect absorber at these distances from the photosphere. The *temperature* in this sense is as defined by the radiation laws. As derived from the random motions of the particles and their degrees of ionization, however, the *kinetic temperature* of the upper chromosphere is 100,000°, and that of the corona is 1,000,000°.

THE SUN'S VISIBLE SURFACE; SUNSPOTS

10·9. Observing the Sun. It is unsafe to look steadily at the sun on a clear day with unprotected eyes; to look at it through a telescope without special precaution invites immediate and serious injury to the eye, because the objective acts as a burning glass. A convenient way to observe the sun with a telescope is to hold a sheet of smooth white cardboard back of the eyepiece, racking the eyepiece out beyond the usual position of focus until the sun's image is sharply defined. In this way many can observe at once. Finer details may be viewed through the telescope with a special solar eyepiece which admits to the eye only enough light to form a clear image of the sun.

Photographs provide permanent records of the changing features of the sun's surface and its surroundings. They are taken frequently at a number of observatories, often with special solar telescopes. Photographs of the sun and its spectrum from high-altitude stations, balloons, and rockets are giving new information. A Princeton University project to photograph the sun from an unmanned balloon made a successful beginning in 1957. The photographs have been taken with a 12-inch telescope at the height of about 80,000 feet (Fig. 10·13).

10·10. Solar Telescopes. Fixed telescopes are especially valuable in optical investigations of the sun. They permit the use of long-focus objectives and high-dispersion gratings with a minimum of mechanical construction. Among the larger examples of fixed telescopes is the 150-foot tower telescope of the Mount Wilson Observatory, which has a 60-foot tower and a horizontal solar telescope as well. There are also the 50-foot and 70-foot tower telescopes of the McMath-Hulbert Observatory.

A tower telescope has a coelostat at its summit. This consists of an equatorially mounted plane mirror, which is rotated around the polar axis at the rate of once in 48 hours, and a second fixed plane

Fig. 10·10.   The McMath-Hulbert Observatory of the University of Michigan.

Fɪɢ. 10·10A.   The McMath Solar Telescope of the Kitt Peak National
Observatory.

mirror beside it, which directs the sunlight to a fixed objective,
either a lens or a mirror. The image of the sun formed at the
base of the tower may be photographed directly, or else the light
from a selected part of the disk may be passed on through a narrow slit to a grating in the well below the observing room, from
which it is returned dispersed into spectra.

The new solar telescope of the Kitt Peak National Observatory
has a sloping tube 500 feet long that is parallel to the earth's axis
and three fifths below the ground. A heliostat, a rotating plane
mirror, 80 inches in diameter, reflects the sunlight down the tube
to the 60-inch objective, a paraboloidal mirror near the bottom.
This mirror, having a focal length of 300 feet, forms an image of
the sun's disk, averaging 33½ inches in diameter through the year,
in the observation room at the ground level. Here the spectrum
of any part of the disk may also be observed.

10·11. The Photosphere is the visible surface of the sun. It is a
layer 250 miles thick, the direct source of practically all the sun's
radiation. Here the sun becomes opaque, so that we cannot see
into it any farther. Yet the gas is still very tenuous in this layer,
producing a pressure not exceeding a hundredth of our atmospheric pressure at sea level. Its opacity is ascribed mainly to the

abundance of negative hydrogen ions, hydrogen atoms which have acquired second electrons.

The sun's disk is less luminous and redder near its edge than near its center. The fading of the light toward the edge is especially conspicuous in photographs with blue-sensitive plates, an effect often partly compensated in the prints for the sake of clearer illustration. The explanation of the effect is that, because of the opacity of the photosphere, the light from the edge emerges from a higher and cooler level, so that it is less bright and redder than the light from the lower levels we can see near the center of the disk. It is the custom to denote the heights of features of the sun from that of the visible edge.

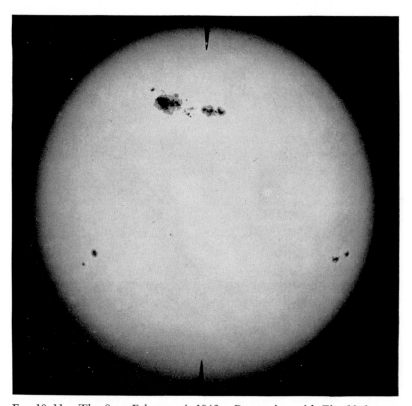

Fig. 10·11. The Sun, February 4, 1946. Comparing with Fig. 10·1, note that the spots have been carried to the right by the sun's rotation. (*Mount Wilson Observatory photograph*)

10·12. Granulations of the Photosphere. As observed with the telescope the photosphere presents a mottled appearance, which in good conditions is resolved into bright *granules*. These are scattered profusely on the less luminous and by contrast grayish background. The granules vary from 150 to 900 miles in diameter and are separated by narrow dark spaces. They are hot spots, hotter by 100° or more than the normal surface, and each one lasts only a few minutes. What we see is a seething surface where hotter gases come up from below and quickly cool.

The granules are not distinct near the edge of the disk. Here we see instead the larger bright areas of the *faculae* (little torches) at somewhat higher levels. The faculae are inseparable companions of sunspots, and they often antedate and survive the associated spots.

10·13. Sunspots are dark spots on the sun's disk, ranging in size from spots scarcely distinguishable from the intergranular spaces to

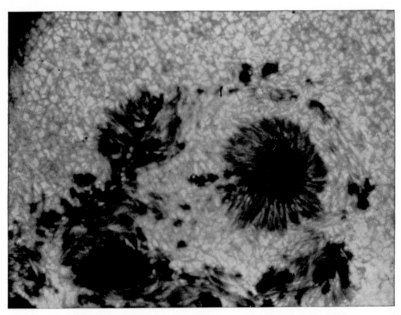

Fig. 10·13. The Sun Photographed August 17, 1957, from an Unmanned Balloon. Photograph from an altitude exceeding 80,000 feet with a special 12-inch Perkin-Elmer telescope in a project directed by Martin Schwarzschild, Princeton University. (*Courtesy of Perkin-Elmer Corporation*)

great spots that are visible to the unaided eye. They appear dark by contrast with their surroundings, although they are brighter than most artificial sources of light. A sunspot generally consists of two parts; the *umbra,* the central darker region, and the *penumbra,* the lighter surrounding region which is three fourths as bright as the photosphere. The penumbra, as it appears in the Princeton photographs, is described by R. E. Danielson as a complex array of predominantly radial bright filaments. The filaments, having lifetimes roughly five times those of the granules, are interpreted by him as convection rolls in the magnetic field of the sunspot.

Sunspots occur in groups. Where a solitary spot is seen, it is likely to be the survivor of a group. The unusually large and long-lived group shown in Fig. 10·11 began coming into view at the sun's eastern edge on January 29, 1946. Its largest spot measured 90,000 by 60,000 miles. The group attained a length of 200,-000 miles and a maximum area of 5700 million square miles which, however, was less than half of 1 per cent of the visible hemisphere of the sun. The group was brought around to the eastern edge three times by the sun's rotation and was last seen disappearing at the western edge on May 8, having survived more than 99 days. A somewhat larger group (Fig. 10·2), the largest so far recorded, was observed from February 5 to May 11, 1947.

10·14. The Life of a Sunspot Group. Rapid development and slower decline characterize the life history of the normal group, as Seth B. Nicholson describes it.

In its very early stages the group consists of two clusters of small spots in about the same latitudes and 3° or 4° apart in longitude. As the group develops, a large compact *preceding spot* dominates the part that is going ahead in the direction of the sun's rotation, while a somewhat less large and compact *following spot* is conspicuous in the part that is moving behind. The following spot is usually a little farther from the equator than the preceding spot. Meanwhile, these *principal spots* draw apart to a difference of 10° or more in longitude. By the end of a week the group generally attains its greatest area and the decline sets in.

The following spot breaks up into smaller spots, which diminish in size and vanish along with other small spots. Finally the preceding spot remains alone, a single umbra at the center of a nearly circular penumbra, which may persist for several weeks or even

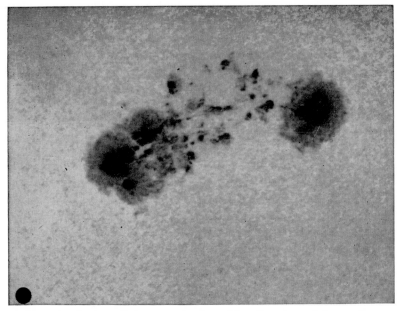

Fig. 10·14. A Normal Sunspot Group. The direction of the sun's rotation is toward the right. The black disk in the corner represents the relative size of the earth. (*Mount Wilson Observatory photograph*)

months. This spot usually disappears after becoming progressively smaller, and not by breaking up as the following spot generally does. Sometimes, as in the case of the great group of early 1946, the following spot is the larger and surviving member.

10·15. The Sunspot Cycle. In some years the sun's disk is seldom free from spots, whereas in other years it may remain unspotted for several days in succession. Sunspots vary in number in a roughly periodic manner. The variation was first announced, in 1843, by Heinrich Schwabe, an amateur astronomer in Germany, after he had observed the sun systematically with a small telescope for nearly 20 years.

The overall average interval between the times of the greatest numbers of spot groups has been 11.1 years, but for the past half-century it has been more nearly 10 years. The rise to maximum spottedness is generally more rapid than the decline. Not only is the period of the sunspot cycle variable, but the number of groups at the maximum also varies from cycle to cycle and is likely to be greater in the short-period cycles. It is accordingly possible to predict only approximately the date of a future maximum and how plentiful the groups will then become.

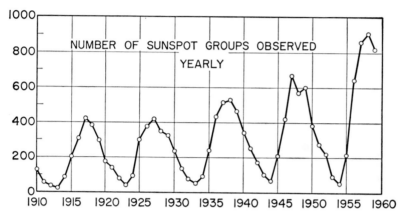

FIG. 10·15. The Sunspot Number Cycle. The point for each year represents the number of spot groups observed during that year. (*From data by Mount Wilson Observatory*)

The maximum of 664 groups reported for 1947 was the highest since the year 1778. The following minimum occurred early in 1954; during that year the sun was observed on 337 days at Mount Wilson and was spotless on 213 days. Although the maximum of 1958 was higher in number of groups than was the preceding one, the groups and individual spots were generally smaller. The next minimum would be expected in 1964.

10·16. The Shifting Sunspot Zones. Sunspots are confined mainly between heliographic latitudes 5° and 30°. Few are seen at the equator or beyond latitudes 45°. At a particular time they occur in two rather narrow zones equidistant from the equator. The zones shift toward the equator in cycles paralleling the variation in the spot numbers.

About a year before sunspot minimum the new cycle is announced by the appearance of spots in the higher latitudes. As these spots vanish and others appear, the disturbance gradually closes in toward the equator. When the minimum of the num-

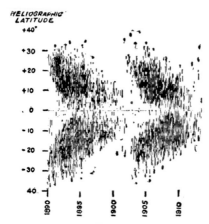

HELIOGRAPHIC
LATITUDE
+40°
+30
+20
+10
0
-10
-20
-30
40

1890 1895 1900 1905 1910

FIG. 10·16.   Shifting of Sunspot Zones.   The disturbed areas gradually draw in toward the sun's equator.   As one cycle dies out near the equator, a new cycle of spots has begun in the higher latitudes.   *(From a diagram by E. W. Maunder)*

bers is reached, the fading cycle is marked by spots near the equator. Meanwhile, the early members of the next cycle have appeared in the higher latitudes. Thus in the year near the minimum of 1954 the Mount Wilson observers recorded 15 groups of the old cycle and 31 groups of the new one.

10·17. The Sunspot Spectrum gives decisive evidence as to two characteristics of the spots:

(1) *Lower temperature of sunspots.* As compared with the normal solar spectrum (10·21): (a) The continuous background of the spot spectrum is weakened progressively from red to violet. (b) Certain dark lines are strengthened; they are lines that are more conspicuous in laboratory spectra of sources at lower temperatures. (c) Other dark lines are weakened; these are lines of ionized atoms which are weaker at lower temperatures when other conditions are unaltered. (d) Dark bands produced by chemical compounds appear in the spot spectrum, compounds which cannot often form at the higher temperatures above the undisturbed surface of the sun. The temperature of the ordinary spot umbra is 1200° below that of the photosphere, according to Pettit.

(2) *Magnetic fields of sunspots.* Many lines in the sunspot spectrum are widened, and some are plainly split. This effect had been known for some time before G. E. Hale, in 1908, demonstrated its association with the magnetism of sunspots.

10·18. Magnetism of Sunspots. The Zeeman effect, known by the name of the physicist who discovered it in the laboratory in 1896, is the splitting of the lines in the spectrum when the source of the light is in a magnetic field. We are concerned here with the effect when the light emerges along the line joining the poles of the magnet. The lines in the spectrum are then divided into pairs, the components of which are circularly polarized in opposite directions.

In the spectrum of a sunspot near the center of the sun many lines are so divided, showing that sunspots have magnetic fields. The field strength, indicated by the amount the lines are separated, ranges from 100 gauss or less for small spots to as much as 3700

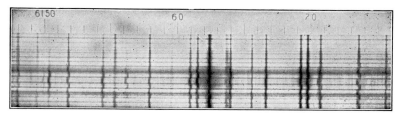

Fig. 10·18. Zeeman Effect in the Sunspot Spectrum. A small part of the Mount Wilson photographic map of the sunspot spectrum. A nicol prism and pieces of mica over the slit of the spectroscope divide the spectrum lengthwise into several strips in which the violet and red components of a line are alternately suppressed. Thus the lines widened by the Zeeman effect have a zigzag appearance.

gauss in the case of the great sunspot of 1946. The *gauss* is the unit of magnetic field intensity.

Strips of mica or other quarter-wave device along with a nicol prism in front of the slit of the spectroscope alternately suppress the components of the lines to facilitate the measurements and to show the *polarity* of the spot, whether its positive or negative pole is toward the observer. Daily polarity records of sunspots are kept at Mount Wilson and elsewhere.

10·19. Polarities of Sunspots. Most sunspot groups are bipolar. Where the leading members of a group have positive polarity, the following members have negative polarity. If the group we are considering is in the sun's northern hemisphere, the statement applies to all other bipolar groups in this hemisphere at the time. For all such groups in the southern hemisphere the situation is reversed; the leading members have negative and the following members positive polarity.

A remarkable feature of sunspot magnetism is the reversal of polarity with the beginning of each new cycle. When the groups of the new cycle appear in the higher latitudes, the parts which had positive polarity by the rule of the old cycle now have negative

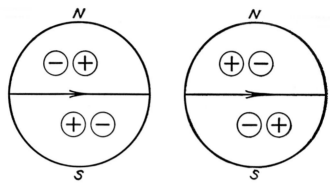

Fig. 10·19. Reversal of Polarities of Sunspots in Successive Cycles. The two diagrams represent preceding and following spots of groups in the two hemispheres of the sun.

polarity, and vice versa. First recorded at Mount Wilson around the sunspot minimum of 1913, this reversal of polarities has been observed at each succeeding minimum.

10·20. Magnetic Fields of the Sun. A scanning process is employed by H. W. and H. D. Babcock at Mount Wilson Observatory for mapping the magnetic fields over the sun's disk. The image of the sun formed by a solar telescope is allowed to drift repeatedly over the slit of a spectrograph, giving a succession of traces parallel to the sun's equator. The Zeeman effect at each point of the disk is recorded at a corresponding point in the tracing by a vertical deflection proportional to the intensity of the field—to the north for positive polarity and to the south for negative polarity. The magnetogram so produced is illustrated in Fig. 10·20. By a supplementary process developed by R. B. Leighton, positive fields can also be shown bright and negative fields dark.

Localized magnetic fields generally within 40° or 50° from the sun's equator are likely to be most intense around sunspot groups or where only conspicuous plages appear, or sometimes even where no visible evidence of special disturbance is observed. Beginning with the 1953 magnetograms, weak fields at higher latitudes were also recorded; they had positive polarity near the sun's north pole and negative polarity near the south pole. The polar fields reversed sign around the time of sunspot number maximum, in 1958.

Thus the sun's general magnetic field could be regarded as having two components: (1) *Polar fields* have opposite polarity around the two poles, and these have reversed sign at sunspot maximum. (2) *Ring-shaped fields* parallel to the equator have opposite field direction in the two hemispheres; they migrate toward the equator in the sunspot cycle and are replaced at sunspot minimum by new fields in the higher mid-latitudes, where the directions are reversed. These fields provide the basis for H. W. Babcock's magnetohydrodynamic interpretation of observed features at and above the solar surface, a theory in which he combines the results of his own studies with conclusions of other investigators.

The ring-shaped magnetic fields are mainly submerged below the surface, as Babcock pictures them. Because of the increasing period of the sun's rotation with distance from its equator, the lines of force are twisted into "magnetic ropes" where, especially in their loops formed by excessive twisting, they can exert pressure comparable with the gas pressure. These equatorial fields undulate like sea serpents. Many loops are brought up to the surface by the convection currents. As they break through the surface, the loops produce pairs of oppositely polarized regions where sunspot groups may form. Anchored to these regions the loops arch above them to support the material of the solar prominences. The author of the theory points out that its adequate development will

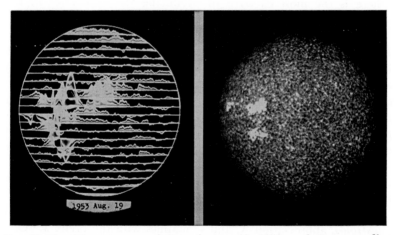

Fig. 10·20. Magnetogram of Sun, August 19, 1953, and Corresponding Calcium Spectroheliogram. North is at the top. Upward deflection of the trace indicates positive polarity toward the observer. (*Magnetogram by H. W. and H. D. Babcock*)

require a body of data which can be obtained only through long-continued observation of the sun's magnetism.

The new field of *magnetohydrodynamics,* or hydromagnetics, combines the previously independent procedures of hydrodynamics and electrodynamics; it deals with the large-scale behavior of an electrically conducting fluid in a strong magnetic field. In most astrophysical applications the fluid consists of ionized gases. The main subjects of the applications, as listed by the Swedish scientist H. Alfvén, are the following. (1) The origin of the earth's magnetic field, and the fields of other planets and of stars. (2) The electromagnetic states of the upper atmosphere and of interplanetary space; this includes the radiation belts around planets, the magnetic storms, and auroras. (3) Solar activities. (4) The magnetism of stars. (5) The physics of interstellar matter, including the dynamics of cosmic clouds.

THE CHROMOSPHERE AND CORONA

It is the custom to speak of the photosphere as the surface of the sun, and of the more nearly transparent gases above it as constituting the sun's atmosphere. The photosphere, as we have noted, is the region from which most of the sunlight emerges. The lowest stratum of the chromosphere immediately above the photosphere is the most effective in producing the dark lines in the solar spectrum.

10·21. The Visible Solar Spectrum is an array of colors from violet to red interrupted by thousands of dark lines, which are known as *Fraunhofer lines* in honor of their discoverer. The German optician Joseph Fraunhofer, in 1814, was the first to distinguish clearly these lines; he mapped several hundred and labeled the most prominent ones with letters of the alphabet, starting at the red end of the spectrum. Thus the pair close together in the yellow are the D lines. The significance of the lines remained unknown until 1859, when it was understood that they are wavelengths abstracted from sunlight chiefly by gases above the photosphere.

These lines are designated by their wavelengths expressed in *angstroms,* abbreviation A, and sometimes with the prefix λ. One angstrom is 10^{-8} cm. Thus 4000 A denotes the wavelength of 4×10^{-5} cm. The visible region of the spectrum is between 3900

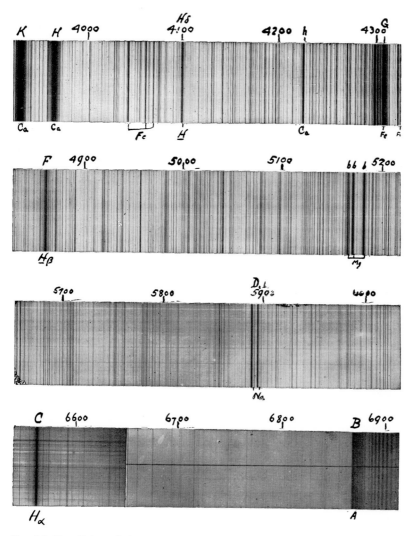

Fig. 10·21. Parts of the Visible Solar Spectrum. Photographed with the 13-foot spectrograph. (*Mount Wilson and Palomar Observatories photograph*)

and 7500 A. Some conspicuous lines and bands in the visible part
of the solar spectrum are the following:

Fraunhofer Letter	Wavelength	Identification
A	7594 A	oxygen (telluric)
B	6867	oxygen (telluric)
C	6563	hydrogen
D	5893	sodium (double)
E	5270	iron
F	4861	hydrogen
H	3968	calcium
K	3934	calcium

By far the strongest lines are the Fraunhofer H and K of calcium
near the termination of the visible spectrum in the violet. Not all
the lines are of solar origin. There are also *telluric bands* produced
by absorption of sunlight in the earth's atmosphere. The Fraunhofer A and B bands are identified with terrestrial oxygen.

10·22. The Ultraviolet Solar Spectrum. Beyond the shortest wavelength visible to the eye, the solar spectrum can be photographed
ordinarily to about 2900 A. Beginning there, the sun's radiations
are absorbed by ozone molecules and other constituents of our
atmosphere. The extreme ultraviolet rays, X rays, and gamma
rays, which would preclude the existence of large molecules of
living matter, are thereby prevented from reaching the ground.
Studies of the extreme ultraviolet solar spectrum are being made
in photographs from rockets above the obstructing atmosphere.

In a spectrogram from an Aerobee rocket at a height of about
120 miles on March 13, 1959 (Fig. 10·22), the Naval Research
Laboratory group of J. D. Purcell, D. M. Packer, and Richard
Tousey observed the major features of the ultraviolet solar spectrum as far as 584 A. Absorption lines of the photosphere crowd
together and finally disappear for this dispersion at about 1700 A.
Shortward from there nearly 100 emission lines of the chromosphere, about 60 of which had not been previously observed, were
identified in the spectrogram. Among these are lines of neutral
neon, silicon, and carbon, and of ionized magnesium, oxygen,
neon, and silicon. The very strong Lyman-alpha line at 1216.7 A,
other lines of that hydrogen series, and part of the Lyman continuum beginning at 910 A were well observed. In later photographs, where stray light was suppressed, the NRL scientists extended their investigations farther into the ultraviolet.

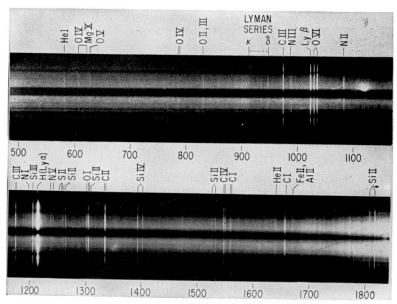

FIG. 10·22. Ultraviolet Spectrum of the Sun. Photographed, March 13, 1959, from a Naval Research Laboratory Aerobee rocket. (*Official U. S. Navy photograph*)

W. A. Rense and T. Violett of the University of Colorado have listed solar spectrum lines as far as 83.9 A, which they have observed in other rocket spectrograms.

10·23. The Infrared Solar Spectrum has been studied photographically to 13,500 A, and the line patterns are clearly resolved to 24,500 A in tracings with the lead sulfide photoconductive cell.

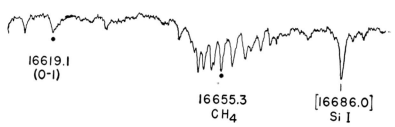

16619.1
(0-1)

16655.3
CH₄

[16686.0]
Si I

FIG. 10·23. A Section of the Solar Spectrum in the Infrared. The methane band at 16655 A is produced in the earth's atmosphere. The silicon line at 16686 A originates in the sun. (*Tracing by McMath, Mohler, and Goldberg with lead sulfide cell, McMath-Hulbert Observatory*)

The gross details have been shown by heat-detecting apparatus as far as 200,000 A. Heavy bands, absorbed particularly by oxygen, carbon dioxide, and water vapor molecules of our atmosphere, conceal much of the infrared region of the sun's spectrum itself. Bands of atmospheric methane are also recognized; one of these is represented in the tracing in Fig. 10·23. Knowledge of the infrared solar spectrum should be greatly improved when the troublesome telluric absorption is avoided in recordings from above our atmosphere.

10·24. The Spectrum of the Chromosphere. The gases above the photosphere, which produce the dark lines of the solar spectrum, give a bright-line spectrum when they are observed alone, as at the

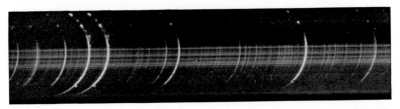

FIG. 10·24. Spectrum of the Chromosphere. Photographed with slit-less spectrograph near the end of the total solar eclipse of January 24, 1925. The pair of long crescents at the left are the H and K lines of calcium. Projections to the right of these lines are prominences. Breaks in the crescents are caused by irregularities in the moon's surface. (*Mount Wilson Observatory photograph*)

time of total solar eclipse. This was called the *flash spectrum* originally, because it flashes into view near the beginning of total eclipse and disappears soon after the end of totality. When the slitless spectroscope is employed (Fig. 10·24), the bright lines are images of the thin crescent left uncovered by the moon. The thickest crescent images are produced by calcium and hydrogen. The strong red line of hydrogen is responsible for the characteristic hue of the chromosphere.

With some exceptions the bright crescents match the dark lines of the normal solar spectrum. The most conspicuous differences are found in the hydrogen and helium lines. All the hydrogen lines of the Balmer series are present in the flash spectrum, but only the first four are noticed in the dark-line spectrum. Helium lines, which are prominent in the spectra of the chromosphere and prominences, are almost entirely absent in the visible dark-line spectrum; a dark triplet of helium, discovered by the Babcocks in 1934, appears in the infrared at about 10,830 A.

Studies of the chromospheric spectrum are now extended to the extreme ultraviolet, as we have seen (10·22), in spectrograms from rockets.

10·25. Chemical Elements in the Sun. More than 60 chemical elements are definitely recognized in the sun, according to a list prepared by H. D. Babcock and Charlotte Moore. These elements have been identified by comparing their laboratory spectra with lines in the solar spectrum. At the high temperatures of the sun the elements exist generally as dissociated atoms. The molecules of 18 compounds are recognized by their characteristic spectrum bands; they are found mainly in the cooler regions of sunspots, but a few hold together above the undisturbed photosphere as well. All the natural elements are presumed to be present in the sun.

Hydrogen is the most abundant element in the sun's atmosphere, and helium is second. These two elements also predominate in the sun's interior, in the stars, and in the universe generally. Hydrogen contributes 55 per cent of the mass of the cosmic material, helium about 44 per cent, and the heavier elements the remainder. Exceptions to these proportions occur in the earth and other smaller members of the planetary system from which most of the lighter gases have escaped.

10·26. Spectroheliograms are photographs of the chromosphere and prominences taken outside eclipse in the light of a single spectral line. These revealing photographs show how the gases of the element are distributed above the sun's surface. They are taken with the *spectroheliograph*, a special adaptation of the spectroscope. The operation of this instrument, which employs two slits, is as follows.

The image of the sun is focused by the telescope objective onto the first slit, which admits the light from a narrow strip of the sun's disk to the diffraction grating. The spectrum produced by the grating falls on a screen containing a second slit parallel to the first. This slit allows the light from only a limited region of the spectrum to pass through to the photographic plate. By a slight rotation of the grating any part of the spectrum can be brought upon the second slit, for example, the "dark" K line of calcium. It will be understood that the dark lines of the solar spectrum are not devoid of light; they appear dark by contrast with the brighter continuous spectrum.

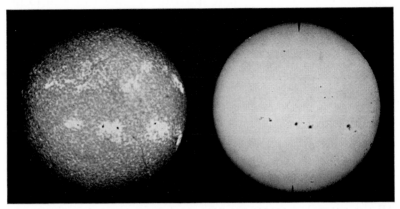

FIG. 10·26. Spectroheliogram and Direct Photograph of the Sun. The spectroheliogram is taken with the K line of calcium. Calcium plages are conspicuous in the sunspot zones and especially near the spots. (*Mount Wilson Observatory photographs*)

The operation so far described would give a photograph of only a narrow strip of the sun's disk in calcium light. When the first slit is moved across the disk and the second slit correspondingly over the photographic plate, the result is a spectroheliogram of as much of the disk as is desired. The spectrohelioscope accomplishes the same result for visual observations. Here the two slits are made to oscillate rapidly enough to give a persistent image of a part of the sun's disk in the light of a spectrum line.

An alternate device is the bifringent filter, a sharp-band monochromator which transmits the whole image of an extended source instead of assembling it by scanning; such a filter may consist of a succession of quartz crystal and polaroid sheets. This filter is useful for both photographic and visual purposes. It is also employed with the coronagraph (10·32) for observing the corona outside eclipse.

10·27. Features of the Chromosphere. The chromosphere rises to a height of 5000 miles or more. Photographed beyond the edge of the sun, it appears as a fairly uniform layer from which many narrow bright *spicules* keep emerging, forming a grass-like upper surface. Each spicule reaches a height of about 10″ above the edge in a few minutes and then disappears. The association of the spicules with the granules of the photosphere has been suggested.

Spectroheliograms and other monochromatic photographs of the sun are commonly made with either the K line of calcium or the C line of hydrogen. The former show the disk mottled with bright calcium *flocculi;* the word flocculus means a tuft of wool. Where these are bunched around sunspot groups and other active centers, they are known as *plages.* Photographs in hydrogen light also show flocculi and plages. Photographed from rockets in the light of the Lyman-alpha line of hydrogen, the chromosphere shows a grosser plage structure and much greater contrast than in the lower-level spectroheliograms. The solar image in X-ray wavelengths (20 to 60 A) has also been photographed.

The hydrogen photographs often show masses of this gas dark against the brighter background and drawn out in filaments which may extend as far as 60° in longitude; they are huge curtain-like structures hanging above the chromosphere. Whenever the dark filaments are carried beyond the edge of the disk by the sun's rotation, they appear bright against the sky. These are the prominences.

10·28. The Solar Prominences are best observed beyond the edge of the sun. They show wide diversity in their behavior. Some are like sheets of flame; some rise to great heights; many move downward. Their red color, contrasting with the white glow of the corona, contributes to the splendor of the total solar eclipse. The prominences are most often observed, however, in monochromatic light at other times than during eclipses.

Our appreciation of how prominences behave began with their photography on motion-picture films, initiated by R. R. McMath and now in frequent use. Continuous records of prominence and chromospheric activity are made automatically on 35-mm film in monochromatic light at a number of solar observatories in America and elsewhere.

Most prominences are of the *active* type; they originate high above the chromosphere and pour their streamers down into it. *Quiescent* prominences are the least active and have the longest lives; their most common form is the "haystack." *Eruptive* prominences are among the rarer types. These rise from material above

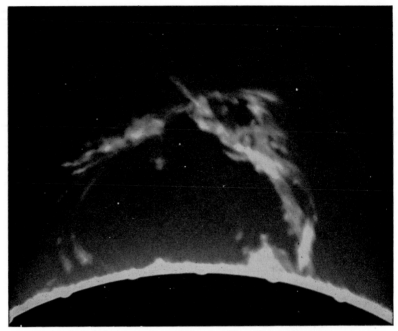

FIG. 10·28. Solar Prominence, February 2, 1957. The scale is indicated by marks placed at intervals of 10° on the circumference of the disk. (*Mount Wilson and Palomar Observatories photograph*)

the chromosphere, attaining high speeds and great altitudes before they vanish. A prominence of 1938 attained a speed of 450 miles a second. A prominence of June 4, 1946, rose to a distance of more than a million miles above the sun's surface.

Cooled gases that supply the prominences may collect near the tops of magnetic arches above bipolar regions, as H. W. Babcock suggests. Here they are precariously supported for a time, perhaps eventually to be propelled outward at high speed by an increase of the strength of the magnetic field.

10·29. Solar Flares appear as sudden increases in brightness of areas near sunspot groups and persist from tens of minutes to as long as several hours; the larger ones are likely to be associated with large and active groups. The flares are most easily observed in the light of the red line of hydrogen and are rarely seen at all in the direct view of the sun. These outbursts are often attended by active dark filaments, the projections on the disk of surge-type prominences. They are sources of intense ultraviolet radiations, high-speed particles, and bursts of noise in the radio frequencies. X-ray emission is one of the major features of the flare outbursts.

Direct evidence of high velocity of the bright flare was first re-

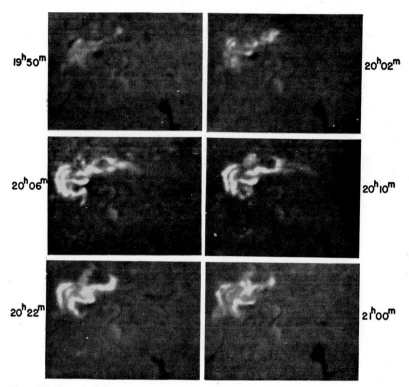

FIG. 10·29. A Solar Flare, May 10, 1949. A series of Hα spectrohelio-grams showing development of the flare. (*Photographs by Helen W. Dodson, McMath-Hulbert Observatory*)

corded by Helen Dodson at the McMath-Hulbert Observatory in photographs with a motion-picture camera. An eruption associ-ated with a flare of May 8, 1951, rose at the edge of the sun's disk in the first minute of its life at the rate of 450 miles a second; it reached the height of 30,000 miles.

Thus the sun is a flare star, perhaps resembling in this respect the red stars that brighten suddenly and repeatedly (13·16).

10·30. The Corona is the tenuous outer envelope of the sun, seen ordinarily only during total solar eclipse. Its feeble light, which

averages only half as bright as the light of the full moon, is generally lost in the glare of the sky around the uneclipsed sun. Half
of this light comes from the inner corona which is within 3', or less
than 100,000 miles, from the sun's surface. The outer corona is
characterized by delicate streamers which may extend more than a

Fig. 10·30. The Corona, August 31, 1932. Near the time of sunspot
minimum. Short, curved polar streamers and long equatorial extensions
characterize the corona at this phase of the sunspot cycle. (*Photograph
by Paul A. McNally, Georgetown University*)

million miles from the edge of the sun and which contribute to
the beauty of the total solar eclipse.

The details of the outer corona exhibit a cycle of changes in the
11-year period of sunspot frequency. Near sunspot maximum the
petal-like streamers extend to about the same distance all around
the disk, so that the corona resembles a dahlia. Near sunspot
minimum short, curved streamers appear around the poles, remindful of the lines of force around the poles of a magnet, and long
streamers stretch far out from the equatorial regions.

The corona proper is a highly ionized gas, glowing partly with sunlight scattered by its free electrons and partly with its own light which is emitted as shattered ions keep recombining with electrons. This light of the true corona is confused with the inner zodiacal light (9·21), which is sunlight scattered by dust particles, and with the blue light of the sky.

10·31. The Spectrum of the Corona shows a continuous background containing dark Fraunhofer lines and a superposed array of

FIG. 10·31. The Corona, February 25, 1952. Photograph by John P. Hagen and David S. Hawkins at Khartoum, Sudan. (*Naval Research Laboratory photograph*)

bright lines. The background consists of two components, which are designated as K and F.

The K-component of the spectrum is the brighter within a solar radius from the sun's edge. It resembles the solar spectrum except that the dark lines are almost completely washed out by Doppler effects of the swiftly moving scattering electrons; only the H and K lines are clearly seen, combined as a darkening 300 A wide. The F-component, caused by the zodiacal light, is a faint replica of the solar spectrum, and the strength of its dark lines shows the fraction of light it contributes to the total. This component is equally bright at equator and poles; it decreases more gradually outward than does the other.

Twenty-seven bright lines are well observed in the region of the spectrum which has been photographed. The most conspicuous ones are at 3388 A in the ultraviolet, 5303 A (the brightest line) in the green, 6375 A in the red, and 10,747 and 10,798 A in the infra-red. The stronger lines were first detected in an extrasolar source by Adams and Joy in the spectrum of the recurrent nova RS Ophi-uchi. They have since been recognized in the spectra of several novae, including Nova Herculis 1960. The identifications of the emission lines were announced in 1942 by the Swedish scientist B. Edlén. They are unusual lines of from 9 to 15 times ionized atoms of iron, nickel, calcium, and argon. The brightest ones are ascribed to iron atoms which have lost from 9 to 13 electrons. Hydrogen and helium are not represented in the spectrum because these less complex atoms would be kept permanently stripped of electrons in these conditions.

Such high degree of ionization and the considerable widths of the emission lines themselves indicate a kinetic temperature of the corona of the order of a million degrees.

10·32. The Corona Outside Eclipse. Until recent years, the sun's corona was not observed at all except during the infrequent mo-ments of total solar eclipse. Its faint glow seemed hopelessly con-cealed by the glare of the sunlit atmosphere, which at 1' from the edge of the sun is from 500 to 1000 times as bright as the coronal light.

In 1930, Bernard Lyot succeeded in photographing features of the inner corona with a special type of telescope, the *coronagraph*, at the Pic du Midi Observatory in the French Pyrenees. This in-strument depends for its effectiveness mainly on the quality and spotlessness of its objective, so that it brings in a minimum of scattered sunlight, and also on the clearer air of the mountains.

In addition to the original instrument, there are a dozen or more coronagraphs now in use at other mountain observatories, includ-ing the High Altitude Observatory at Climax, Colorado, and the

Sacramento Peak Observatory at Sunspot, New Mexico. The coronagraph is also useful for observing the chromosphere and prominences outside eclipse.

Wider extension of the corona has been recorded with radio telescopes. The evidence was first obtained while the sun in its annual circuit of the heavens was passing the Crab nebula, an intense radio source. The radiation from this source was found to be scattered and dimmed by the solar corona out to a distance of 30 or 40 solar radii from the sun. In 1960, O. B. Slee of the Radiophysics Laboratory, Sydney, Australia, observed this effect on a dozen fainter radio sources as well, and was able to determine the amount of the scattering at 350 points in the corona. He reported that the extended corona was an ellipse about 110 by 80 solar radii in size; it was similar in shape to the corona in visual light at that stage of the sunspot cycle.

10·33. Radio Reception from the Sun. The reception of radiation from the sun at radio wavelengths was recorded in 1942 at radar defense stations in Great Britain, but was not then published. The radiation was in excess of what was expected from thermal radiation at the sun's surface; and the very high kinetic temperature of the corona implied by Edlén's identification of its emission lines in that year had not yet become well known. The radiation is now being studied with radio telescopes at wavelengths from about 1 cm to 15 meters. The shortest of these are emitted from the lower chromosphere and the longer lengths from the corona.

The distinction is drawn between the quiet sun and the active sun. From the *quiet sun,* around sunspot minimum, the strength of the radio reception is near the thermal values. From the *active sun,* when sunspots, plages, and flares occur in great centers of activity, increased radiation and irregular *bursts* of much greater strength are superposed on the quiet sun emission. *Outbursts* of very great strength and lasting for minutes occur when large solar flares are observed. These have been attributed to streams of protons and other ions sucked out by the flares and propelled outward at speeds of the order of 1000 miles a second. They begin to disturb the ionized gas of the corona in seconds, causing the radio outbursts, and reach the earth a day later to produce our magnetic storms.

ASSOCIATED IONOSPHERIC DISTURBANCES

10·34. Magnetic Storms.   The appearance of a large solar flare is likely to be the signal for the deterioration of our radio communications in the higher frequencies.   Strong ultraviolet radiations arrive from the sun with the visible evidence of the flare.   These radiations disrupt ionized layers of the upper atmosphere, which normally reflect our radio beams back to the ground.   This effect and the magnetic storm which follows are most pronounced when the flare appears in a large sunspot group near the central meridian of the sun's disk.

Geomagnetic storms are unusual agitations of the earth's magnetic field; they are indicated by erratic gyrations of the compass needle.   They occur when streams of ions from the solar disturbance arrive here, a day or more after the flare is seen.   These effects are sometimes accompanied by strong induced earth-currents, which can interfere with our communications by wire.   The incoming protons also cause the primary glow of the aurora in the upper atmosphere.

A good example of the association between solar and ionospheric disturbances was inaugurated by a brilliant solar flare on September 28, 1961.   Two days later, a fine auroral display was observed in the northeastern United States.   Three photographs of the flare from a series taken by G. E. Moreton at the Lockheed Solar Observatory and some pictures of the aurora are shown in *Sky and Telescope* for November, 1961.

10·35. The Aurora.   Characteristic of many displays of the "northern lights" of our hemisphere is a luminous arch across the northern sky, having its apex in the direction of the geomagnetic pole. Rays like searchlight beams reach upward from the arch, while bright draperies may spread to other parts of the sky, altogether often increasing its brightness from 10 to 100 times that of the ordinary night sky.   These displays, which also occur in the southern hemisphere, are likely to be especially spectacular when large spot groups appear on the sun.

Auroral displays are most frequently observed in two zones centered about 23° from the two magnetic poles.   The zone in North America extends from Alaska across Hudson Bay to northern Labrador.   The southern boundary of auroral visibility is normally

FIG. 10·35. The Aurora. (*Photograph by Lewis Larmore*)

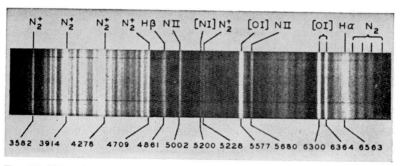

FIG. 10·35A. Spectrum of a Green Aurora. (*Photograph by Joseph W. Chamberlain, Yerkes Observatory, in* Sky and Telescope)

a parallel through San Francisco, Memphis, and Atlanta. Auroras have appeared on rare occasions as far south as Mexico City and Cuba. The southward shifting of this zone at the maxima of the sunspot number cycle strengthens the correlation that is found between the frequencies of auroras and sunspots.

The light of the aurora is believed to be produced by streams of protons and electrons, which emerge from solar upheavals and are trapped by the earth's magnetic field. The arches, as A. B. Meinel has explained, are caused mainly by the focusing of protons by the magnetic field in narrow bands, where they combine with electrons already in the ionosphere to form normal hydrogen atoms with the emission of light. The arches are subsequently broken into rays and draperies by impacts of streams of electrons, which combine with ionized atoms of oxygen and molecules of nitrogen. These effects are greatest at altitudes of 50 to 100 miles, but may extend to heights of several hundred miles.

Most of the light of an auroral display is produced in the colors green, red, and blue by the combining of electrons with oxygen atoms and nitrogen molecules. Hydrogen combinations contribute red and blue-green light. The great display of February 10–11, 1958, contained a remarkable intensity of red light from oxygen at high levels in our atmosphere.

10·36. The Airglow is permanently suffused over the sky day and night. It is caused by excitation of air molecules and atoms by energy coming from outside and presumably from the sun. The glow appears between altitudes of 60 to 120 miles. When it was first detected, it was called the "permanent aurora."

The night airglow gives us twice as much light as do all the stars, according to C. T. Elvey and F. E. Roach. It places a limit on the durations of exposures in direct celestial photography before the plates become hopelessly fogged. Almost invisible to the eye, it is studied effectively by use of the photoelectric cell and filters. The glow is faintest overhead and reaches its greatest intensity 10° above the horizon, where we look through a greater thickness of air. The night airglow is mainly at 4 wavelengths: (1) the green line of oxygen at 5577 A; (2) the red line of oxygen at 6300 A; (3) the yellow line of sodium at 5893 A; (4) the very strong infrared line of hydroxyl (OH) at about 10,000 A, which has been ascribed to impacts of incoming protons on ozone molecules.

The *twilight airglow* is 100 times as intense as the night airglow, but is not detected by the eye because of the brighter sky. This is believed to be caused by action of direct sunlight on the air molecules.

REVIEW QUESTIONS

1. Sunspots move across the sun's disk with the solar rotation in the direction of the sun's east to west apparent daily motion across the sky. Yet the sun has direct rotation like the earth, from west to east. Explain.

2. Explain that the apparent period of the sun's rotation as determined by observations of a sunspot is longer than the true period in that latitude because of the earth's revolution.

3. If the absolute temperature of a body is doubled, what is the effect on its total radiation? on the wavelength of its maximum radiation?

4. Why does the sun appear as a sharply defined disk? Why does the brightness of the disk diminish toward the edge?

5. Trace the growth and decline of a normal spot group, mentioning the usual difference in the decline of the two principal spots.

6. Describe and correlate the cyclic variations in the numbers and latitudes of sunspots.

7. What features of sunspot spectra show that the spots are cooler than the surrounding surface of the sun? that the spots are magnetic?

8. Describe the polarities of bipolar spot groups in the northern and southern hemispheres and their change with succeeding cycles.

9. How is it possible to distinguish between features of solar and terrestrial origin in the spectrum of sunlight? By what means are the studies of the spectrum being extended into extreme ultraviolet and infrared regions?

10. "Direct photographs" of the sun are frequently made by setting the second slit of the spectroheliograph on a continuous part of the solar spectrum. Explain why the result resembles the ordinary view of the photosphere.

11. Describe two means of photographing the prominences around the uneclipsed sun.

12. Explain that the bright-line spectrum of the corona reveals a surprising degree of atomic activity in that region.

13. Describe the solar flares and the terrestrial disturbances frequently associated with them.

14. Distinguish between the aurora and the airglow.

REFERENCES

Abetti, Giorgio, *The Sun*. Revised edition. The Macmillan Company, New York, 1957.

Kuiper, Gerard P., editor, *The Sun*. University of Chicago Press, Chicago, 1954.

Menzel, Donald H., *Our Sun*. Revised edition. Harvard University Press, Cambridge, 1959.

11

THE STARS

DISTANCES OF THE STARS — MOTIONS OF THE STARS —
STELLAR SPECTRA — MAGNITUDES OF THE STARS —
LUMINOSITIES OF THE STARS

In our studies of the stars we first consider the basic data of observation, how they are determined and in what terms they are expressed. These are the distances of the stars, their motions relative
to the sun, the character of their spectra, and their relative brightness.

DISTANCES OF THE STARS

11·1. The Parallax of a Star. While the earth is revolving around
the sun, a nearer star seems to be describing a little orbit with
respect to more distant stars. This apparent orbit has almost the

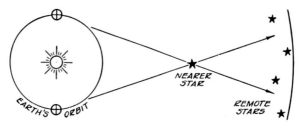

Fig. 11·1. The Parallax of a Star. Because of the earth's revolution, the
nearer star appears to oscillate annually relative to more remote stars.

same form as the aberration orbit (2·21); it varies from nearly a
circle for a star at the ecliptic pole to a straight line for a star at
the ecliptic. It is much smaller than the aberration orbit even for
the nearer stars and shrinks to imperceptible size for the more
distant ones.

The *heliocentric parallax* of a star is half the major axis of the
parallax orbit, with slight correction for the eccentricity of the
earth's orbit. It is otherwise the greatest difference between the
directions of the star as seen from the earth and sun during the
year. We refer to it as the *parallax* of the star.

After Copernicus had proposed the heliocentric theory of the planetary motions, the inability of astronomers to detect the parallax displacements of stars meant either that the earth was stationary after all or that the stars are enormously more remote than they were believed to be at that time. When the earth's revolution was decisively demonstrated by the discovery of the aberration of star-light, the search for perceptible parallaxes was renewed as a promising means of determining the distances of stars.

It was not until the years 1837–39 that the attempts to observe this effect finally met with success. The parallax of Vega was announced by F. G. W. Struve at Dorpat in 1837, of 61 Cygni by F. W. Bessel at Königsberg in 1838, and of Alpha Centauri by Thomas Henderson at the Cape of Good Hope in 1839. Up to 1904, fairly reliable parallaxes of 55 stars had been observed by various means. The early visual methods were adequate to deal only with the larger parallaxes.

11·2. Measurements of Parallax. The modern photographic method of measuring stellar parallaxes was developed, in 1903, by

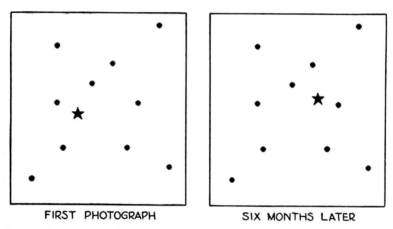

FIRST PHOTOGRAPH   SIX MONTHS LATER

FIG. 11·2. Parallax Displacement of a Nearby Star Relative to More Remote Stars. Two photographs, however, are not sufficient to determine the parallax reliably.

Frank Schlesinger with the 40-inch Yerkes refractor. He attained such greatly increased accuracy that other astronomers with long-focus telescopes were encouraged to enter this exacting and important field. The latest *General Catalogue of Trigonometric Stellar*

Parallaxes of Yale Observatory (1952) lists 5822 stars with known direct parallaxes.

The parallax of a star is determined by observing its change of position relative to stars that are apparently close to it, but are

FIG. 11·2A. Double-Slide Plate Holder of the 40-inch Telescope, Yerkes Observatory. It carries a small eyepiece containing cross wires, with which the observer guides on a star near the edge of the field while the exposure is in progress.

really so much farther away from us that they are not greatly affected by the earth's revolution. Sets of photographs of the region are obtained at intervals of about 6 months, when the star under investigation appears near the extremities of its small parallax orbit. Two sets are not enough, because the star is also moving in a straight line with respect to the more distant stars and it accordingly advances among them in a series of loops. At least 18 sets of photographs are usually required to extricate the parallax accurately.

It will be noted that the result obtained is the *relative parallax;* for the comparison stars themselves appear to be shifted slightly by the earth's revolution in the same directions as the parallax star. The *absolute parallax* is derived by making a correction not exceeding a few thousandths of a second of arc, which depends on the brightness of the comparison stars and can be statistically estimated.

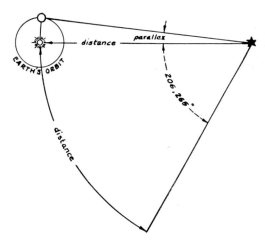

FIG. 11·3. Relation Between Parallax and Distance. The radius of a circle laid off along the circumference subtends an angle, the radian, equal to 206,265″. From the two sectors we have the proportion: distance of the star is to the radius of the earth's orbit as 206,265″ is to the parallax.

11·3. Units of Distance: the Parsec and the Light Year. When the star's parallax, p, has been measured, its distance is found by the relation (Fig. 11·3):

$$\text{Distance (in astronomical units)} = 206{,}265''/p''.$$

Since 1 astronomical unit, the earth's mean distance from the sun, equals 149,500,000 km, or 92,900,000 miles, we have the star's distance:

$$\text{Distance (in kilometers)} = (206{,}265''/p'')1.495 \times 10^8.$$
$$\text{Distance (in miles)} \quad = (206{,}265''/p'')9.290 \times 10^7.$$

The distance of a star expressed in miles or even astronomical units is an inconveniently large number. It is better to use larger units, either the parsec or the light year.

The *parsec* is the distance at which a star would have a *pa*rallax of 1 *se*cond of arc. This distance by the above relations is 206,265 astronomical units, or 3.08×10^{13} km, or 1.92×10^{13} miles. The advantage of the parsec is its simple relation to the parallax:

$$\text{Distance (in parsecs)} = 1''/p''.$$

The *light year* is the distance traversed by light in 1 year; it is equal to the speed of light, 2.998×10^5 km/sec, multiplied by 3.156×10^7, the number of seconds in a year. The light year is therefore 9.46×10^{12} km, or 5.88×10^{12} miles (nearly 6 million million miles). One parsec equals 3.26 light years. Thus:

$$\text{Distance (in light years)} = 3''.26/p'',$$

or $3.26 \times$ distance in parsecs.

As an example, consider the brightest star, Sirius, also one of the nearest, having a parallax of $0''.379$. The distance of Sirius in astronomical units is $206,265''/0''.379$, or somewhat more than half a million astronomical units, which amounts to about 50 million million miles. The distance in parsecs is $1''/0''.379$, or 2.6 parsecs. The distance in light years is $3''.26/0''.379$, or 8.6 light years.

11·4. The Nearest Stars. Fifteen stars are known, counting a double star as one system, within the distance of $3\frac{1}{2}$ parsecs from the sun. Data concerning these, furnished by W. J. Luyten, are listed in Table 11·I. Although three of the very brightest stars in our skies are included, more than half of the nearest stars are invisible without the telescope, for their magnitudes are numbers greater than 6; and it is probable that other faint stars will eventually be added to the list. It is to be noted in passing that the annual proper motions (11·6) of the nearest stars exceed their parallaxes, and also that several of these stars are double.

The distinction of being the sun's nearest neighbor is held by the bright double star Alpha Centauri. A star of the 11th magnitude, sometimes called "Proxima," is a member of this system; it is situated a little more than 2° from the two bright stars and seems to be slightly nearer us than they are.

11·5. Limitations of the Direct Method. The direct, or trigonometric, method of determining stellar parallaxes diminishes in accuracy as more distant stars are observed. The probable error of the most reliable parallaxes, in which several independent meas-

TABLE 11·I THE NEAREST STARS

Name	Right Ascension (1950)	Declination (1950)	Apparent Visual Magnitude	Annual Proper Motion	Absolute Parallax	Distance (Light Years)
* Alpha Centauri	14ʰ 36ᵐ	−60°.6	† −0.3, 1.7	3″.68	0″.760	**4.3**
Barnard's star	17 55	+4.5	9.7	10.25	.544	**6.0**
Wolf 359	10 54	+7.3	13.5	4.70	.402	**8.1**
BD + 36° 2147	11 1	+36.3	7.6	4.78	.390	**8.4**
* Luyten 726–8	1 36	−18.2	11.9, 12.4	3.38	.380	**8.6**
* Sirius	6 43	−16.6	−1.4, 8.4	1.32	.379	**8.6**
Ross 154	18 47	−23.9	11	0.67	.350	**9.3**
Ross 248	23 39	+43.9	12.2	1.58	.318	**10.2**
Epsilon Eridani	3 31	−9.6	3.8	0.97	.303	**10.8**
* 61 Cygni	21 5	+38.5	5.6, 6.3	5.22	.298	**10.9**
Tau Ceti	1 42	−16.2	3.6	1.92	.298	**10.9**
* Procyon	7 37	+5.4	0.4, 10.8	1.25	.294	**11.1**
Luyten 789–6	22 36	−15.6	12.3	3.27	.293	**11.2**
Ross 128	11 45	+1.1	11.1	1.40	.288	**11.3**
Epsilon Indi	22 0	−57.0	4.7	4.67	.288	**11.3**

* Visual double star.

† A third star of magnitude 11 belongs to the system.

ures are averaged, is of the order of 0″.005. For the very nearest stars this error is less than 1 per cent of the parallax. The percentage of probable error increases as the parallax decreases; it is 10 per cent for a parallax of 0″.05. If the observed parallax is as small as 0″.01 ± 0″.005, it follows from the definition of the probable error that the chance is one half that the true value lies between 0″.015 and 0″.005, or that the star's distance is between 67 and 200 parsecs. It is equally probable that the true value is outside these limits.

Thus the percentage of error in measuring the distances of stars by the direct method increases with the distance and becomes very large for distances exceeding 100 parsecs, or about 300 light years. Because the success of many investigations of the stars depends on the knowledge of their distances, astronomers have sought for and have discovered indirect ways of determining the parallaxes of more remote stars. These will be noted as we proceed.

MOTIONS OF THE STARS

Edmund Halley, in 1718, was the first to demonstrate that the stars are not "fixed." He showed that certain bright stars had moved from the places assigned them in Ptolemy's ancient catalog by about the moon's apparent diameter. The stars are moving in various directions relative to one another. Their movements through space are often swift, but seem very slow to us because of the great distances of the stars.

11·6. Two Projections of a Star's Motion. (1) *Proper motion* is the rate of change in the star's direction, or apparent place on the celestial sphere; this *angular* rate decreases, in general, as the star's dis-

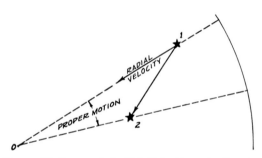

Fig. 11·6. Proper Motion and Radial Velocity. As the star moves from *1* to *2*, its proper motion is the angular rate of its change in direction viewed from *O*; its radial velocity is the linear rate of its approach to or recession from the observer.

tance is greater. (2) *Radial velocity* is the star's speed of approach or recession; this *linear* rate is independent of the distance and is often the only projection of the motion that can be measured. The observed motion may be referred to the sun by correcting for the effects of the earth's motions.

Proper motions, radial velocities, and distances of the stars constitute the basic data in the studies of stellar motions.

11·7. Proper Motions of stars are determined by comparing their right ascensions and declinations in catalogs of star positions that are separated by sufficient intervals of time. The rates of change in these coordinates are the required data, after allowance has been made for apparent displacements of the stars caused by precession and other motions of the earth. By this procedure the proper motions of all lucid stars have become known and of multitudes of telescopic stars as well.

Many thousand stars with large proper motions have been detected and measured by Luyten and others by comparison of star positions in two photographs of the same region of the heavens obtained at different times. This comparison is relatively simple and rapid because precession, aberration, and other apparent displacements of stars, with the exception of parallax, are nearly the same over a small area of the sky.

The method of "blinking" is effective for the detection of any differences between two photographs that are being compared. The two plates are arranged under a blink microscope so that corresponding star images appear superposed. By mechanical means the plates are alternately hidden several times a second. If all the stars in the region have not moved appreciably between the exposure times, the appearance is the same as before the blinking began. If a star is displaced on one plate relative to the other, the result is a jumping effect, which at once attracts the observer's attention.

11·8. Stars with Large Proper Motions. The largest known proper motion is that of a telescopic star called "Barnard's star" after the

August 23, 1894   May 30, 1916

FIG. 11·8. Proper Motion of Barnard's Star. The star has moved an eighth of the moon's apparent diameter in the interval of 22 years between the dates of the photographs. (*Yerkes Observatory photographs*)

name of the astronomer who first noticed its swift motion. This 10th-magnitude star in Ophiuchus is moving with respect to its neighbors at the rate of 10″.3 a year, so that it advances in 175 years through an angle equal to the moon's apparent diameter. If all the stars were moving as fast as this and at random, the forms of the constellations would be altered appreciably in the course of a lifetime. As it is, the known proper motions of only about 330 stars exceed 1″ a year, according to Luyten, and the average for all the naked-eye stars is not greater than 0″.1 a year.

We have noted that the proper motion is angular. A star having a large proper motion may actually be in rapid motion, or it may be nearer us than most stars, or both, as is true of Barnard's star. We have also noted that the proper motion relates only to that part of the star's motion that is transverse to the line of sight.

11·9. Radial Velocities. A star's rate of motion directly toward or away from us, or its *radial velocity,* is shown by the displacement of

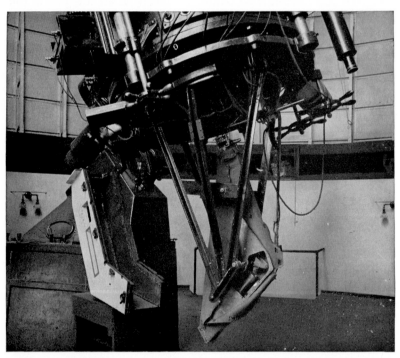

Fɪɢ. 11·9. Single-Prism Spectrograph. Attached to the 37-inch reflecting telescope, University of Michigan Observatory. The case is removed to show the prism.

the lines of its spectrum from their normal positions. By the Doppler effect (4·9), the wavelengths are shortened if the star is approaching us and are lengthened if the star is receding; and the amount of the change in their lengths is directly proportional to the star's radial velocity. For the visual region of the spectrum, the lines are displaced respectively toward the violet or the red end. The more general terms *shortward* and *longward* denote without ambiguity the direction of the displacement of the lines in any region of the spectrum. For a line of a particular wavelength the relation is:

$$\text{Radial velocity} = \frac{\text{change of wavelength}}{\text{wavelength}} \times \text{velocity of light.}$$

If, for example, a line at 4000 angstroms is displaced 1 angstrom toward the violet, the star is approaching us with a speed of

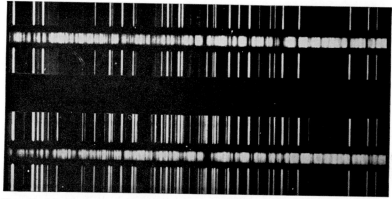

Fig. 11·9A. Doppler Displacements in Stellar Spectra. In the spectrum of the star HD 6497 (above) the displacement of the dark lines to the violet (left) represents the velocity of approach to the earth of 108 km/sec. In the spectrum of HD 39045 (below) the displacement to the red (right) represents the velocity of recession of 116 km/sec. The bright comparison lines are the spectrum of the iron arc. (*Photographs by David Dunlap Observatory, University of Toronto*)

$\frac{1}{4000} \times 186{,}300$ miles a second; its radial velocity is -46.6 miles a second. Approach is indicated by the minus sign, recession by the plus sign.

The spectroscope is attached at the eye end of the telescope, with the slit at the focus of the objective. With it the bright-line spectrum of a laboratory source, often iron or titanium, may also be photographed above and below the star's spectrum. The photograph, or *spectrogram* (Fig. 11·9A), is observed under a microscope, and the positions of the star-lines are measured micrometrically with respect to the *comparison lines* of the laboratory source, which have no Doppler displacements.

A recent catalog by R. E. Wilson lists the radial velocities of more than 15,000 stars. Velocities up to 30 km/sec, or about 20 miles a second, are common; those exceeding 100 km/sec are rare.

11·10. Annual Variation in the Radial Velocities. The earth's revolution around the sun causes a variation in the observed radial velocities of the stars during the year. When the earth is moving

Fig. 11·10. Annual Variation in the Radial Velocity of a Star. Because of the earth's revolution, the lines in the spectrum of a star oscillate in a period of a year. The effect is greatest for a star on the ecliptic.

toward a star, the lines in the star's spectrum are displaced to shorter wavelengths; when the earth is moving away from the star, the lines are displaced to longer wavelengths than they would otherwise have. The observed radial velocities may be corrected for this and some other effects of the earth's motions.

The annual variation in the radial velocities provides another means (7·16) of determining the earth's distance from the sun. The English astronomer H. Spencer Jones derived in this way the value 92,870,000 miles, which is not far from the mean distance currently adopted.

As a simplified example, consider a star at the ecliptic and at rest. Once in a year the earth is moving directly toward the star. Six months later it is moving directly away from the star. On each occasion the radial velocity of the star as determined from the displacement of its spectrum lines is numerically equal to the speed of the earth's revolution. Suppose that this value is 18½ miles a second and that the earth's orbit is a circle. Multiplying 18½ miles per second by 31,558,150, about the number of seconds in the sidereal year, we find for the circumference of the orbit nearly 584 million miles. Dividing this value by 2 × 3.1416 we have for the mean radius of the orbit about 92,900,000 miles.

11·11. Space Velocities. When the annual proper motion, μ, of a star and its parallax, p, are known, the tangential velocity, T, can be calculated. The *tangential velocity* is the star's velocity with

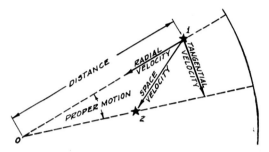

Fig. 11·11.   Relation Between Space Velocity, Tangential Velocity, Radial Velocity, Proper Motion, and Distance of a Star.

respect to the sun at right angles to the line of sight; it equals 4.74 μ/p km/sec.

When the star's radial velocity, V, is known as well, the *space velocity, v*, which is the star's velocity with respect to the sun, is the

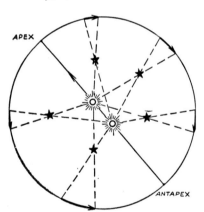

Fig. 11·12.   Apparent Motions of Stars Caused by the Solar Motion. The stars seem to be drifting away from the point on the celestial sphere toward which the sun is moving.

diagonal of the right triangle given by the relation: $v^2 = V^2 + T^2$. The space velocities of the stars in the sun's vicinity are generally of the same order as the velocities of the planets in their revolutions around the sun; the majority are between 5 and 20 miles a second. Among the brightest stars, Arcturus has the highest space velocity; it is 135 km/sec, or 84 miles a second.

11·12. The Sun's Motion. Although the space velocities of the stars are referred to the sun, the sun itself is one of the stars and is in motion among them. It is therefore important to determine how the sun is moving and to be able to correct the space velocities for the effects of this motion.

If the sun with its planetary system is moving in a certain direction among the stars around it and if the stars have random motions, these stars should seem to be passing by in the opposite direction. The stars ahead of us should seem to be opening out from the *apex* of the sun's way, the point of the celestial sphere toward which the sun's motion is directed. The stars behind us should seem to be closing in toward the opposite *antapex*. So reasoned William Herschel, English astronomer and pioneer in the study of sidereal astronomy. Although the proper motions of only 13 stars were then available, he determined, in 1783, the position of the apex within 10° of the place now assigned to the "standard apex."

11·13. The Standard Apex of the Sun's Way is referred to the average of the stars visible to the naked eye. It is situated approximately in right ascension $18^h 0^m$ and declination $+30°$, in the constellation Hercules about 10° southwest of the bright star Vega. With respect to these stars the solar system is moving in this direction at the rate of 20 km/sec, or about 12 miles per second. In the course of a year we progress through the local field of stars 4 times as far as the distance from the earth to the sun. The corresponding antapex is in the constellation Columba, about 30° south of Orion's belt.

The more recent determinations are based on the proper motions and also the radial velocities of thousands of stars. When the radial velocities are employed, the apex is evidently the point around which the stars have the greatest average velocity of approach, while around the antapex they have the greatest average velocity of recession; and this average is the speed of the sun's motion relative to these particular stars. The positions from the proper motions and radial velocities nearly agree, as they should, because the reference stars are in both cases in the sun's neighborhood.

When the motions of more distant stars are studied, the apex of the sun's way is displaced progressively toward the northeast. Thus, from their analysis of the proper motions of 18,000 of the brighter telescopic stars, P. van de Kamp and A. N. Vyssotsky locate the apex in right ascension $19^h.0$ and declination $+36°$, in the constellation Lyra. As we note later, this is because the sun and the stars in its vicinity are moving swiftly toward Cygnus in the rotation of our galaxy.

11·14. Stellar Distances from the Solar Motion. We have seen that the direct parallax method is limited to the nearer stars. For the more distant ones the diameter of the earth's orbit is too short to serve as an adequate base line. At first sight it might seem that the sun's motion could provide an ideal base for measuring stellar parallaxes. In only one year it takes us a distance twice as great as the diameter of the earth's orbit. If this longer base line is still too short to afford appreciable parallax of the distant stars, we could wait two years or perhaps a hundred, until it would become long enough.

Because the stars have motions of their own, it is generally impossible to say what part of a star's proper motion is a parallax effect and what part is peculiar to the star itself. Thus the longer base line provided by the sun's motion cannot be used to determine the distances of individual stars, although it has given reliable average parallaxes of groups of stars.

STELLAR SPECTRA

11·15. Photographs of Stellar Spectra are made in two different ways. One method employs a complete spectroscope with its slit

Fig. 11·15. Four-Degree Objective Prism of the 24-inch Schmidt Telescope, Warner and Swasey Observatory.

at the focus of the telescope objective (Fig. 11·9). Reflecting prisms over the ends of the slit bring in the light of a laboratory source on either side of the beam of starlight. The bright comparison lines of the source appear in the photograph adjacent to the star's spectrum; these can serve as standards for measuring wavelengths and Doppler shifts in the star's spectrum. This method gives the spectrum of only one star at a time and is rather wasteful of light. The present limit for the 200-inch telescope with a 1-night exposure is a low-dispersion spectrum of an 18th-magnitude star.

The objective prism method is preferred when the spectra of many stars are to be examined, as in the classification of stellar spectra. A large prism of small angle is placed in front of the telescope objective, so that the whole apparatus becomes a spectroscope without slit or collimator. The photograph shows appropriately widened spectra of all stars of sufficient brightness in the field of view. Exposure times are restricted by the light of the sky, as in direct photography. The method is now limited to stars brighter than photographic magnitude 12 or 13.

11·16. The Classification of Stellar Spectra. The photographic study of stellar spectra with the objective prism was inaugurated, in 1885, by Edward Pickering at Harvard Observatory. This work was carried on for many years under the immediate direction of Annie J. Cannon. *The Henry Draper Catalogue,* in 9 volumes completed in 1924, gives the approximate positions, magnitudes, and spectral types of 225,300 stars in all parts of the heavens. Its extensions, particularly to fainter stars in the Milky Way, contain almost as many more stars.

One of the outstanding results of the program was the discovery that the great majority of stellar spectra can be arranged in a single continuous sequence. This gradation is the basis of the *Draper Classification,* for which Miss Cannon was chiefly responsible. Various stages in the sequence are denoted by the principal types O, B, A, F, G, K, and M, which are subdivided on the decimal system. Thus a G5 star is halfway between G0 and K0; B2 is nearer to B0 than to A0. Fully 99 per cent of the stars are included in the types from B to M.

Four additional types complete the Harvard sequence. These are W now paired with O at the blue end, and R-N and S, which form two side branches near the red end; the first branches off between G and K, and the second between K and M. All together, it is a sequence of diminishing surface temperature and increasing redness of the stars. We note here the main features of the changing patterns along the sequence in the visible region of the spectrum, leaving further description and explanation for the following chapter.

11·17. The Sequence of Stellar Spectra. The Harvard classification was based on gradations in the patterns of the spectral lines and was independent of theoretical considerations. The sequence is characterized particularly by the rise and decline in the strength of the hydrogen lines throughout its extent. Lines of other elements become prominent at different stages of the sequence, and bands of chemical compounds appear toward the end of the se-

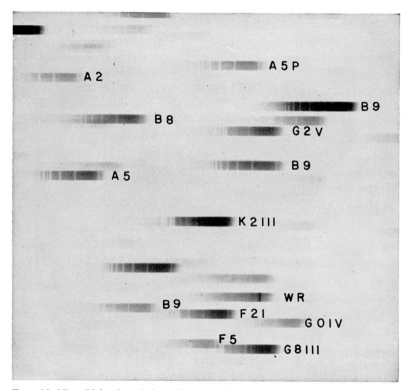

Fig. 11·17. Objective Prism Spectra of Stars. Negative print from a small part of a photograph centered in R.A. 22ʰ 14ᵐ, Decl. +56°. The spectra are labeled with spectral types and luminosity classes (12·19) of the stars. (*Photograph with the Schmidt telescope and 4° prism, Warner and Swasey Observatory*)

quence. The main features in the visual spectra of the different types are as follows:

Type O. Lines of ionized helium, oxygen, and nitrogen appear along with those of hydrogen. *Type W* contains the bright-line Wolf-Rayet stars.

Type B. Lines of neutral helium are most intense at B2 and then fade, until at B9 they have practically disappeared. Hydrogen lines increase in intensity throughout the subdivisions. Examples are Spica and Rigel.

Type A. Hydrogen lines attain maximum intensity at A2. Examples are Sirius and Vega. B and A stars are blue.

Type F. Hydrogen lines are declining. Lines of metals are increasing in intensity, notably the Fraunhofer H and K of ionized calcium. Canopus and Procyon are examples.

Type G. Lines of metals are prominent. These stars are yellow. The sun (type G2) and Capella are examples.

Type K. Lines of metals now surpass the hydrogen lines in strength. Bands of cyanogen and other molecules are becoming prominent. These stars are reddish. Examples are Arcturus and Aldebaran.

Type M. Bands of titanium oxide become increasing prominent up to their maximum at M7. The cooler members are classified by J. J. Nassau and associates to M10 by the strengthening of vanadium oxide bands. Betelgeuse and Antares are examples of this red type.

Types R and *N* show bands of carbon and carbon compounds, *type S* of zirconium oxide and lanthanum oxide.

MAGNITUDES OF THE STARS

11·18. The Scale of Magnitudes. The grading of the naked-eye stars in early times into 6 magnitudes (1·25) was intended primarily to assist in identifying the stars. There is no evidence that the choice of 6 groups, rather than some other number, was governed by any definite idea of fixed numerical relations between the groups. For many centuries afterward, the magnitudes of the stars were accepted as they appeared in Ptolemy's catalog. It was not until the comparatively recent times of the Herschels that stellar magnitudes began to enter as important factors into astronomical investigations, as in statistical studies of the structure of the stellar system.

About 1830, John Herschel concluded that a geometrical progression in the apparent brightness of the stars is associated with the arithmetical progression of their magnitudes. The problem was then to ascertain the constant ratio of brightness corresponding to a difference of 1 magnitude that would best represent the magnitudes already assigned to the lucid stars. Pogson, at Radcliffe in 1856, proposed the adoption of the ratio having the logarithm 0.4, a convenient value nearly equal to the average ratio derived from his observations and those of other astronomers. He adjusted the zero of this fixed scale so as to secure as good agreement as possible with the early catalog at the 6th magnitude. This is the present scale.

Pogson's rule is a special case of a general psycho-physical relation established, in 1834, by the physiologist Weber and given a more precise phrasing later by Fechner. By Fechner's law, $S = c \log R$, where S is the intensity of a sensation, R is the stimulus producing it, and c is a constant factor of proportionality. Pogson had evaluated the constant in the corresponding relation: $m - n = c \log (l_n/l_m)$, where l_m and l_n are the apparent brightnesses of two stars having the magnitudes m and n, respectively. The constant is 2.5, or $1/0.4$, or $1/\log 2.512$. If the difference, $m - n$, is 1 magnitude, $l_n/l_m = 2.512$.

11·19. Relation Between Brightness and Magnitude.

We have seen that the ratio of brightness between two stars differing by exactly 1 magnitude is the number having the logarithm 0.4, which is about 2.512. A few values where the magnitude difference is a whole number are as follows:

Magnitude Difference	Ratio of Brightness
1.0 magnitude	2.512
2.0 magnitudes	6.31
3.0 magnitudes	15.85
4.0 magnitudes	39.8
5.0 magnitudes	100.0

In general, the ratio of apparent brightness, l_n/l_m, of two stars or other sources of light of magnitudes m and n can be derived by the formula:

$$\log (l_n/l_m) = 0.4(m - n).$$

It is to be noted that the number expressing the magnitude diminishes algebraically as the brightness increases, and that the
choice of the zero point makes the magnitudes of the very brightest celestial objects negative. The apparent visual magnitude of
the brightest star, Sirius, is -1.4, of the planet Venus at greatest
brilliancy is -4.4, of the full moon is -12.6, and of the sun is -26.8.
The photographic magnitude of the faintest star recorded with the
200-inch telescope is $+23.9$.

The following examples illustrate some of the uses of the relation between apparent brightness and magnitude:

(1) How much brighter is Sirius (magnitude -1.4) than a star of the
magnitude $+23.9$?
Answer: $\log (l_n/l_m) = 0.4 \times 25.3 = 10.12$
$l_n/l_m =$ about 13,200 million times.

(2) Nova Aquilae, in the course of two or three days in June, 1918, increased in brightness about 45,000 times. How many magnitudes did it
rise?
Answer: $\log (l_n/l_m) = \log 45,000 = 4.65 = 0.4(m - n)$
$m - n = 4.65/0.4 =$ about 11.6 magnitudes.

(3) The bright star Castor, which appears single to the naked eye, is resolved by the telescope into two stars of magnitudes 1.99 and 2.85. What
is the magnitude of the two combined?
Answer: $\log (l_n/l_m) = 0.4 \times 0.86 = 0.344$
$l_n/l_m = 2.21$; $(l_m + l_n)/l_m = l_x/l_m = 3.21$
$\log (l_x/l_m) = 0.507 = 0.4(m - x)$
$m - x = 0.507/0.4 = 1.27$
$x = 2.85 - 1.27 = 1.58$, the combined magnitude.

11·20. Visual and Photographic Magnitudes. The *apparent magnitude* of a star refers to its observed brightness, depending on its
actual brightness and its distance from us. The value for a particular star varies with the region of the spectrum to which the
receiver of the star's radiation is sensitive. If the receiver is the
eye alone or the eye at the telescope, it is also the visual magnitude that is determined.

Visual methods for determining magnitudes are now generally
replaced by the more reliable photographic and photoelectric
methods. By use of a suitable color filter and a specially stained
plate, or still more accurately with a filter and photocell, it is possible to determine the magnitude on the visual scale. This *photo-*

visual magnitude is usually meant when we refer to the visual magnitude.

The *photographic magnitude* of a star is its magnitude as shown in a blue-sensitive photograph. It is generally determined by the size of the star's round image, which is larger and also denser as the star is brighter, and by comparison with stars of known magnitudes in the same photograph. The desired magnitude is sometimes simply estimated by viewing the plate with an eyepiece. For greater accuracy the star's image is measured with special apparatus. A single measure with the iris-diaphragm Eichner photometer can determine the brightness of a star with a probable error of about 0.03 magnitude.

Fig. 11·20. Diameter of a Star Image Photographs Larger as the Star Is Brighter. Sirius and other stars of Canis Major. (*Photograph by F. E. Ross, Yerkes Observatory*)

11·21. The Brightest Stars. The 22 stars brighter than apparent visual magnitude +1.5 are listed in order of brightness in Table 11·II. The magnitudes, as given by H. L. Johnson, have been measured photoelectrically. The spectral types and luminosity classes are on the Morgan-Keenan system (12·19); they refer to the brighter components where the stars are visual doubles. Types from B to M are represented. The bluest stars, having the largest negative color indexes (11·24), are Alpha and Beta Crucis and Spica; the reddest are Betelgeuse and Antares.

These 22 stars are generally not the brightest in the sky because

TABLE 11·II THE BRIGHTEST STARS

Name	Spectrum	Apparent Visual Magnitude	Apparent Photographic Magnitude	Parallax	Absolute Visual Magnitude
Sirius	A1 V	−1.43	−1.43	0″.379	+1.5
Canopus	F0 Ia	−0.73	−0.58	.018	−4.4
d α Centauri	G2 V	−0.27	+0.39	.760	+4.1
Arcturus	K2 III	−0.06	+1.17	.090	−0.3
Vega	A0 V	+0.04	+0.04	.123	+0.5
Capella	(G0)	0.09	0.89	.073	−0.6
Rigel	B8 Ia	0.15	0.11	.005	−6.4
Procyon	F5 IV	0.37	0.78	.288	+2.7
Achernar	B3 V	0.53	0.37	.023	−2.7
d β Centauri	B0 V	0.66	0.45	.016	−3.3
v Betelgeuse	M2 I	0.7	2.6	.017	−2.9
Altair	A7 IV	0.80	1.02	.198	+2.3
v Aldebaran	K5 III	0.85	2.37	.048	−0.7
d α Crucis	B0 V	0.87	0.63	.015	−3.2
dv Antares	M1 Ib	0.98	2.78	.019	−2.6
Spica	B1 V	1.00	0.77	.021	−2.4
Fomalhaut	A3 V	1.16	1.25	.144	+2.0
Pollux	K0 III	1.16	2.17	.093	+1.0
Deneb	A2 Ia	1.26	1.35	.006	−4.8
β Crucis	B0 IV	1.31	1.08	(.011)	−3.5
Regulus	B7 V	1.36	1.25	.039	−0.7
ε Can. Maj.	B2 II	1.49	1.32	(.012)	−3.1

d Visual double star with brightness difference less than 5 magnitudes; combined magnitudes are given.

v Variable star. Visual magnitude range for Betelgeuse, 0.4 to 1.0; Aldebaran, 0.75 to 0.95; Antares, 0.90 to 1.06.

they are the nearest to us. Although Alpha Centauri, Sirius, and Procyon are among the nearest stars, others such as Rigel, Canopus, and Deneb are so remote that they must be highly luminous to appear so bright. The significance of the last column of the table is explained later in this chapter.

All but six of the brightest stars are visible at some times in the year throughout the United States. Those six become visible in their seasons south of about the following north latitudes: Canopus, 38°; Achernar, 33°; Alpha and Beta Centauri and Beta Crucis, 30°; Alpha Crucis, 28°.

11·22. Photoelectric Photometry has superseded photographic methods of measuring star magnitudes where the greatest possible accuracy is required. The photoelectric cell at the focus of the telescope admits the beam of starlight through a clear window and thereupon releases electrons from its inner, sensitive surface. In the photomultiplier tube now employed, the electrons accelerated by an electric field impinge successively on other photosensitive surfaces in the cell, where more electrons are jostled out to add to the current and hence to the sensitivity of the cell.

These active surfaces in the tube are generally coatings of antimony-cesium where the radiations transmitted to the cell by filters have wavelengths shorter than 6000 angstroms, and of cesium oxide for longer wavelengths, as far as 10,000 angstroms into the infrared.

When the electron stream has encountered a dozen such surfaces, the current may have a million times its strength at the start. It then goes to the recorder, where the amount of deflection of a pen on a moving tape denotes the relative intensity of the light. After allowance is made for sky light entering the cell around the beam of starlight and also for "dark current" in the cell itself, the observer has a measure of the star's brightness. Magnitudes can be measured with the phototube for stars as faint as can be photographed with the same telescope.

An important advantage of photoelectric photometry as contrasted with the photographic method is that the release of electrons in the cell is directly proportional to the intensity of the light; and this linear relation is maintained through the whole range of brightness of the celestial bodies. A disadvantage is that only one star can be measured at a time. It is also difficult to allow for the sky light in congested areas, as in the Milky Way. Where many stars are to be observed, the procedure is generally to set up magnitude standards in the area with the cell and then to go on with photography.

11·23. Magnitude Standards. In many investigations that involve the apparent magnitudes of stars, the magnitudes must all conform to the same scale. Standard magnitude sequences have been set up as a means of control for all observers. They are sequences of stars in limited areas, having their magnitudes well determined and grading in brightness by small steps. The Mount Wilson north polar sequence of F. H. Seares long served as primary standards for photovisual and photographic magnitudes.

The greater accuracy of photoelectric photometry is employed in the newer sequences. The Mount Wilson and Palomar sequences in certain areas are based on magnitudes of selected stars of the original north polar sequence and are extended to the fainter magnitudes observed with the 200-inch telescope.

A system of standard magnitudes determined photoelectrically with specified color filters has been established for the ultraviolet (U), blue, or photographic (B), and yellow, or visual (V) regions of the spectrum by H. L. Johnson and W. W. Morgan for stars in various parts of the sky; for the red (R) at 7000 angstroms by Robert Hardie, and infrared (I) at 8250 A by G. E. Kron.

11·24. Color Index. The *color index* of a star is the difference between its magnitudes determined in two colors. It is frequently

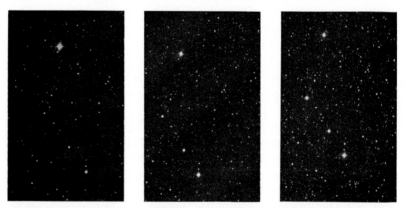

Fig. 11·24. Comparison of Photographs in Blue, Red, and Infrared. The four bright stars from top to bottom are of types B, M5, K5, and K2, respectively. (*Warner and Swasey Observatory photographs*)

given as the blue minus the visual $(B - V)$ magnitude. This difference becomes greater as the star is redder, because a red star appears brighter in yellow light and therefore has a numerically smaller magnitude than in blue light. The two scales are adjusted so that $B - V$ is zero for a star of spectral type A0, such as Sirius. Thus the bluest stars have slightly negative color index and the reddest stars have large positive index.

Color index is a numerical measure of the star's color and therefore of its spectral type if nothing intervenes in space to redden the light. If the spectral type is also known and if the measured color index is greater than would normally be expected for a star of this type, the excess reveals the presence and effect of an intervening cosmic dusty medium, as we note in a later chapter. Values of $B - V$ for the different spectral types are given in Table 12·II and may be found for the brightest stars from Table 11·II.

LUMINOSITIES OF THE STARS

11·25. Absolute Magnitudes. The apparent magnitude of a star relates to its brightness as we observe it. This depends on the star's *luminosity,* or brightness at a specified distance, and on its actual distance. One star may appear brighter than another only because it is the nearer; thus the sun appears brighter than Capella. In order to rank the stars fairly with respect to luminosity, it is necessary to place them all at the same distance from us or, what amounts to the same thing, to calculate how bright they would appear if they were placed at the same distance. By agreement the standard distance is 10 parsecs, or 32.6 light years.

The *absolute magnitude* of a star is the apparent magnitude it would have at the distance of 10 parsecs (parallax $0''.1$).

When the parallax, p'', is known and the apparent magnitude, m, has been determined by observation, the absolute magnitude, M, can be calculated by the formula:

$$M = m + 5 + 5 \log p, \text{ or}$$

$$M = m + 5 - 5 \log r,$$

where r is the distance in parsecs. This important formula is derived from the relation between brightness and magnitude (11·19) and the fact that the brightness of a point source of light varies inversely as the square of its distance. The absolute magnitude is of the same sort as the apparent magnitude employed in its calculation; it may be visual, photographic, or some other kind.

When the absolute magnitudes, M_1 and M_2, of any two stars are known, the ratio of their luminosities, L_2 and L_1, is given by the formula:

$$\log (L_2/L_1) = 0.4(M_1 - M_2),$$

which is the same relation already given for the apparent magnitudes.

11·26. Relative Luminosities. It is the custom to express the luminosity of a star in terms of the sun's luminosity, that is, as the number of times the star would outshine the sun if both were the same distance from us. This ratio can be calculated by substituting the absolute magnitudes of the sun and star in the preceding formula.

The sun's apparent visual magnitude, m, is -26.8; its parallax, p, on the same basis as those of the stars, is the radian, 206,265″, of which the logarithm is 5.314. By the first formula of the preceding section, the sun's absolute visual magnitude, M, is $-26.8 + 5 + 26.6$, or $+4.8$. At the standard distance of 10 parsecs the sun would appear as a star of nearly the 5th magnitude, only faintly visible to the naked eye.

The expression for the star's visual luminosity relative to that of the sun is accordingly:

$$\log (\text{luminosity}) = 0.4(4.8 - \text{star's absolute magnitude}).$$

Because the majority of the brightest stars are more remote than 10 parsecs, they must be more luminous than the sun. Indeed, this is true of all the stars of Table 11·II, as is shown by their absolute magnitudes. Rigel and Deneb are of the order of 10,000 times as luminous as the sun. On the other hand, we have noted in Table 11·I that many stars nearer us than the standard distance of 10 parsecs are visible only with the telescope, so that they must be considerably less luminous than the sun. The conclusion is that the stars differ very greatly in luminosity. The foregoing formula is employed in the following examples.

(1) Compare the visual luminosities of Sirius and the sun. The absolute visual magnitude of Sirius is $+1.5$.

Answer: $\log L = 0.4(4.8 - 1.5) = 1.3$. Thus Sirius is 20 times as luminous as the sun.

(2) Compare the luminosities of Barnard's star (absolute visual magnitude +13.3) and the sun.

Answer: $\log L = 0.4(4.8 - 13.3) = -3.4 = 6.6 - 10$. Thus Barnard's star is 0.0004 as luminous as the sun.

11·27. Stars of the Main Sequence. When the absolute magnitudes of stars in our neighborhood are plotted against their spectral classes, as in Fig. 11·27, the majority of the points are arrayed in a band running diagonally across the diagram. The middle line of this band drops rather steadily along the spectral sequence from absolute magnitude −3 for B stars to fainter than +10 for M stars. This band is known as the *main sequence*.

The sun, a yellow star of type G2 and absolute visual magnitude

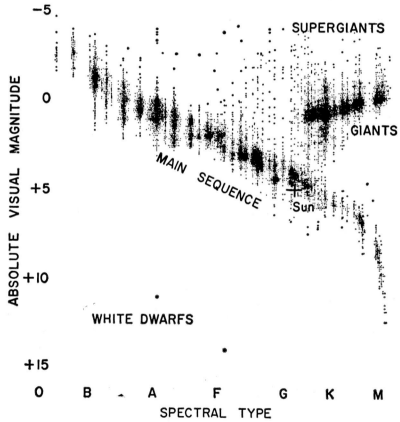

FIG. 11·27. Spectrum-Luminosity Diagram. The points represent 6700 stars in the sun's region of the Galaxy. (*Diagram by Lund Observatory*)

+4.8, is a main-sequence star. It is about 100 times less luminous than the average blue star and the same amount brighter than the average red star of the sequence. Because the sun as viewed from a distance of 10 parsecs would be a faint star to the naked eye, the red stars of the sequence must generally be telescopic objects. Red stars such as Betelgeuse and Antares, however, are among the apparently brightest stars. More distant than 10 parsecs, they are much more luminous than the sun. These and other stars of high luminosity are represented by points that appear above the band of the main sequence.

11·28. Giant and Dwarf Stars. Since its introduction by H. N. Russell in 1913, the spectrum-luminosity diagram has played a leading part in directing the studies of the stars. The Danish astronomer Ejnar Hertzsprung had previously drawn attention to the sharp distinction between red stars of high and low luminosity and had named them giant and dwarf stars, respectively. The original term *dwarf stars* is commonly used today to denote main-sequence stars fainter than about absolute visual magnitude +1.

The spectrum-luminosity diagram is accordingly known as the Hertzsprung-Russell diagram, or the H-R diagram. It is now often superseded by the equivalent color magnitude diagram (15·5), because the color indexes of stars may be measured more precisely than the spectral types can be estimated, and may also be determined to fainter magnitudes.

Giant stars, such as Arcturus and Capella, are decidedly more luminous than main-sequence stars of similar spectral types and therefore having about the same surface temperatures as these; they are brighter because they are larger than the main-sequence stars. *Supergiant stars* are extraordinarily large and luminous giants. Examples are Antares and Betelgeuse. *Subgiants* are between the giants and the main sequence, and *subdwarfs* are somewhat below this sequence. *White dwarf stars* are far less luminous than main-sequence stars of corresponding colors.

11·29. White Dwarf Stars have a deceptive title, because some are yellow and at least one is red. Although their masses average half the sun's mass, their diameters generally range between one half and four times the earth's diameter. Their densities average 2×10^5 times the sun's density and may have much greater values. The companion of Sirius was among the earliest of this remarkable type of stars to become known.

White dwarfs comprise an estimated 3 per cent of all the stars of our galaxy. Their low luminosity, however, permits only the very nearest ones to be observed. W. J. Luyten lists about 200 stars of this type, the majority of which he has discovered. In his photographic search over more than a quarter of a century for stars of large proper motion, which are accordingly nearby, Luyten has found that most of the faint stars among them are red members of the main sequence. An occasional one has proved to be either a white dwarf or a subdwarf, between the main sequence and the white dwarfs in the color-magnitude diagram.

A white dwarf star is described by Greenstein as mainly a degenerate mass devoid of hydrogen, surrounded by a nondegenerate envelope 65 miles deep, and above this an atmosphere of a sort only a few hundred feet deep. *Degenerate matter* conforms to an equation of state different from the ordinary gas laws. According to the theory, the radius of a completely degenerate star is inversely proportional to the mass, which cannot exceed 1.4 times the sun's mass.

11·30. Spectra of White Dwarf Stars. Greenstein has reported on his studies of the spectra of 50 white dwarf stars, which he has already photographed with the 200-inch telescope in his undertaking to record the spectra of all that are available to apparent mag-

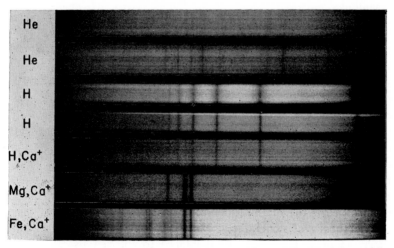

Fig. 11·30. Spectra of White Dwarf Stars. From the ultraviolet at the left to Hβ at the right. Chemical elements prominently represented in the spectra are denoted at the left. (*Photographs by Jesse L. Greenstein with the Hale telescope, Palomar Observatory*)

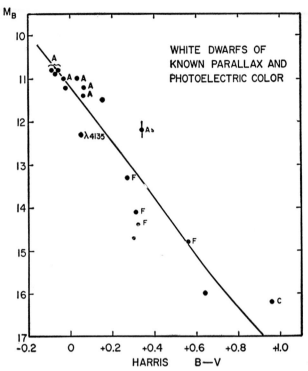

Fig. 11·30A. Color-Absolute Magnitude Diagram of White Dwarf Stars. Magnitudes and color indexes are by Daniel Harris. (*Diagram by Jesse L. Greenstein*)

nitude 16. Some spectra (Fig. 11·30) show prominent helium absorption, others show strong dark hydrogen lines, and at least one spectrum has only the H and K lines of ionized calcium and a line of neutral magnesium. The lines are generally much widened by compression of the very dense stars, and in some cases (type DC) are not seen at all. The other preliminary types assigned to white dwarfs are DB, DA, DF, DG, and DK; these are in order of increasing color index of the stars. Although there is not a simple relation between the spectra and colors of these stars, the color-magnitude diagram (Fig. 11·30A) reveals a rather convincing sequence below the main sequence.

The theory of general relativity predicts that the lines in the spectrum of a star should be displaced to the red by an amount that is directly proportional to the cube root of the star's mean density. In the case of the sun the predicted displacement corresponds to a velocity of recession of only 0.6 km/sec and is masked by other effects. For the very dense white dwarfs the displacements should be much greater.

D. M. Popper has observed about the expected relativity shift of the lines in the spectrum of the 9th-magnitude white dwarf companion of the star 40 Eridani. His measured redshift is equivalent to a velocity of recession of 21 km/sec, which is considered in satisfactory agreement with the predicted value of 17 km/sec corresponding to a diameter of 14,000 miles for this star.

11·31. The Luminosity Function. The relative numbers of stars for successive intervals of absolute magnitude in a sample volume of space constitute the *luminosity function* for that sample. The broken line of Fig. 11·31 refers to samples in the sun's vicinity, studied especially by P. J. van Rhijn in Holland and S. W. Mc-Cuskey at Warner and Swasey Observatory. The supergiants, at the left of its bright end, are scarce. Beyond the faint end, at the right, the numbers are still increasing. For stars within 5 parsecs

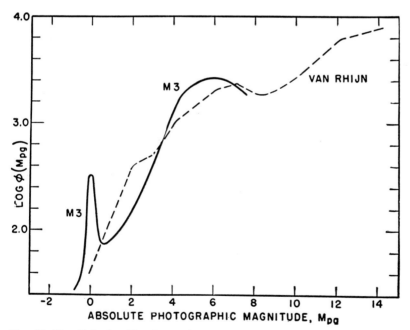

Fig. 11·31. Relative Numbers of Stars of Different Luminosities. The logarithms of the numbers for successive intervals of absolute magnitude for stars in the sun's vicinity are represented by the broken line, and for stars of the globular cluster M 3 by the full line. (*Diagram by Allan R. Sandage*)

of the sun, W. J. Luyten has shown that the maximum number is reached at absolute photographic magnitude +15.

Stars of low luminosity are evidently in the great majority in a sample volume of space around the sun. As we see them in the sky, however, the stars of high luminosity are the most numerous. The reason is that the less luminous stars must be nearer in order to be visible.

As examples, consider the lucid stars. The greatest distance, r in parsecs, at which a star of absolute visual magnitude M is visible to the naked eye is found by the formula (11·25): log r = $(6.2 - M + 5)/5$. Here we suppose that the faintest lucid star is of apparent visual magnitude +6.2 and that no cosmic dust intervenes. By this formula, the limiting distance is 1740 parsecs for a supergiant star of absolute magnitude −5 and is reduced to 17 parsecs for a star as bright as the sun. The limit would be only 0.17 parsec, or slightly more than half a light year, for a star having M = +15; such a star would have to be much nearer us than the nearest known star in order to be visible to the naked eye.

The full curve of the figure refers to stars of a different sample, studied by Sandage in the globular cluster M 3 (16·17).

REVIEW QUESTIONS

1. Explain that two photographs taken 6 months apart (Fig. 11·2) are not enough to determine the parallax of a star.

2. The parallax of Arcturus is not far from 0″.1. Using this value, calculate approximately the star's distance in astronomical units, miles, parsecs, and light years.

3. Explain that a star's distance is required as well as its proper motion and radial velocity in order to calculate its space velocity.

4. How is the apex of the sun's way located by means of (a) the proper motions of stars? (b) their radial velocities?

5. What is the advantage (a) of the slit spectroscope for determining the radial velocities of stars? (b) of the objective prism method for observing the spectral classes of many stars?

6. Of the apparently brightest stars (Table 11·II) name (a) the brightest of all; (b) the reddest; (c) the bluest; (d) the most luminous; (e) the nearest to us.

7. Spica (type B1) and Antares (type M1) are about equally bright to the unaided eye. How do they compare in brightness as (a) viewed with the telescope? (b) photographed with blue-sensitive plates? (c) with red-sensitive plates?

8. State an important advantage of the photoelectric method of measuring star magnitudes. Why is this method supplemented by photography, especially in regions where stars are very numerous?

9. Define color index. Explain that the blue minus visual index of a star in magnitudes has a greater positive value as the star is redder.

10. What is gained by comparing the absolute magnitudes of stars rather than their apparent magnitudes?

11. Explain that when the apparent magnitude of a star has been determined, (a) the absolute magnitude can be calculated if the distance is known, or (b) the distance can be calculated if the absolute magnitude of the star is independently known.

12. Distinguish between main-sequence, giant, supergiant, and white dwarf stars.

13. Account for the greater luminosity of a giant star as compared with a main-sequence star of the same spectral class.

14. Explain that a red star visible to the naked eye is likely to be a giant or supergiant.

PROBLEMS

1. The parallax of Alpha Centauri is $0''.760$. Calculate the star's maximum parallax change in position in photographs taken with the 26-inch Yale telescope in the southern hemisphere. The scale of these plates is $18''.82$ to the millimeter.

Answer: 0.08 mm, or about 0.003 inch.

2. The parallax of Vega is $0''.123$. Calculate the star's distance in parsecs and light years.

Answer: 8.1 parsecs; 26 light years.

3. Show that the tangential velocity, T, of a star equals $4.74 \, \mu''/p''$ km/sec, where μ is the annual proper motion, p the parallax, and d the distance in astronomical units.

Answer: $T = (\mu''/206,265'') \times d$; $d = 206,265''/p''$. Convert from astronomical units per year to km/sec.

4. Calculate the ratio of the apparent brightness of Sirius and the sun.

Answer: The sun appears about 10,000 million times as bright as Sirius.

5. Calculate the ratio of the visual luminosity of Capella and the sun.

Answer: Capella is 145 times as luminous as the sun.

6. Derive the relation: $M = m + 5 - 5 \log r$, where M would be the magnitude of a star if it were distant 10 parsecs, and m is the magnitude at its actual distance, r parsecs.

Answer: By the formula of $11 \cdot 19$, $0.4(M - m) = \log (l_m/l_M)$. Since the brightness of a star varies inversely as the square of its distance, the right side of the equation becomes $2 - 2 \log r$.

REFERENCES

Morgan, W. W., Philip C. Keenan, and Edith Kellman, *An Atlas of Stellar Spectra.* With an outline of spectral classification. University of Chicago Press, Chicago, 1943.

Schlesinger, Frank, and Louise F. Jenkins, *Catalog of Bright Stars.* Containing all important data known in January, 1940, relating to all stars brighter than 6.5 visual magnitude and to some fainter ones. Second edition. Yale University Observatory, New Haven, 1940.

12

STELLAR ATMOSPHERES
AND INTERIORS

ATOMIC STRUCTURE AND RADIATION — STELLAR
ATMOSPHERES — EXTENDED ATMOSPHERES AND
ENVELOPES — INTERIORS OF THE STARS

Like the sun, the stars are globes of intensely hot gas. Their radiations emerge from their photospheres and filter through their atmospheres, where dark lines are formed in their spectra. The atmospheres around some stars are extended enough to imprint bright lines in the spectra, and larger envelopes may be visible directly with the telescope.

This chapter describes evidence given by stellar spectra concerning the exteriors of the stars. It then considers what the interiors may be like to produce the exterior phenomena and what processes in the interiors may supply the energy to keep the stars shining. These subjects are introduced by a brief account of some relations between the constituents of a gas and the radiations they absorb and emit.

ATOMIC STRUCTURE AND RADIATION

12·1. Constituents of the Atom. Atoms are the building blocks of all material. They are composed essentially of electrons, protons, and neutrons. The *electron* is the lightest of these constituents; its mass is 9.1055×10^{-28} grams and it carries unit negative charge of electricity. The *proton* is 1836.57 times as massive as the electron and carries unit positive charge. The *neutron* has about the same mass as the proton and is electrically neutral.

The nucleus of the atom ranges progressively from the single proton of the ordinary hydrogen atom to compact groups of protons and neutrons in the heavier atoms. Each added proton contributes one unit to the positive charge on the nucleus. In the normal atom the nucleus is surrounded by negatively charged electrons equal in number to the protons, so that the atom as a whole is electrically neutral.

Among the products that issue from atoms when they are vigorously bombarded or disintegrate spontaneously are positrons and photons. The *positron* has the same mass as the electron but carries unit positive charge. The *photon* is a unit bundle of energy. There are also mesons and particles having masses greater than that of the proton. All these constituents and products of atoms are considered to be wave formations, but are often pictured as particles.

The following descriptions of some atomic processes employ the conventional model of the atom proposed, in 1913, by the Danish physicist Niels Bohr. They begin with the atom of hydrogen, the simplest and also the most abundant in the universe.

12·2. Model of the Hydrogen Atom. The normal hydrogen atom consists of one proton attended by a single electron. In the Bohr model the electron revolves around the proton analogous to a planet

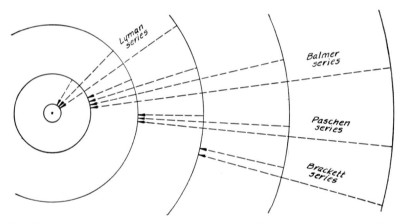

FIG. 12·2. Conventional Representation of the Hydrogen Atom. Possible orbits of the electron around the nucleus are shown as circles.

revolving around the sun. The force holding the electron in its orbit is that of the attraction between the unlike electric charges which, like the gravitational force, is inversely proportional to the square of the distance between them. Whereas a planet in a two-body system would remain always in the same orbit, the electron may be found at different times in a variety of possible orbits.

The radii of the permitted orbits around the proton (Fig. 12·2) are proportional to the squares of the integers; that of the innermost orbit is about half an angstrom. The atom does not absorb or emit radiation as long as the electron remains in the same orbit. It absorbs energy, as from radiation that strikes it, only when it can find the right quantity to raise its electron to a higher orbit against the attraction of the proton. At once the electron falls back again, releasing as radiation the energy it absorbed. Here is justification of the rule previously stated (4·8), that a gas abstracts from light passing through it the same wavelengths that the gas itself emits.

The relation between the gain or loss of energy by the atom in such a transition and the frequency of the radiation absorbed or emitted is $E_1 - E_2 = h\nu$. E_1 is the energy of the atom when the electron is in one orbit, and E_2 is the energy when the electron is in another orbit. The difference between the two states is the photon, $h\nu$, which is absorbed and then emitted. The quantity of this unit bundle of energy is given by the constant h times the frequency, ν, of the radiation. Thus the frequency of the radiation absorbed or emitted is higher, and the wavelength is shorter, as the energy difference between the two orbits is greater.

12·3. Series of Hydrogen Lines. A prominent feature of the spectra of the hotter stars as ordinarily photographed is a long series of hydrogen lines. Beginning with the Fraunhofer C line

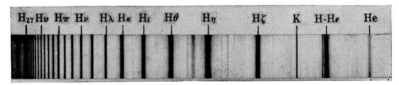

Fig. 12·3. Hydrogen Lines in the Spectrum of Zeta Tauri. Showing the Balmer series of lines from Hε in the violet to the limit of the series in the ultraviolet. (*Photograph by R. H. Curtiss, University of Michigan Observatory*)

in the red, the lines appear along the spectrum at diminishing intervals, like a succession of telegraph poles receding in the distance, until they close up in the near ultraviolet. These lines of the *Balmer series* (Fig. 12·3) are designated in order: Hα, Hβ, Hγ, and so on. More than 30 are identified in stellar spectra and in the sun's chromosphere.

Balmer, a Swiss physicist, derived in 1885 an empirical formula by which the wavelength of any line in the series may be calculated. In the more general form, which applies to other hydrogen line series as well, the formula is:

$$1/\lambda = R(1/m^2 - 1/n^2),$$

where λ is the wavelength of the line in centimeters; R is about 109,678; m is the number of the orbit in the Bohr model from which the electron is raised to produce a dark line and to which it returns to produce a bright line in the spectrum; n is any whole number greater than m, representing the number of the orbit to which the electron is raised. A single hydrogen atom can promote only one electron transition at any instant; but in a gas containing very many atoms all possible transitions are likely to be in progress.

In the Balmer series, $m = 2$ and n is put equal to 3, 4, 5, and so on. Four other series have been observed in celestial and laboratory spectra. These are the *Lyman series* ($m = 1$) in the extreme ultra-violet, the *Paschen series* ($m = 3$), the *Brackett series* ($m = 4$), and the *Pfund series* ($m = 5$), all in the infrared. The lines in the spectra of some other chemical elements are also arrayed in series.

12·4. The Chemical Elements. Table 12·I lists the names, symbols, atomic numbers, and atomic weights of 96 chemical elements. Numbers 93 to 96, and more recently to 103, were produced in radiation laboratories.

The *atomic number* of an element is the number of protons in the nucleus and also the number of electrons around the nucleus of the normal atom. All atoms having the same atomic number belong to the same chemical element.

The *atomic weight* is the mass of the atom. The unit of mass employed in the table is one sixteenth the mass of the average oxygen atom, taken as weight 16.0000; the value of the unit is 1.660×10^{-24} grams. The atomic weight given here is frequently the average for two or more different kinds of atoms, or *isotopes*, of the same element, which differ in mass because their nuclei have different numbers of neutrons.

The *mass number* of an atom is its atomic weight rounded off to the nearest whole number, the sum of its protons and neutrons. Thus the mass numbers of hydrogen, helium, and lithium corresponding to their weights in the table are, respectively, 1, 4, and 7. In formulas of nuclear reactions a particular atom is conveniently designated by its symbol having the atomic number as subscript and

TABLE 12·I THE CHEMICAL ELEMENTS

Element	Symbol	Atomic Number	Atomic Weight *	Element	Symbol	Atomic Number	Atomic Weight *
Hydrogen	H	1	1.0080	Indium	In	49	114.82
Helium	He	2	4.003	Tin	Sn	50	118.70
Lithium	Li	3	6.940	Antimony	Sb	51	121.76
Beryllium	Be	4	9.013	Tellurium	Te	52	127.61
Boron	B	5	10.82	Iodine	I	53	126.91
Carbon	C	6	12.01	Xenon	Xe	54	131.30
Nitrogen	N	7	14.008	Cesium	Cs	55	132.91
Oxygen	O	8	16.0000	Barium	Ba	56	137.36
Fluorine	F	9	19.00	Lanthanum	La	57	138.92
Neon	Ne	10	20.183	Cerium	Ce	58	140.13
Sodium	Na	11	22.99	Praseodymium	Pr	59	140.92
Magnesium	Mg	12	24.32	Neodymium	Nd	60	144.27
Aluminum	Al	13	26.98	Promethium	Pm	61	(145)
Silicon	Si	14	28.0	Samarium	Sm	62	150.35
Phosphorus	P	15	30.975	Europium	Eu	63	152.0
Sulfur	S	16	32.066	Gadolinium	Gd	64	157.26
Chlorine	Cl	17	35.457	Terbium	Tb	65	158.93
Argon	A	18	39.944	Dysprosium	Dy	66	162.51
Potassium	K	19	39.100	Holmium	Ho	67	164.94
Calcium	Ca	20	40.08	Erbium	Er	68	167.27
Scandium	Sc	21	44.96	Thulium	Tm	69	168.94
Titanium	Ti	22	47.90	Ytterbium	Yb	70	173.04
Vanadium	V	23	50.95	Lutetium	Lu	71	174.99
Chromium	Cr	24	52.01	Hafnium	Hf	72	178.50
Manganese	Mn	25	54.94	Tantalum	Ta	73	180.95
Iron	Fe	26	55.85	Tungsten	W	74	183.86
Cobalt	Co	27	58.94	Rhenium	Re	75	186.22
Nickel	Ni	28	58.71	Osmium	Os	76	190.2
Copper	Cu	29	63.54	Iridium	Ir	77	192.2
Zinc	Zn	30	65.38	Platinum	Pt	78	195.09
Gallium	Ga	31	69.72	Gold	Au	79	197.0
Germanium	Ge	32	72.60	Mercury	Hg	80	200.61
Arsenic	As	33	74.91	Thallium	Tl	81	204.39
Selenium	Se	34	78.96	Lead	Pb	82	207.21
Bromine	Br	35	79.916	Bismuth	Bi	83	209.00
Krypton	Kr	36	83.80	Polonium	Po	84	210
Rubidium	Rb	37	85.48	Astatine	At	85	(210)
Strontium	Sr	38	87.63	Radon	Rn	86	222
Yttrium	Y	39	88.92	Francium	Fa	87	(223)
Zirconium	Zr	40	91.22	Radium	Ra	88	226.05
Niobium	Nb	41	92.91	Actinium	Ac	89	227
Molybdenum	Mo	42	95.95	Thorium	Th	90	232.05
Technetium	Tc	43	(99)	Protactinium	Pa	91	231
Ruthenium	Ru	44	101.1	Uranium	U	92	238.07
Rhodium	Rh	45	102.91	Neptunium	Np	93	(237)
Palladium	Pd	46	106.4	Plutonium	Pu	94	(242)
Silver	Ag	47	107.880	Americium	Am	95	(243)
Cadmium	Cd	48	112.41	Curium	Cm	96	(245)

* Atomic weights, except those in parentheses, are from the *Journal of the American Chemical Society* (1956). The numbers and names of transuranic elements more recently produced are: 97 berkelium, 98 californium, 99 einsteinium, 100 fermium, 101 mendelevium, 102 nobelium, 103 lawrencium.

the mass number as superscript. As an example, the iron isotope $_{26}Fe^{56}$ contains 26 protons and 30 neutrons.

12·5. The Electron Shells. Turning from the simple hydrogen atom to more complex ones, we find less confusion of electron transitions than might at first be expected. Most of the electrons are so

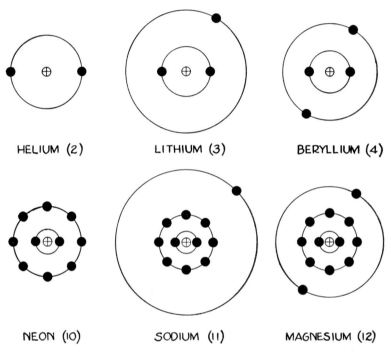

HELIUM (2)   LITHIUM (3)   BERYLLIUM (4)

NEON (10)   SODIUM (11)   MAGNESIUM (12)

FIG. 12·5.   Electron Structures of Some Lighter Atoms.

firmly held in filled shells that they are not easily raised to higher levels.

The *shells* are the same as the Bohr hydrogen orbits. They are filled in order of distance from the nucleus when they acquire $2n^2$ electrons, where n is the number of the Bohr orbit. Thus the first shell is filled by 2 electrons, the second by 8, the third by 18, and so on. A filled shell will not receive additional electrons and is reluctant to release any that it possesses. As examples, Fig. 12·5 shows the outer structures of a number of lighter atoms having their electrons in the lowest possible orbits.

The normal hydrogen atom (atomic number 1) has its single electron in the first orbit, from which it can be raised with moderate effort. The helium atom (number 2) has its two electrons filling the first shell, which is not easily broken. The lithium atom (number 3) has two electrons locked in the inner shell and a third in the second orbit, from which it is easily removed. In the successively heavier atoms: beryllium, boron, carbon, and so on, electrons are added one at a time to match the added protons in the nucleus. In the neon atom (number 10) the second shell is filled. The sodium atom (number 11) has two filled shells and the additional electron in the third orbit ready to jump out on slight provocation.

Some of the atoms represented in the figure have shells in the making and others have only filled shells, as in the cases of the chemically inactive elements helium and neon. Evidently the amount of energy the atom must absorb to raise an electron from its normal position to a higher level depends on the number of protons attracting from within and the arrangement of the other electrons in the superstructure. Each kind of atom presents its peculiar demands in this respect. Here we have the explanation of the principle (4·8) that each gaseous element produces its characteristic pattern of spectrum lines.

12·6. Neutral and Ionized Atoms.

The *neutral atom* has its full quota of electrons, equal to the number of protons in the nucleus, so that it is electrically neutral. The *ionized atom* has generally lost one or more electrons. It has absorbed enough energy to transfer these electrons beyond the outermost orbit. They have become *free electrons,* free to dart about independently until they are captured by ionized atoms.

The *singly ionized atom* has lost a single electron and has thereby acquired a single unit positive charge. The *doubly ionized atom* has lost two electrons and has an excess of two positive charges. Each succeeding ionization requires a greater amount of energy to promote it. The extent of the ionization is indicated by adding a Roman numeral to the symbol for the element (number I designates the neutral atom). Thus singly ionized helium is written He II.

The removal of an electron leaves the superstructure of the atom similar to that of the next lower atomic number. As an example, the singly ionized helium atom has one electron left and in this respect resembles the neutral hydrogen atom. The important difference between the two is that the helium nucleus has two positive charges and thus holds the electron 4 times as tenaciously as does the hydrogen nucleus with its single charge. The energy required to raise the electron to a higher level is accordingly 4 times as great, so that the spectrum line produced by the transition has 4 times the frequency, or one fourth the wavelength of its hydrogen counterpart. The lines of ionized helium ordinarily observed correspond to the Brackett series of hydrogen in the infrared.

Thus the pattern of lines in the spectrum of a gas, whether it is in the laboratory or surrounding a star, reveals not only what chemical elements are represented but also to what extent their atoms are ionized. Certain negative ions are permissible, where the atom has an electron in addition to its normal number. The negative hydrogen ion is an important source of continuous absorption in stars like the sun.

12·7. The Energy-Level Diagram (Fig. 12·7) substitutes energy levels in the atom for the orbits of the original Bohr model. The present theory of atomic structure assigns to each energy level a distinctive wave pattern having properties that can be expressed

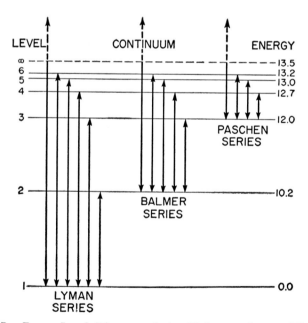

Fig. 12·7. Energy-Level Diagram of the Hydrogen Atom. The levels correspond to the Bohr orbits. The numbers at the right are proportional to the energy required to raise the electron from the lowest level.

mathematically. A spectrum line corresponds to a transformation from one wave pattern to another.

The lowest level, corresponding to the innermost Bohr orbit, is the base of electron transitions producing the Lyman series of lines in the hydrogen spectrum. Level 2 is the base of the Balmer series, 3 of the Paschen series, and 4 of the Brackett series. The vertical lines in the figure represent transitions of electrons from lower to various higher levels and conversely, and the lengths of these lines are proportional to the energy expended or released in the transitions.

Fig. 12·7A. The Balmer Continuum. Spectrum of π^1 Cygni, showing the Balmer series of hydrogen lines and the continuum at the left. (*Photograph by L. H. Aller at Lick Observatory*)

The higher the level, the less is the additional energy required to raise the electron to the next higher level against the weakened attraction of the more distant nucleus. Near the top level only a little more energy is needed to remove the electron completely and thus to ionize the atom.

A *continuum,* or continuous absorption, extends from the head of the Balmer series far into the ultraviolet (Fig. 12·7A) in the spectra of the hotter stars. It is produced when the energy absorbed by electrons at the second level is in excess in various amounts of that barely necessary to remove them from the atoms. Conversely, the continuum in emission is produced when free electrons having different velocities are captured by the atoms and fall to the second energy level. A dark or bright continuum may also appear beyond the limits of other line series.

12·8. Molecular Spectra. A *molecule* is here defined as a combination of two or more atoms, whereas in chemistry it may also include separate atoms. The astrophysical distinction between the atom and the molecule arises from the difference between the spectra of the two. Atomic spectra contain only lines. Molecular spectra are characterized by series of bands. Each *band* is many angstroms long and is composed of systematically spaced lines.

As the simplest case, the diatomic molecule consists of two positive ions surrounded by electrons. It may be pictured as a rotating dumbbell having an elastic rod. Its energy at any instant is derived from: (1) Its rotation on an axis at right angles to the line joining the two ions; (2) its vibration along that line; (3) its energy states analogous to those of the atom. The spectrum of the molecule may be interpreted by extensions of models of the atom.

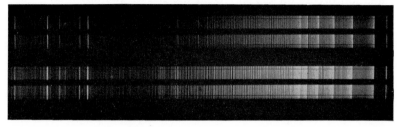

Fig. 12·8. Cyanogen Bands in the Spectrum of the Carbon Arc. These bands are conspicuous in the spectra of some red supergiant stars. (*Mount Wilson Observatory photograph*)

Molecules such as the oxides of titanium and zirconium and compounds of carbon appear prominently in the spectra of the cooler stars. Molecules of water vapor, carbon dioxide, and oxygen are abundant in the earth's atmosphere where their dark bands obscure celestial spectra over large ranges of wavelength.

STELLAR ATMOSPHERES

Although the absorption and the continuous spectrum of a star are produced in the same layers, it will be useful for our purpose to think of the dark lines as originating in the atmosphere above the star's photosphere. We are concerned here with effects of temperature and density in stellar atmospheres as shown by the spectra.

12·9. Temperature by the Radiation Laws. The *effective temperature* of a star is the temperature that a perfect radiator of the same size must have to produce the same output of radiation. It is calculated by the radiation laws (10·5) from the observed quantity of the star's radiation.   One calculation, by Stefan's law, employs the radiation of all wavelengths as measured by its heating of a thermocouple, and resembles the evaluation of the sun's temperature from the solar constant.

A second calculation of the temperature, by Planck's formula, is based on the intensities of the star's radiation in various wavelengths.   The intensities are measured in different parts of the available regions of the spectrum, and most accurately by use of the photoelectric cell attached to a spectroscope.   In such procedures it is necessary to allow for whatever absorption of the radiation occurs on the way from the star to the observer.

12·10. Temperatures and Color Indexes.   The effective temperatures of stars at intervals of spectral type in Table 12·II are as

TABLE 12·II   EFFECTIVE TEMPERATURES AND COLOR INDEXES

Spec-trum	Tempera-ture	Color Index B − V	Spec-trum	Main Sequence		Giants	
				Tempera-ture	Color Index B − V	Tempera-ture	Color Index B − V
		mag.			mag.		mag.
O5	50,000°K	......	F5	6,600°K	+0.44	6,470°K	......
B0	25,000	−0.32	G0	6,000	+0.60	5,300	......
B5	15,600	−0.16	G5	5,520	+0.68	4,650	......
A0	11,000	0.00	K0	5,120	+0.82	4,200	+1.01
A5	8,700	+0.15	K5	4,400	+1.18	3,550	+1.52
F0	7,600	+0.30	M0	3,600	+1.45	3,340	+1.56
F5	6,600	+0.44	M5	.....	+1.69	2,710	......

given by P. C. Keenan and W. W. Morgan, except the first one. These are tied to an adopted surface temperament of 5730° for the sun, type G2; they may be in error by several hundred degrees, according to these investigators, so that the last significant figure is valid only in comparing the relative values.

The temperature diminishes as the spectral type progresses from O to M.   The temperature change itself is mainly responsible for the succession of spectral patterns, as has been noted before; the explanation of this relation is given in following sections. Yellow and red stars of the main sequence have temperatures considerably higher than those of giant stars of corresponding types. It will be seen presently that the character of the spectrum is determined by the density as well as the temperature of the stellar atmosphere.

The color indexes, blue minus visual magnitude, of these types in the table are as determined photoelectrically by H. L. Johnson and W. W. Morgan. With diminishing temperature of the stars the most intense radiation is increasingly shifted toward the red in accordance with Wien's law, and the color index increases; it is set at zero for type A0. Thus the bluest stars have negative color indexes and the reddest ones have the largest positive indexes.

12·11. Excitation and Ionization of Atoms. The *normal atom* has its electrons as close as possible to the nucleus. When the atom absorbs energy so that an electron is raised to a higher level, it becomes an *excited atom*. If the atom absorbs energy enough to remove an electron, it becomes ionized. The energy may be provided by a photon or a fast-moving particle. As the temperature of the gas is greater, its particles dart about more rapidly and their collisions are more vigorous. Such collisions cause *thermal excitation and ionization* of the atoms.

The physicist M. N. Saha of India, in 1920, developed the rules of thermal ionization of atoms. His work ranks along with the Bohr model among the classics of atomic investigation. Saha presented an analogy between the evaporation of a liquid and the removal of electrons from atoms.

12·12. Thermal Ionization. When a covered container partly filled with a liquid is put in a sufficiently warm place, the liquid begins to evaporate. The amount of liquid diminishes until the space above it becomes saturated, so that just as much vapor is returning to the liquid as is coming out of it. The extent of the evaporation before this steady state is reached depends on 3 conditions. (1) The amount of liquid evaporated is greater as the temperature is higher. (2) The evaporation is greater at a particular temperature as the space above the liquid is more nearly empty at the start. (3) It is greater at a particular temperature and vapor pressure for some liquids than for others; compare, for example, the evaporation of ether and water.

Consider the parallel case of the removal of electrons from the atoms of a gas. (1) The extent of the ionization is greater at higher temperatures, where the particles are colliding more vigorously. (2) It is greater in a rarer gas where fewer free electrons are available to replace the ones removed. (3) It is greater in similar conditions for atoms to which electrons are more loosely bound. We now examine the third relation.

12·13. The Energy Required to Ionize an Atom is conveniently pictured in terms of an electron colliding with an atom. It is equivalent to the kinetic energy an electron acquires when it is accelerated across a potential difference of a specified number of volts. This *ionization potential* is accordingly expressed as a number of *electron volts*. We may here, if we choose, simply note the numbers themselves. An atom having a small ionization potential is ionized at a lower temperature, where it is subjected to more moderate collisions, than an atom having a larger number.

Table 12·III gives the ionization potentials of some chemical elements which are represented by prominent lines in stellar spectra.

TABLE 12·III   IONIZATION POTENTIALS OF SELECTED ELEMENTS

Element	Symbol	Stage of Ionization		
		I	II	III
Helium	He	24.5	54.2	....
Nitrogen	N	14.5	29.5	47.2
Oxygen	O	13.6	35.0	54.7
Hydrogen	H	13.5	....	....
Carbon	C	11.2	24.3	47.7
Silicon	Si	8.1	16.3	33.3
Iron	Fe	7.8	16.2	30.5
Magnesium	Mg	7.6	15.0	79.9
Titanium	Ti	6.8	13.6	28.0
Calcium	Ca	6.1	11.8	51.0
Strontium	Sr	5.7	11.0	43.0
Sodium	Na	5.1	47.1	71.3

The column headed I refers to the neutral atom, II to the singly ionized atom, and III to the doubly ionized atom. Neutral sodium with a single electron in its outer shell has a small number, as would be expected. This atom should be excited or singly ionized in the atmospheres of the cooler stars. Neutral helium with its two electrons locked in the innermost shell has the largest number in this column. Its lines should be prominent only in the spectra of the hotter stars, where lines of ionized atoms of other elements should also appear. Note that the numbers in the table increase with successive stages of ionization.

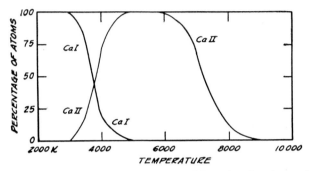

FIG. 12·13. Effect of Temperature on Calcium in the Atmospheres of Main-Sequence Stars. All calcium atoms are neutral (Ca I) at temperatures up to about 3000°K, where singly ionized atoms (Ca II) begin to appear. The second ionization begins at about 6000°. (*Adapted from a diagram in* Atoms, Stars and Nebulae *by Leo Goldberg and L. H. Aller*)

As an example, Fig. 12·13 shows the effect of increasing temperature on the spectra of calcium atoms in the atmospheres of main-sequence stars.

12·14. Effect of Temperature on Stellar Spectra. Saha's theory of thermal ionization of atoms has been amplified and given more precise form. For a gas at an assigned temperature and pressure the Boltzmann formulas permit the calculation of the fraction of atoms in any stage of ionization and of these the fraction at any level of excitation. It is accordingly possible to predict how the patterns of lines in the spectra of stars must change with increasing temperature of the stars. Conversely, the pattern observed in the spectrum of a particular star informs us of the surface temperature of that star.

Consider the dark magnesium line at wavelength 4481 A, which is prominent in the spectra of blue stars such as Sirius. To produce this line the magnesium atom must have lost one electron and must have a second electron already raised to the level next above the lowest possible one. The strength of the line thus depends on the fraction of the magnesium atoms in the star's atmosphere that are singly ionized and on the fraction of these having the second electron raised to the required level.

Fig. 12·14 shows how the calculated fractions and the resulting strength of the line vary with temperature. This magnesium line begins to appear at about the sun's temperature, attaining its greatest strength around 10,000°K, and declines at higher temperatures.

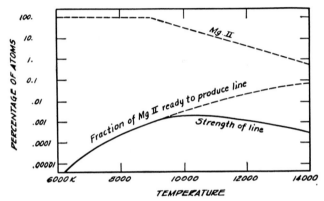

FIG. 12·14. Relative Strength of Mg II Absorption Line 4481 A at Different Temperatures. Showing the percentage of magnesium atoms in stellar atmospheres that are singly ionized at different temperatures, the fractions of these that are ready to produce the line, and the strength of the line. (*Diagram by C. H. Payne-Gaposchkin*)

We have seen that stellar spectra can be arrayed in a single sequence, except for some branching at the ends. Along the sequence from the red to the blue stars, as we observe again in Fig. 12·15, the patterns of bands and lines gradually change. It is in order to explain the spectrum changes as effects of increasing temperatures of the stellar atmospheres. Later we will consider the effects of the different densities of these atmospheres as well.

12·15. Interpretation of the Spectral Sequence; the Coolest Stars.
At the relatively low temperatures of the red stars the spectra show lines of neutral atoms and molecular bands. The lines are particularly those of elements, such as sodium, calcium, and iron, which have easily excited atoms, as indicated by their low ionization potentials (Table 12·III). Hydrogen lines are present despite the higher ionization potential of these atoms from their lower levels, because hydrogen is a very abundant element.

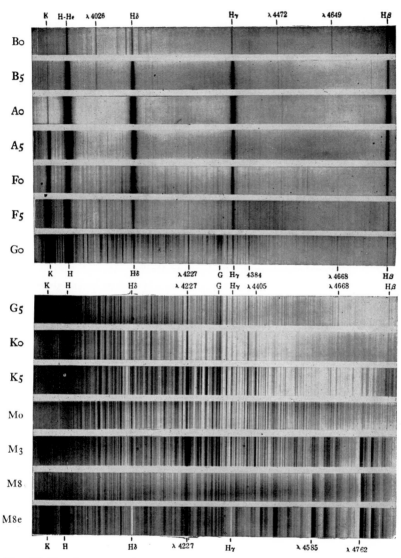

FIG. 12·15. Sequence of Stellar Spectra. Types B to M. *(University of Michigan Observatory photographs)*

The bands are especially of carbon compounds, titanium oxide, and zirconium oxide; these provide a basis for classifying the red stars. The presence of carbon bands and the absence of titanium oxide bands characterize the spectra of types R and N. Titanium oxide bands are prominent in the spectra of M stars and vanadium oxide bands strengthen for the very coolest ones. Zirconium oxide is conspicuous and titanium oxide is usually absent in the S stars.

The division of red stars into three branches is ascribed to difference of chemical composition. In this view the atmospheres of N stars have more carbon than oxygen; the carbon combines with the available oxygen to form unobservable carbon monoxide and then produces other compounds. The atmospheres of M and S stars contain more oxygen than carbon. After exhausting the carbon, the oxygen has combined with titanium and vanadium or with zirconium, which are believed to have different abundances in these two types of stars.

12·16. Stars of Intermediate Temperature. At the higher temperatures of the yellow stars the compounds are being disrupted and their bands are no longer prominent in the spectra. Titanium oxide bands have disappeared at type K0; but cyanogen (CN), hydrocarbon (CH), hydroxyl (OH), and other combinations are still present at the temperature of the sun.

The Fraunhofer H and K lines of singly ionized calcium dominate the spectra of yellow stars. Here all calcium is singly ionized (Fig. 12·13) and the second ionization is about to begin. Hydrogen lines are becoming stronger as more of these atoms are excited. The complex patterns of neutral metals, such as iron and magnesium, are still conspicuous, but these lines are fading in the hotter F stars. With the removal of an electron the atom produces a different set of lines, as we have seen; and the strong lines of many ionized metals lie in the far ultraviolet that is cut out by the earth's atmosphere. Thus with increasing temperature and degree of ionization in stellar atmospheres the visible spectrum becomes less complex.

12·17. Spectra of the Hottest Stars. The hydrogen lines are most conspicuous in type A2. They decline in still hotter stars as more of the atoms become ionized. Having had only one electron to lose, the singly ionized hydrogen atom cannot absorb light. The

lines of this abundant element persist even in type O where only
1 in 100,000 atoms of hydrogen remains neutral, as Aller points
out. Neutral helium is latest to appear, in type B9; its lines become strongest at B3 and quickly fade, being replaced by lines of
ionized helium in O stars.

In addition to hydrogen and helium, the spectra of very hot stars
show prominent lines of doubly ionized oxygen, nitrogen, and
carbon, a simple pattern visually because most strong lines are in
the far ultraviolet. The hottest stars are O5. At the theoretical
upper limit, type O0 at a temperature of 100,000°K or more should
show no lines at all in the ordinarily observable regions of the
spectrum.

The changing patterns along the spectral sequence are therefore
caused mainly by changing surface temperatures of the stars. At
any stage in the sequence the prominence of a particular set of
lines is conditioned by the excitation and ionization potentials of
the atoms which produce them. It remains to consider the effect of
different densities of stellar atmospheres on the spectra they form.

12·18. Spectra of Giant and Main-Sequence Stars. The effective
temperatures of giant stars are lower than those of main-sequence
stars of the same spectral type (Table 12·II). The reason is given
by the theory of thermal ionization. According to this theory the
degree of ionization in stellar atmospheres increases with the temperature, and at any specified temperature is greater when the pressure of the gases is low. The atmospheres of giant stars are less
dense than those of main-sequence stars. Thus the giants attain
a particular degree of ionization and the corresponding type of
spectrum at a lower temperature.

The following account of some differences within the same spec-
tral types was kindly written and illustrated for this book by W. W.
Morgan, the senior author of the monograph *An Atlas of Stellar
Spectra.*

Although the spectra of giant and main-sequence stars of the
same type are often similar in general appearance, certain lines are
stronger in the case of giant stars and some are weaker. For example, in Fig. 12·18 the hydrogen lines (marked with dots below
them) are stronger in main-sequence stars of types B and A, while
lines of singly ionized iron (marked with dots above them) are
enhanced in the A supergiants. Lines due to ionized metals (three

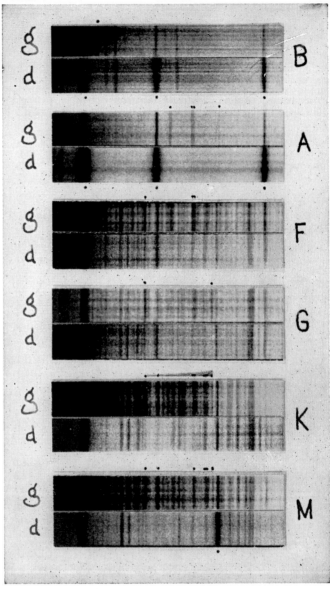

FIG. 12·18.   Representative Spectra of Giant (g) and Main-Sequence (d) Stars for the Principal Spectral Types.   The range of spectrum is from 3920 A (left) to 4380 A (right).   (*Prepared by W. W. Morgan, Yerkes Observatory*)

marked by dots above) in general are stronger in F supergiants than in main-sequence stars.

The lower spectrum of type G is that of sunlight observed as reflected by Jupiter's 3rd satellite. The two lines marked in the figure for this type are due to ionized strontium, which is far stronger in F, G, K, and M giants than in main-sequence stars (Fig. 12·20). At type K the great absorption caused by the molecule cyanogen furnishes the principal difference between the two spectra. At type M the feature showing the greatest difference is the strong line of neutral calcium, which is marked below it. It will be noted that differences between two spectra of the same type are in some cases as well distinguished as are those from one type to another.

12·19. The Yerkes Classification of Stellar Spectra of W. W. Morgan and P. C. Keenan assigns *luminosity classes* as well as the lettered Draper types. These are numbered in order beginning with the most luminous stars, which have the least dense atmospheres. The numeral I refers to supergiant stars, Ia for the more luminous and Ib for the less luminous supergiants; II refers to bright giants, III to normal giants, IV to subgiants, and V to main-sequence stars. Thus the two-dimensional designation in Table 11·II for Deneb is A2 Ia; Antares, M1 Ib; Epsilon Canis Majoris, B2 II; Aldebaran, K5 III; Procyon, F5 IV; Vega, A0 V.

12·20. Spectroscopic Parallaxes. We have seen that more luminous yellow and red stars are cooler than are less luminous stars of

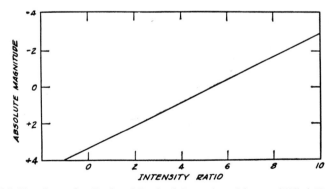

FIG. 12·20. Intensity Ratio of Ionized Strontium Line at 4215 A Relative to Neutral Iron Line at 4260 A in Stellar Spectra of the Same Type. (*Diagram by Dorrit Hoffleit, Harvard Observatory*)

the same spectral type. Although this effect is partly compensated by the rare atmospheres of the more luminous stars so that the spectra remain about the same through the type, the lines of certain elements show conspicuous differences of intensity. For example, the line of ionized strontium at 4215 A becomes stronger and that of neutral calcium at 4227 A becomes weaker as the stars are more luminous. These and other criteria are the basis of *spectroscopic parallaxes,* the means of determining the distances of stars by examining their spectra.

In Fig. 12·20 the intensity ratio of the sensitive strontium line to a neighboring constant iron line is represented for stars of the same type and of known absolute magnitude. We note that the two lines are equally intense for a star of absolute magnitude +2.7; the strontium line is 4 times as intense for magnitude +0.7 and 8 times as intense for magnitude −2.0. Whenever such a relation has been established for two lines, the absolute magnitude, M, can be determined from the spectrum of any star of that particular type. The star's parallax, p, can then be found by the formula (11·25): $M = m + 5 + 5 \log p$.

As an example, the strontium line at 4215 A is twice as intense as the iron line at 4260 A in the spectrum of a star of the type represented in the diagram. The star's apparent magnitude m, is +7.0 and is not increased numerically by intervening dust. Required the parallax of the star.

From Fig. 12·20 the star's absolute magnitude is +2.0. Thus $\log p = (M - m - 5)/5 = (2.0 - 7.0 - 5.0)/5 = -2.0 = 8.0 - 10$. The parallax is $0''.01$, so that the star's distance is 100 parsecs.

The parallaxes of several thousand stars have been determined by this and other spectral criteria, beginning with the pioneer work of W. S. Adams and A. H. Joy at Mount Wilson. The probable error of a spectroscopic parallax is 15 per cent of its value, whereas that of a direct parallax is around $0''.008$ regardless of its value. Thus the two methods should be equally reliable for a parallax of $0''.05$. The direct parallax is likely to be the more dependable for stars nearer than 20 parsecs, and the spectroscopic parallax for more distant stars.

EXTENDED ATMOSPHERES AND ENVELOPES

Many hot stars have envelopes so much larger than the photospheres that considerable portions lie outside the cones joining the photospheres to the observer. Much of the light of the surrounding gases is not balanced by their absorption of the radiations from the stars within them. Their bright-line spectra appear superposed on the dark-line spectra of the stars themselves. Extended atmospheres are recognized around type B emission stars, P Cygni stars, and Wolf-Rayet stars by their bright-line spectra. Envelopes around certain novae (13·21) are extensive enough to be visible directly with the telescope, and those of the nearer planetary nebulae are still more conspicuous. Mira and Alpha Herculis are examples of red stars having extended atmospheres.

12·21. Type B Emission Stars have spectra in which bright lines of hydrogen and sometimes of other elements are present, frequently being superposed on corresponding broader dark lines. Around 4000 such stars are known. About 10 per cent of B0 and B3 stars show emission lines in their spectra and a progressively smaller proportion from B5 to A4 do so. In some cases the bright lines have made their appearance in the spectra of what seemed before to be normal B stars and have subsequently disappeared.

Otto Struve has explained that these emission lines occur generally in the cases of rapidly rotating stars and are widest where the axes of the stars are nearly at right angles to the line of sight. Gases emerge, particularly from the equators where gravity is most diminished by the swift rotations, and form unstable extended atmospheres rotating around the stars. The bright lines in the spectra are broadened by the Doppler effect of the rotation, some of the light coming from parts of the atmosphere that are approaching us and some from parts that are receding from us.

12·22. Pleione, a Shell Star. Narrow dark lines of hydrogen and other elements make their appearance in the spectra of some blue emission stars in addition to the bright lines. The narrow lines then present a striking pattern far into the ultraviolet. Examples of such stars, designated as *shell stars,* are Pleione, 48 Librae, and Gamma Cassiopeiae.

Pleione is one of the brighter members of the Pleiades cluster. Bright hydrogen lines, which had been observed in its spectrum since 1888, disappeared in 1905, so that the spectrum resembled that of an ordinary B5 star. The reappearance of broad bright lines and presently of narrow dark lines as well was reported in 1938. Both sets of lines grew stronger until 1946 and weakened thereafter, until in 1951 they were almost gone.

After the long period of earlier stability, as Merrill has explained, there began a slight but persistent acceleration of the atoms outward from the star's normal atmosphere. The acceleration of the streams of atoms increased until the outward velocities were 50 km/sec or more, becoming greater for the ultraviolet lines of the Balmer series of hydrogen than for those in the visible region. The first result was an emitting extended atmosphere; the second was the absorbing shell at a distance from the photosphere which has been estimated as 2 or 3 times the radius of the star. Eventually the supply of atoms failed and the shell blew away.

Some stars such as Gamma Cassiopeiae have had temporary shells of shorter duration. Others have shells which are more stable than that of Pleione, and their dark lines show the same velocity as from the star within them. In all cases these lines are narrow because they are absorbed at high levels where the density is low, and they are not broadened by the rotation.

12·23. The P Cygni Stars comprise a group of blue emission stars showing features quite different from the ones already mentioned. Like the others, these stars are mainly type B and a few are early

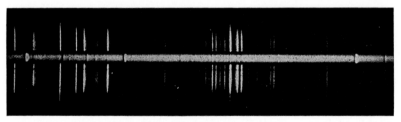

Fig. 12·23.   Spectrum of P Cygni.   (*Photograph by N. T. Bobrovnikoff, Perkins Observatory*)

A; but their bright lines have dark lines at their violet edges rather than near their centers. Hydrogen lines are the most prominent. The prototype P Cygni burst out like a nova twice in the 17th century and thereafter became invariable at the 5th apparent magnitude.

The picture here, according to P. W. Merrill, is that of gases passing out through a shell which itself does not expand. The bright lines in the spectrum are somewhat widened, some parts coming from the gas on our side of the star, which is approaching us, and other parts from the gas beyond the star, which is receding from us. The dark lines displaced to the violet are absorbed by the part of the envelope immediately in front of the star, where the gas has the maximum speed of approach.

12·24. Wolf-Rayet Stars are named after two astronomers at the Paris Observatory who discovered, in 1867, the first 3 known stars of this remarkable type. About 200 are now recognized; the brightest is the 2nd-magnitude southern star Gamma Velorum. Formerly included with the dark-line stars of type O, these stars are now grouped by themselves in type W. Of average absolute magnitude −5, they are among the hottest stars, having surface temperatures of 50,000°K. Averaging twice the sun's diameter, they are surrounded by much larger atmospheres.

The spectra contain broad bright lines on a much fainter continuous background and sometimes bordered by weak and diffuse dark lines at their violet edges. The prominent lines are mainly of helium, oxygen, silicon, nitrogen, and carbon in various stages of

Fig. 12·24. Spectrum of a Wolf-Rayet Star. (*Photograph by* **L. H. Aller** *at Lick Observatory*)

ionization; but where nitrogen is conspicuous, carbon is practically absent, and vice versa. Hydrogen lines are surprisingly weak.

One interpretation of the Wolf-Rayet stars pictures a star surrounded by a gaseous envelope where the material might seem to be streaming outward as fast as 3000 km/sec, as indicated by the widths of the bright lines. An alternate interpretation is that the lines may be widened mainly by random motions in the envelope. A number of these stars are spectroscopic binaries and a few are known to be eclipsing stars. It is suspected that all may be components of close pairs, the W stars revolving with larger type O companions, a situation that may provide an important clue to the still mysterious behavior of Wolf-Rayet stars.

12·25. Planetary Nebulae are so named because the nearer ones appear with the telescope as greenish disks somewhat remindful of the disks of Uranus and Neptune. They are gaseous envelopes around central stars, having diameters 20,000 to more than 100,000 times the earth's distance from the sun. Planetary nebulae are of three general types, as O. C. Wilson describes them: (1) Ring-like, often having a bright inner ring and a fainter outer ring; (2) amorphous, consisting of "roundish blobs"; (3) irregular.

Several hundred planetary nebulae are recognized, including 73 new ones found by A. G. Wilson and G. O. Abell in the Palomar Sky Survey. All invisible to the naked eye, they appear with the telescope in a variety of sizes. They range in this respect from the relatively nearby ring-like NGC 7293 in Aquarius (Fig. 12·25), having half the apparent diameter of the moon, to objects so reduced by distance that they can be distinguished from stars only by their peculiar spectra. Many faint planetaries were discovered by R. Minkowski in a systematic search for objects showing the red line of hydrogen and very little continuous spectrum, and by K. G. Henize by the same procedure in the southern hemisphere.

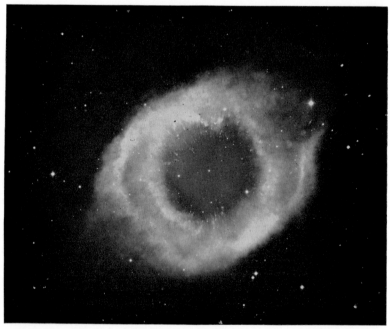

Fig. 12·25. Planetary Nebula NGC 7293 in Aquarius. Photographed in red light with the 200-inch telescope. (*Mount Wilson and Palomar Observatories photograph*)

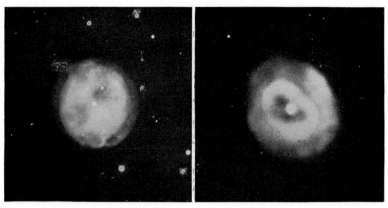

Owl Nebula in Ursa Major.   NGC 7662 in Andromeda.
Diameter 200″   Diameter 30″

FIG. 12·25A.   Two Planetary Nebulae. *(Mount Wilson Observatory pho-tographs)*

The Ring nebula in Lyra (Fig. 12·26) is among the most familiar of the planetaries. Unlike some other ring-like planetaries, it is a true ring, as R. Minkowski and D. E. Osterbrock have demonstrated. This ring is 20 times as bright as the space inside it, whereas a ratio of 2 would be predicted if the nebula were actually a hollow ellipsoidal shell. An example of a true ring seen edge-on might well be NGC 650 and 651, cataloged as a double nebula. The meaning of the NGC numbers is explained later (15·1).

The central stars of planetary nebulae are about as massive as the sun but are much smaller than the sun, so that they have high densities. They are among the hottest stars, having surface temperatures of 50,000°K, or more. Thus they furnish a rich supply of ultraviolet radiation to illuminate the nebulae. Because their radiation is mainly in the ultraviolet, these stars are less easy to see than are the nebulae, but they come out as clearly in the blue photographs.

12·26. Expansion of Planetary Nebulae. When the image of a planetary nebula is centered on the slit of the spectroscope, the bright lines of the spectrum tend to be double in the middle. The part of the line formed in the near side of the nebula is displaced toward the violet, showing that the gas is approaching us; and the part from the far side is displaced toward the red, showing that the

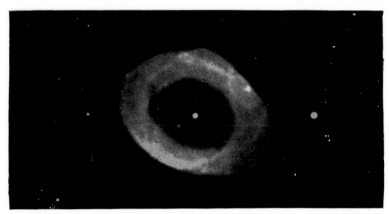

FIG. 12·26.   The Ring Nebula in Lyra.   (*Mount Wilson Observatory photograph*)

gas is there receding from us.   Thus the planetary nebulae are moving outward from the central stars.   The speeds of expansion in the radii range from 10 to 50 km/sec and may have decelerated moderately since the outburst of the material from the central stars.   After lifetimes of 20,000 years, the nebulae begin to disintegrate by breaking into separate clouds of gas.

It will be noted later (13·21) that planetary nebulae differ from the expanding envelopes of novae in their slower rates of expansion and their much longer lives.   There is also a pronounced difference in the amount of material involved; the mass of a planetary nebula is about one tenth of the star's mass, whereas the mass of a nova envelope does not exceed 1/10,000 of the mass of the star.

THE INTERIORS OF THE STARS

12·27. A Star in Equilibrium.   Studies of the interior of a main-sequence star such as the sun proceed on the assumption that the star is in mechanical equilibrium under its own gravity.   By this we mean that the weight of the gas above any level in the interior is exactly supported by gas and radiation pressures at that level. The assumption is reasonable, because the star would shrink if the internal pressure were inadequate or else expand if it were excessive; and the sun is not observed to be doing either at present.

The weight of overlying gas to be supported at a particular level depends on the mass of that gas and the acceleration of gravity. These values can be derived for a star of known mass and radius if it is also known how the density of the material diminishes with distance from the center of the star. The pressure required to balance the weight depends on the temperature and composition of the gas at that level. If the composition is known, then it becomes possible to calculate the temperature there and, similarly, at all other levels in the star's interior.

In order to preserve the balance between weight and pressure, the rate at which the energy is liberated in the central region of the star and is passed on up to the surface must remain equal to the rate of radiation at the surface. The required rate of energy liberation is determined by the luminosity of the star. If this rate diminishes, the star will cool and contract; if it increases, the star will grow hotter and expand. One important objective of studies of stellar interiors is to learn the process by which the energy is liberated and how it is likely to affect the future of the star.

12·28. Gas and Radiation Pressures. The *gas pressure* at any point inside a star is produced by the turmoil of the gas particles in that vicinity. The relation between the pressure, p, the density, ρ, and the absolute temperature, T, of the gas is given by the gas law: $p = R\rho T/\mu$, where R is a constant and μ is the mean weight of the gas particles. These particles are constituents of shattered atoms. In the laboratory a gas compressed to a density exceeding one tenth the density of water ceases to conform to this law; but in the very hot interior of a star, where atomic superstructures are disrupted, the law continues to operate at densities far exceeding that of water.

The *radiation pressure* results from the outward flow of radiation through the star. Radiation pressure at any point is directly proportional to the rate of radiation there, which by Stefan's law (10·5) varies as the fourth power of the temperature. Thus with increasing temperature the ratio of radiation to gas pressure increases. The share of radiation pressure in keeping the star inflated, however, is considered negligible where the star's mass does not exceed 2 or 3 times the mass of the sun.

12·29. Effect of Chemical Composition. The atoms in the deep interiors of the stars are highly ionized. The result is a confusion of atomic nuclei, partly or entirely separated from their electrons, and the electrons themselves. For example, a neutral atom of iron (atomic weight 55.8 and number 26) would become 27 particles of average weight 55.8/27, or 2.1, if entirely ionized. The average values for the "metals," meaning here all the elements except hydrogen and helium, are so nearly the same that the proportions in which they occur are not important in the gas law. What has to be determined is the proportion between the metals and the lightest gases, hydrogen and helium, whose particles have average weights of only 0.5 and 1.3, respectively.

Consider two stars having the same size, density, and density distribution, the first star composed mainly of iron and the second entirely of hydrogen. By the formula the temperature at a particular point in the first star would be 2.1/0.5, or about 4, times that at the corresponding point in the second star in order to produce the same gas pressure. If the sun were composed mainly of metallic gases, its central temperature would be 4×10^7 degrees K. If it contained only hydrogen, the central temperature would be 10^7 degrees and it would shine only 1 per cent as brightly as the metallic sun.

Thus chemical composition is an important factor in determining the interior temperatures and also the luminosity of a star. The procedure has been to find by trial and error a composition giving a central temperature appropriate to the observed luminosity of the star. Calculations of this sort have recently assigned a smaller percentage of metals, and accordingly a lower central temperature, than they did previously.

12·30. The Interior of the Sun. In the sun, where the liberation of energy may not yet have produced pronounced changes, the chemical elements are believed to be in about the same proportions from the chromosphere almost to the center. Hydrogen contributes nearly 75 per cent of the mass, helium about 25 per cent, and the metals 1 per cent or so in the models recently discussed by Bengt Strömgren. The temperature increases rapidly from the surface to a central value of 13 million degrees K. The gases around the center are 90 times as dense as water. Martin Schwarzschild has employed a more recent model of the sun by R. Weymann, where the hydrogen content at the center is reduced to 50 per cent. The central temperature is thereby increased to 15 million degrees and the density to 134.

Energy is liberated in the deep interior of the sun in the form of very high-frequency radiation. It is passed on upward mainly by absorption and emission of the gas particles, until it reaches the surface and escapes into space. In this process the frequency is gradually stepped down, so that much of the energy emerges as visible sunlight.

12·31. What Keeps the Stars Shining? A major problem of astronomy has been to locate the stores of energy which supply the radiations of the stars during their long lives. The stars cannot continue to shine simply because they are extremely hot; energy must come from some source to keep them so highly heated. Nor are the stars kept heated by combustion. Even in the cooler regions of the sun's atmosphere the atoms are generally not combining. The sun is too hot to burn.

We dismiss any idea that adequate amounts of energy are being stoked into the sun from outside. Meteors must fall into the sun in great numbers, it is true, and their impacts are great as they arrive with speeds approaching 380 miles a second. A yearly fall of meteoric material 3500 times the earth's mass would be needed to supply as much energy as the sun radiates in a year. The actual amount falling into the sun can be only a very small fraction of this requirement.

Another early idea of how the sun and other stars keep shining seemed more promising. The idea was that all the necessary heat may be supplied by their contraction.

12·32. The Contraction Theory. In 1854, the German physicist H. L. F. von Helmholtz explained that a yearly contraction of 140 feet in the sun's present radius would supply enough heat to keep the sun shining. The process could not continue indefinitely. After a few million years, as it then seemed, the sun would become so compressed that it could contract no further; then the sun would quickly cool, bringing to us the "end of the world."

The theory that the sun shines only because of its contraction does not conform with the present cosmic time-scale. To have continued shining as it does today as the result of contraction alone, the sun must have shrunk to its present size in less than 5×10^7 years. That duration of the sunshine may have seemed quite long enough a century ago, but it is far too short today when geologists are dating the beginning of life on the earth at least 10^9 years in the past.

Thus contraction is not the only factor in the continued shining of the sun and stars. In current theories of stellar evolution it enters as a means of heating youthful stars to the point where their internal supplies of energy can be released; it assists in important ways thereafter and ultimately assumes control when these supplies are exhausted.

Having failed to find adequate supplies of energy elsewhere, the scientists now look more confidently within the atoms. The inquiry is guided by a relation derived from the theory of relativity.

12·33. Relation Between Energy and Mass. Early in the present century, Albert Einstein showed that energy and mass are related by the formula: Energy equals mass times the square of the speed of light. The energy is expressed in ergs, the mass in grams, and the speed of light in centimeters a second. By this formula there is a vast amount of energy in a very small quantity of matter. For example, the energy released by the destruction of a single gram of matter could lift a weight of 7 million tons from the earth's surface to the height of a mile above it.

We now approach the answer to the question: What keeps the stars shining? In the present view, the energy required to keep the stars shining is converted from the excess material when atoms of lighter chemical elements are built up into atoms of heavier ones in the stellar interiors.

12·34. Fusion of Hydrogen into Helium. The great abundance of hydrogen in the stars has directed the search for processes which can transform hydrogen into heavier elements. At the central temperature of the sun the collisions of gas particles are vigorous enough to unite hydrogen nuclei into helium nuclei. This transformation can operate on a scale sufficient to keep the sun shining at the present rate. The arithmetic of the operation is as follows:

The relative weight of the hydrogen nucleus is 1.0076 and that of the helium nucleus is about 4.003. Where hydrogen in stellar interiors is being converted to helium, each combination of 4 hydrogen nuclei into a single helium nucleus involves a mass loss of about $4.030 - 4.003 = 0.027$, or seven tenths of 1 per cent of the original mass. The unrecovered mass is released as energy.

Two means of transforming hydrogen into helium in the stars have received much attention. They are the proton-proton reaction and the carbon cycle. The first of these is considered the more effective at the temperatures in the sun and the redder stars of the main sequence. The carbon cycle becomes effective at somewhat higher central temperatures.

12·35. The Proton-Proton Reaction combines 6 hydrogen nuclei to form a helium nucleus and at the end puts 2 hydrogen nuclei back into circulation. One process of this type, proposed by W. A. Fowler and C. C. Lauritzen, is represented by the following succession of formulas, in which the subscripts are the atomic numbers and the superscripts are the atomic weights to the nearest whole number. The symbol β^+ denotes a positron, or positive electron, and γ denotes a γ-ray, or a unit of high-frequency radiation. The steps are:

$$_1H^1 + {}_1H^1 \rightarrow {}_1H^2 + \beta^+ \tag{1}$$

$$_1H^2 + {}_1H^1 \rightarrow {}_2He^3 + \gamma \tag{2}$$

$$_2He^3 + {}_2He^3 \rightarrow {}_2He^4 + 2{}_1H^1 \tag{3}$$

In this reaction: (1) Two protons, or normal hydrogen nuclei, combine to form a deuteron. One proton becomes a neutron and a positron, which soon unites with a negative electron in the vicinity to add to the energy. A neutrino formed in this step promptly escapes from the scene. (2) The deuteron combines with a third proton to form helium of weight 3, with the release of a γ-ray. (3) Two helium-3 isotopes combine to produce an ordinary helium nucleus and 2 protons. The available energy released in the formation of each helium nucleus equals about 4×10^{-5} ergs.

The fusion of hydrogen into helium, which provides the energy of the hydrogen bomb, may become the principal source of power on the earth as well as in the stars. Although the quantity of deuterium in a gallon of ordinary water is very small, it has an energy content equivalent to that of 350 gallons of gasoline. The amount of deuterium in the oceans is enough to supply all foreseeable demands for power in the world for billions of years to come if a method of controlling the fusion reaction can be discovered.

12·36. The Carbon Cycle. This process, known as the carbon cycle because carbon is its promoter, was suggested, in 1938, by the physicist H. A. Bethe, who also proposed the chain of the proton-proton reaction in a form somewhat different from the one given in the preceding section. The cycle is:

$$_6C^{12} + _1H^1 \rightarrow _7N^{13} + \gamma \tag{1}$$

$$_7N^{13} \rightarrow _6C^{13} + \beta^+ \tag{2}$$

$$_6C^{13} + _1H^1 \rightarrow _7N^{14} + \gamma \tag{3}$$

$$_7N^{14} + _1H^1 \rightarrow _8O^{15} + \gamma \tag{4}$$

$$_8O^{15} \rightarrow _7N^{15} + \beta^+ \tag{5}$$

$$_7N^{15} + _1H^1 \rightarrow _6C^{12} + _2He^4 \tag{6}$$

In the turmoil of the star's interior: (1) A carbon nucleus of weight 12 combines with a proton to form radioactive nitrogen, with the release of a γ-ray. (2) The nitrogen degenerates into carbon of weight 13 and a positron. (3) The carbon combines with a second proton and forms ordinary nitrogen, with the release of a γ-ray. (4) This nitrogen combines with a third proton to form radioactive oxygen with the release of a γ-ray. (5) The oxygen degenerates into nitrogen of weight 15 and a positron. Here and in the second step a neutrino is released. (6) The heavy nitrogen combines with a fourth proton to produce the original carbon and a helium nucleus.

In this cycle 4 hydrogen nuclei unite to form a helium nucleus, and the excess mass is released as energy. The carbon is recovered and can be used repeatedly. The energy made available in the formation of a single helium nucleus is about the same as in the former process.

12·37. The Unmixed Model of a Star.

Consider a main-sequence star, such as the sun, which contains at the outset the same mixture of chemical elements throughout and where conversion of hydrogen to helium has begun in the interior. Vigorous stirring is not to be expected, except near the photosphere and in the central core where the conversion is occurring.

When the hydrogen in the core is nearly exhausted, the fusion into helium spreads to surrounding regions. The core contracts, until it may become hot enough for the transformation of helium into carbon, oxygen, magnesium, and still heavier elements. These processes are considered in Chapter 16.

Review Questions

1. What particular electron transition in the atomic model corresponds to the Hα line in the spectrum of hydrogen? Why do the other lines of the Balmer series have progressively shorter wavelengths?

2. Explain that less energy is required to excite the normal atom of lithium than of helium.

3. Why do color indexes, blue minus visual magnitude, of stars (Table 12·II) have greater positive values as the surface temperatures are lower?

4. Recalling the kinetic theory of gases, explain why the atoms of a gas become increasingly excited and ionized as the temperature of the gas is higher.

5. Referring to Table 12·III, account for the prominence of the following features successively in stellar spectra from the cool to the hot stars:

(a) Band spectra of molecules.
(b) Lines of neutral sodium and calcium.
(c) Lines of neutral iron and ionized calcium.
(d) Lines of hydrogen.
(e) Lines of neutral helium.
(f) Lines of ionized helium, nitrogen, and oxygen.

6. Why does a giant star have a lower surface temperature than a main-sequence star of the same spectral class?

7. Explain how the distance of a star can be determined from an examination of its spectrum.

8. The spectra of Wolf-Rayet stars contain broad bright lines sometimes having narrow dark lines at their violet edges. Give a possible explanation.

9. Describe the characteristic features of planetary nebulae. Name two examples of such nebulae.

10. By what means is it possible to estimate the central temperature of the sun? Why are recent values considerably lower than earlier ones?

11. Describe the probable character of the material in the deep interior of the sun.

12. Show that radiation pressure within a star increases relative to gas pressure as the temperature is higher.

13. Why is contraction by itself inadequate to account for the long-continued radiation of the sun?

14. Describe the proton-proton reaction within a star and how it liberates energy.

References

Allen, C. W., *Astrophysical Quantities*. John de Graff, New York, 1955.

Aller, Lawrence H., *The Atmospheres of the Sun and Stars*, and *Nuclear Transformations, Stellar Interiors, and Nebulae*. The Ronald Press Company, New York, 1953, 1954.

Flügge, S., editor, *Handbuch der Physik*, vol. 50-54, *Astrophysics*. Springer-Verlag, Berlin.

Greenstein, Jesse L., editor, *Stellar Atmospheres*. University of Chicago Press, Chicago, 1960.

Herzberg, Gerhard, *Atomic Spectra and Molecular Structure*. D. Van Nostrand Company, Princeton, 1950.

Hynek, J. Allen, editor, *Astrophysics*, A topical symposium. McGraw-Hill Book Company, New York, 1951.

Liller, William, editor, *Space Astrophysics*. McGraw-Hill Book Company, New York, 1961.

McCrea, William H., *The Physics of the Sun and Stars*. Longmans, Green, and Company, New York, 1950.

The 210-foot Radio Telescope, Australian National Radio Astronomy Observatory at Parkes, N.S.W. Operated by the Radiophysics Laboratory, Sydney, Australia. (*Courtesy of E. G. Bowen*)

13

INTRINSIC VARIABLE STARS

PULSATING STARS – RED VARIABLE STARS – ERUPTIVE
STARS

Variable stars are stars that vary in brightness and frequently in
other respects as well. The second edition (1958) of the *General
Catalogue of Variable Stars* lists 14,708 variables in our galaxy.
All variable stars, according to the *Catalogue,* may be divided into
three main classes: eclipsing, pulsating, and eruptive variables,
each of which is subdivided into several types. We consider here
stars that are intrinsically variable, from causes inherent in the
stars themselves, leaving the eclipsing stars for the following chapter on binary stars.

13·1. The Light Curve of a star shows how its magnitude varies
with time. It is the curve representing the array of points where

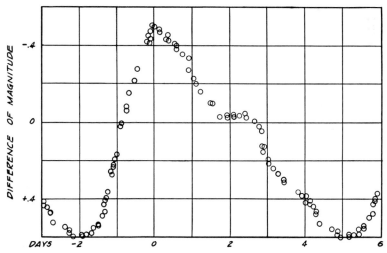

FIG. 13·1. Light Curve of Eta Aquilae. A classical cepheid having a
period of about 7 days. (*Photoelectric light curve by C. C. Wylie*)

383

the observed magnitudes of the star are plotted against the times
of their observations. If the same variation is repeated periodically,
the times of successive maximum and minimum brightness can be
derived eventually, and from these are found the *elements* of the
light variation. They are the *epoch,* or time of a well-defined place
on the curve, and the *period* of the variation. The light curve for
a single cycle may then be obtained more precisely by plotting all
the observed magnitudes with respect to *phase,* or interval of time
either in days or in fractions of the period since the epoch preceding each observation.

As an example, the elements for the cepheid variable star
Eta Aquilae are: Maximum brightness $= 2,414,827.15 + 7^d.1767 \cdot E$,
where the first number is the epoch expressed in Julian days and
the second is the period in days. In order to predict the times of
future maxima we have simply to multiply the period by $E = 1$,
2, . . . and to add the results successively to the original epoch.

The *Julian Day* is the number of days that have elapsed since the beginning of the arbitrary zero day at noon Greenwich mean time on January
1, 4713 B.C. It is a device often used in astronomical records to avoid the
complexity of the calendar system. When the interval between two events
is required, especially where they are widely separated in time, it is easier
to take the difference between the Julian dates. The Julian day numbers
are tabulated for each year in the *American Ephemeris and Nautical
Almanac.* J.D. 2,436,934.5 corresponds to January 1, 1960 at Greenwich
mean midnight.

13·2. The Designation of Variable Stars follows a plan that started
simple enough but became complicated when the discoveries of
these stars ran into many thousands. Unless the star already has a
letter in the Bayer system (1·24), it is assigned a capital letter, or
two, in the order in which its variability is recognized, followed by
the possessive of the Latin name of its constellation. For each constellation the letters are used in the order: R, S, . . . , Z; RR, RS,
. . . , RZ; SS, . . . , SZ; and so on until ZZ is reached. Subsequent
variables are AA, AB, . . . , AZ; BB, . . . , BZ; etc. By the time
QZ is reached (the letter J is not employed), 334 variable stars are
so named in the constellation. Examples are R Leonis, SZ Herculis,
and AC Cygni. Following QZ the designations are V 335, V 336,
and so on; an example is V 335 Sagittarii.

13·3. The Observation of Variable Stars. After the discovery of
a variable star, the next step is to recognize the character of its

variability and to decide whether its continued study is likely to contribute to knowledge of such stars or of stars in general. The magnitudes at the various phases of its fluctuation are determined by comparison with neighboring stars of known magnitudes.

Studies requiring the highest precision are made with the photoelectric cell and may be extended by use of filters for transmitting

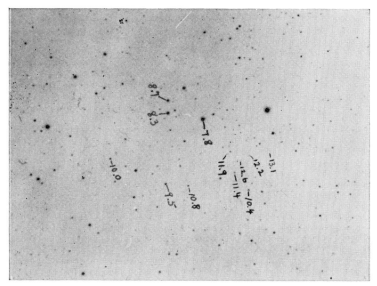

Fig. 13·3.   A Magnitude Sequence.   Negative photograph of a small area of the sky with a magnitude sequence by Leon Campbell.

different colors of the starlight to the cell (Fig. 13·8). For many purposes the magnitudes are determined photographically, either measured by appropriate means or simply estimated in photographs with reference to sequences of known magnitudes (Fig. 13·3). The photometric determinations are often supplemented by studies of the star's spectrum, where the character and displacements of the lines may give additional information.

Visual observations of the magnitudes are employed as well, especially where the light variation is of large range and somewhat irregular. Amateur astronomers with small telescopes find here an interesting and useful field. The American Association of Variable Star Observers, of which Margaret W. Mayall is the director, has contributed many more than a million magnitude determinations.

Many supergiant and giant stars are variable in brightness because they are alternately contracting and expanding, becoming hotter and cooler in turn. These pulsating stars include prominently the cepheid and RR Lyrae variables.

13·4. Cepheid Variable Stars are named from one of the earliest recognized examples, Delta Cephei. They are of two types: classical cepheids and type II cepheids.

Classical cepheids are so called because they resemble the prototype. About 500 are known in our galaxy, where they congregate near the central line of the Milky Way. Their periods range generally from 1 to 50 days and are most commonly around 5 days. Those of shorter periods are generally steady in period and form of light curve. The increase in brightness is likely to be more rapid than the decline, and the maximum of the light curve is often more sharply defined than is the minimum. The visual range of the variation is frequently around 1 magnitude.

Classical cepheids are yellow supergiants, not redder than type G0 at their maxima. Very rare in space, their high luminosities raise them to prominence in the sky out of proportion to their actual number. About a dozen are visible to the naked eye; the brightest are Polaris, Delta Cephei, Eta Aquilae, Zeta Geminorum, and Beta Doradus. Polaris has the smallest range of all, which is 0.17 magnitude in the ultraviolet and 0.04 in the infrared.

Type II cepheids have been recognized more frequently in the globular clusters and near the center of our galaxy. Their light curves have broader maxima and are more nearly symmetrical than those of the classical cepheids. Their periods are mostly from 12 to 20 days. An example is W Virginis.

13·5. RR Lyrae Variables were first observed in the globular clusters (15·10) and are often called *cluster variables,* although they are now recognized in greater numbers outside the clusters. The periods of their light variations are around half a day, ranging from 1½ hours to about a day, and are slowly changing. Especially in the clusters the light curves are nearly symmetrical for the shorter periods; at about half a day they change abruptly to curves having very steep upslopes and extreme amplitudes, effects which moderate as the periods are longer. Variations in magnitude are generally

less in ultraviolet than in blue light, because of increased absorption by the Balmer continuum (12·7) as the stars rise to their
higher temperatures.

These stars are blue giants, which vary between types A0 and F5.
They occupy by themselves a small section of the horizontal giant

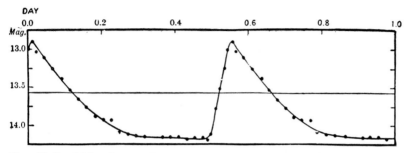

FIG. 13·5.   Light Curve of an RR Lyrae Variable.   The very rapid rise
to maximum light is characteristic of many variable stars of this type.
(Harvard Observatory diagram)

branch in the color-magnitude diagram.   Although they far out-
number the classical cepheids, their lower luminosity makes them
less conspicuous in the sky.   Not one is bright enough to be visible to the naked eye; the brightest examples are the prototype, RR
Lyrae, and VZ Cancri, both of the 7th apparent magnitude.

13·6. The Spectra of Cepheids and RR Lyrae Stars show two features which are especially significant for the interpretation of these
stars:

(1) *The spectral type is variable.*   From maximum to minimum
light the spectral type advances.   In the case of Delta Cephei the
change is from F4 to G2, signifying a drop of about 1500°C in
surface temperature.   Thus the surface of this star is hotter at
maximum brightness and cooler at minimum.

(2) *The spectrum lines oscillate* in the period of the light variation.   The curve representing the variation of radial velocity with
time is not far from the mirror image of the light curve.   Near
maximum brightness of the star the lines are displaced farthest
toward the violet, and near minimum brightness they are displaced
farthest toward the red end of the spectrum.   This is the Doppler
displacement owing to the motion in the line of sight of the atmosphere in front of the star.   At maximum light these gases are approaching us and at minimum light they are receding from us.

The correspondence between the velocity and light curves is only approximate. The differences between the two depend on the part of the spectrum that is examined; also with increasing period of the variation the greatest velocity of approach tends to lag behind the light maximum, as A. H. Joy has shown.

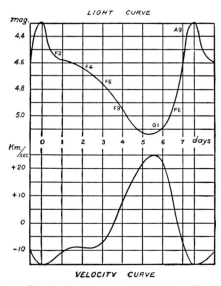

Fig. 13·6. Light and Velocity Curves of W Sagittarii. Maximum brightness of this classical cepheid occurs at about the time of greatest negative velocity (of approach); minimum light at about greatest positive velocity (of recession). (*Diagram by R. H. Curtiss*)

These oscillations of the spectrum lines seemed in earlier times to signify the mutual revolutions of the stars with companions; but there was no convincing idea of how the light variations could be caused by the revolutions. Suggestions that both spectrum and light variations could be shown by single pulsating stars received little attention until Harlow Shapley, in 1914, advocated the pulsation theory.

13·7. Pulsating Stars. In the original form of the pulsation theory the star was supposed to expand and contract alternately all in phase. On this theory the star should be hottest and therefore brightest and bluest when it is most contracted. Actually it reaches that state almost a quarter of the period later when its spectrum lines are farthest displaced toward the violet, showing that the gases which cause the lines are moving outward fastest. The original plan was oversimplified.

The current pulsation theory, proposed in 1938 by Martin Schwarzschild at Princeton, is more flexible and can lead to more complex results. The star's interior is supposed to pulsate in unison as before. Compressional waves run upward through the outer layers, reaching the higher levels later than the lower ones. Greatest compression of the gases in and above the photosphere may occur when the waves are moving outward fastest. The delay in the time of maximum brightness in light of longer wavelength, as is clearly shown in the case of Delta Cephei (Fig. 13·8), is consistent with the theory in its newer form. Although the cause of the pulsation is not clearly understood, it is supposed to be a transitory disturbance in the life of a star as it evolves across the top of the color-magnitude diagram. The region of instability in the color-absolute visual magnitude diagram, according to Sandage, is a strip of width about $0^m.2$ in color index. This strip extends from $M = +4$, $B - V = 0.0$, to $M = -6$, $B - V = 0.7$; it includes all cepheid and RR Lyrae variable stars.

A remarkable confirmation of the pulsation theory was first observed independently by Otto Struve at McDonald Observatory and R. F. Sanford at Mount Wilson in the spectrum of RR Lyrae. Midway between the times of minimum and maximum brightness of the star, one set of narrow dark hydrogen lines formed at a higher level in the star's atmosphere is displaced toward the red, showing that these gases are still moving inward. A second set of broad dark lines from a lower level is displaced to the violet; there the gases have begun to move outward again. In addition, the appearance of narrow undisplaced bright hydrogen lines represents energy released by collision of the two strata. Similar features were later observed in the spectra of W Virginis and other pulsating stars.

13·8. Light Curves of Delta Cephei at three wavelengths are shown in Fig. 13·8. The light of the different colors was transmitted by appropriate filters placed in front of a photoelectric cell. The range of the light variation is 1.48 magnitudes in the ultraviolet and only 0.43 in the infrared, showing that the star is bluer at maximum than at minimum brightness. Maximum and minimum light come progressively later with increasing wavelength of the

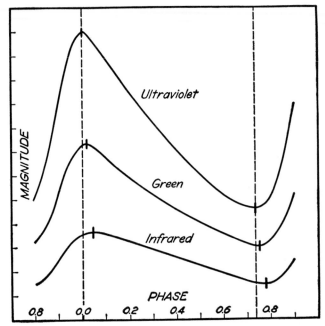

Fig. 13·8.   Light Curves of Delta Cephei in Ultraviolet, Green, and Infrared.   (*Determined photoelectrically by Joel Stebbins*)

light that is observed.   They are 0.27 day later in the infrared than
in the ultraviolet.   Thus when the star has begun to grow fainter
at the shorter wavelengths it is still brightening at the longer ones.

13·9. The Period-Luminosity Relation.   Cepheid variables fluctuate in longer periods as the stars are more luminous.   The relation
is illustrated by the curves of Fig. 13·9, which show how the logarithm of the period increases as the median absolute magnitude is
brighter.   (The *median magnitude* is the average between the magnitudes at maximum and minimum brightness.)   First established
in useful form by Shapley in 1917, the period-luminosity relation
has especial importance in providing a cosmic distance scale, because these very luminous stars are visible at great distances.
Cepheids observed in photographs of 30 exterior galaxies with the
200-inch telescope are available as distance indicators if we can
be sure that the relation for these galaxies is the same as for our
own galaxy.   Two modifications of the earlier single curve are
made necessary by more recent investigations.

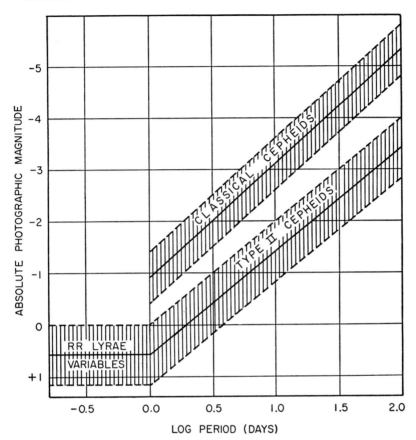

Fig. 13·9. Period-Luminosity Relations for Cepheids. The median absolute photographic magnitude of a cepheid can be read from the appropriate band when the period of the light variation and the median surface
temperature of the star are known. The median magnitudes of all RR
Lyrae variables are around +0.6. (*From preliminary data supplied by
H. C. Arp*)

(1) The absolute magnitudes of classical cepheids are brighter
than was formerly supposed. The curve in the diagram of Fig.
13·9 is raised 1.5 magnitudes above the curve previously used.
The correction was announced by Walter Baade in 1952. An unexpected means of verifying this correction and of supplying data
for a second one was later provided by J. B. Irwin's discovery of
classical cepheids in galactic clusters, for which distances are accurately known; the first correction multiplied by the factor 2 the

distances already determined from the periods of classical cepheids. The curve for the type II cepheids replaced the original curve.

(2) The period-luminosity relation for both types of cepheids must be represented by bands at least 1 magnitude wide rather than by simple curves. This modification resulted from H. C. Arp's studies of cepheids in the Small Magellanic Cloud, and was explained by A. R. Sandage. From the known relation between the period and mean density he deduced that the absolute magnitude of a cepheid is related not only to the period of its pulsation but also to the star's mean surface temperature, or color. This would apply to all pulsating stars. The correctness of the explanation is confirmed by studies by R. P. Kraft and others of the few known cepheids in galactic clusters, where the surface temperatures can be accurately determined. These studies also show that for stars having the larger variations in brightness the absolute magnitudes are represented more nearly by the central curves of the bands of the diagram.

When the period and mean color of a cepheid of either kind is observed, the star's median absolute magnitude, M, can be read from the appropriate band of the diagram. When the median apparent magnitude, m, is also observed, the star's distance, r in parsecs, can be calculated by the formula (11·25): $\log r = (m - M + 5)/5$. In the use of this and similar photometric formulas, allowance must be made for any dimming of starlight by intervening cosmic dust, which would otherwise cause the distance to come out too great.

RR Lyrae stars are assumed to have median photographic magnitude $+0.6$ in the average regardless of period. Wherever one of these stars is found, its approximate distance is given by the formula: $\log r = (m - 0.6 + 5.0)/5$. The relation of luminosity to period and surface temperature is also shown by a band in Fig. 13·9; but the width of the band and the magnitude of its central line are not yet certainly established. RR Lyrae stars are useful for determining distances within our own galaxy. They are not bright enough to be observed with present telescopes beyond the nearest exterior galaxies.

Effects of differences in surface temperatures of the stars are neglected in order to simplify the examples of distance calculations that follow.

(1) The classical cepheid SY Aurigae has a period of 10 days. Its apparent photographic magnitude varies from 9.8 to 11.0. Determine its approximate distance, supposing that no cosmic dust intervenes.

Answer: The median apparent magnitude is 10.4.   The logarithm of the period is 1.0, and the corresponding absolute magnitude from the period-luminosity curve is -3.1.   Thus $\log r = (10.4 + 3.1 + 5.0)/5 = 3.70$.   The resulting distance is 5000 parsecs.

(2) Required the approximate distance of the RR Lyrae variable RX Eridani, which has a period of 0.6 day and median apparent magnitude 9.2.   We again suppose no intervening dust.

Answer: The median absolute magnitude of an RR Lyrae variable is assumed to be $+0.6$.   Thus $\log r = (9.2 - 0.6 + 5.0)/5 = 2.72$.   The distance is 520 parsecs.

13·10. Beta Canis Majoris Variables are pulsating stars of spectral types B1 and B2.   The few known examples have been studied intensively, especially by Otto Struve and associates.   They form a band in the color-magnitude diagram, which begins with Gamma Pegasi near the main sequence and extends to the left and above that sequence as far as the prototype.   The periods of the light variations increase progressively in this direction from $3\frac{1}{2}$ to 6 hours.

The light variations have small and often variable ranges from cycle to cycle and the spectrum lines oscillate in the same periods, as with other pulsating stars.

13·11. RV Tauri Variables.   Among the yellow and reddish variable stars, around types G and K, which do not conform to the principal patterns, 40 or more form a sort of connecting link between the cepheids and the red variables.   They are known as RV Tauri stars after one of their members.   Their variations in light in a semiregular manner are ascribed at least partly to pulsations. Like the cepheids, these stars are redder at minimum light and are separated into type I and II groups.

RV Tauri itself can serve as an example, although the pattern is not the same throughout the group.   Its light curve (Fig. 13·11) shows a semiregular variation of about a magnitude in a period around 79 days.   A cycle comprises two maxima of nearly equal brightness and two unequal minima; meanwhile, the spectrum varies between G4 and K5.   In this case there is also a superim-

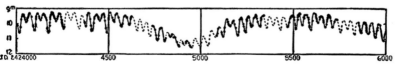

FIG. 13·11.   Light Curve of RV Tauri.   (*Diagram by Leon Campbell and Luigi Jacchia*)

posed variation of more than 2 magnitudes in a period of about 1300 days.

RED VARIABLE STARS

Many red giants and supergiants are variable in brightness. Their variability involves temperature variations of the photo-spheres and may in some stars be enhanced by variable veiling by clouds of solid or liquid particles alternately forming and dispers-ing in the outer regions of their atmospheres. These variable stars are of two general types: (1) Mira-type, or long-period, variables, having an approach to regularity; (2) irregular variables, where the fluctuations are less readily predictable. The red giant variables have been often regarded as pulsating stars, and are so classified in the *General Catalogue of Variable Stars*.

Some red stars and certain others of the main sequence are also irregularly variable in brightness.

13·12. Mira-Type Variables are variable in cycles of from 3 months to more than 2 years, and most commonly around 10 months. Their periods and ranges in brightness have an approach to regularity which is remindful of the cycles of sunspot numbers. The range in their light variations averages 5 magnitudes and may be as much as 10 magnitudes in the extreme case of Chi Cygni (Fig. 13·12). This star at maximum brightness in its different

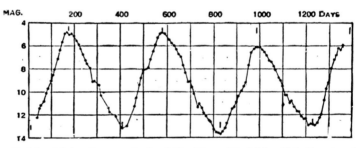

FIG. 13·12. Light Curve of the Mira-Type Variable Chi Cygni. (*De-termined by the American Association of Variable Star Observers*)

cycles is sometimes plainly visible and at other times is still invis-ible to the naked eye. Meanwhile, the total radiations of Mira-type variables, as determined by their heating of a thermocouple at the focus of a telescope, vary only about 1 magnitude.

The spectra are mainly of type M, but S, R, and N are represented as well. They contain the dark lines and bands characteristic of red stars, and also bright lines, particularly of hydrogen, which have been the means of discovering many of these variable stars. The bright hydrogen lines, which are first formed at lower levels than the dark ones, often make their appearance about midway between minimum and maximum brightness of the stars, become most intense about a sixth of the period after maximum, and disappear around the next minimum.

As with the cepheids, the spectral type moves toward the blue end of the sequence from minimum to maximum light, and the surface temperature increases accordingly. We can best consider the problem presented by the Mira-type variables by referring to the prototype as a particular example.

13·13. Mira (Omicron Ceti) itself is the best-known and at times the brightest of these variable stars; its light variations have been observed for more than $3\frac{1}{2}$ centuries. It was in fact the first variable star to be recognized, aside from two or three novae, and was therefore called *stella mira*. Mira is a red supergiant at least 10 times as massive as the sun, having a diameter 300 times as great, and an average density only about a 3-millionth that of the sun. Its greatest brightness ranges in the different cycles generally from the 3rd to the 5th apparent visual magnitude, and its least brightness from the 8th to the 10th magnitude. The average period of its light variation is 330 days.

HδEquation   λ 4227   Hγ   λ 45 85   λ 47 62

Fig. 13·13. Spectrum of Mira. Titanium oxide bands are prominent at the right. Hydrogen lines are bright. (*University of Michigan Observatory photograph*)

From minimum to maximum brightness of the star the spectrum of Mira varies from M9 to M6. The surface temperature rises from 1900° to 2600°C, increasing by the factor 1.37. By Stefan's law (10·5) the rate of the star's total radiation increases as the 4th power of this quantity, or by the factor 3.5. Yet the visible light increases an average of 5 magnitudes, or by the factor 100. The large difference between these factors is ascribed to the temperature change and the diminished veiling of the star by its molecular bands and clouded envelope as the star becomes hotter.

A. H. Joy's long-continued studies of the spectrum of Mira have served to guide the thinking about the cause of its variability. The dark lines show a slight longward displacement around maximum light, especially at the brighter maxima. The behavior of the bright lines has seemed more significant for the interpretation. They are most displaced toward the violet around maximum light of the star, as with the cepheids, but there is a one-way shifting during a cycle rather than an oscillation. Indeed, there is little evidence from the spectrum or from measurements with the interferometer that Mira is alternately expanding and contracting.

13·14. The Nature of Mira-Type Variability is not yet completely explained. In somewhat earlier times the pulsation theory was invoked to interpret the variability of the red as well as the blue and yellow giant stars. More recently, this type of pulsation has come to be considered as a trigger mechanism or else as inoperative in these red stars. In a lecture in 1955, P. W. Merrill expressed his preference for a main hypothesis of "hot fronts," perhaps like shock waves, moving outward successively from below the photosphere and disappearing at the higher levels as a new disturbance forms below. Merrill's description of the proposed process may be summarized as follows:

The impact of each disturbance at the visible levels of the star is spread over an interval of weeks or months as the wave travels outward with moderate speed. The earlier arrival of its infrared radiations brings a general warming and brightening of the photosphere. The ultraviolet radiations arrive later to cause the bright lines in the spectrum.

At length comes the kinetic impact of the wave itself, which then proceeds outward and after months of travel reaches the uppermost layers of the atmosphere. Here the dissipating wave may cause the gases to condense into droplets which evaporate slowly in much the same way that a slowly disappearing train of white particles is set up by an airplane above us. The variable veiling of the photospheres, along with the varying strength of the titanium oxide bands in the spectra, may contribute to the large ranges in brightness which characterize the Mira-type variables.

13·15. Irregular Variable Stars. Many red supergiant and giant stars vary irregularly in brightness in narrower limits often not exceeding half a magnitude. Betelgeuse is the brightest of these. Another example, the type M5 supergiant Alpha Herculis, varies unpredictably between visual magnitudes 3.0 and 4.0. Its distance from us is 500 light years and its diameter is 500 times the sun's diameter. A. J. Deutsch's studies of the spectrum have shown that this red star has an envelope extending out at least as far as its visual companion, a distance of 700 astronomical units. The material of the envelope is moving outward at a rate exceeding the velocity of escape from the star. At very high levels the gas may condense into patchy clouds, which disappear by dilution and are replaced by others. Their partial veiling of the red star is believed to contribute to its variability.

Other irregular variable stars include the T Tauri variables (16·16) and the flare stars.

13·16. Flare Stars are red main-sequence stars that are subject to intense outbursts of very short durations remindful of the solar flares (10·29). They are designated in the *General Catalogue* as UV Ceti-type variables after a typical representative first recognized by W. J. Luyten in 1948. This star is the fainter component of the binary Luyten 726-8. The main outbursts of UV Ceti occur at average intervals of $1\frac{1}{2}$ days, when the rise in brightness of the star is generally from 1 to 2 magnitudes. On one occasion in 1952, however, an increase of 6 magnitudes was observed, the greatest flare on record for any star. Between the outbursts the light of the star varies continuously and irregularly in smaller amplitude.

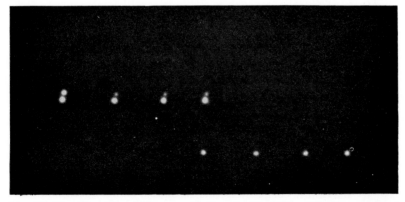

FIG. 13·16. Flare-Up of Krueger 60 B, July 26, 1939. The last of the 4 successive exposures (left) on the double star and its distant optical companion shows the brightening of the fainter star of the pair. (*Sproul Observatory photograph*)

About two dozen flare stars are recognized. Their spectra, which normally contain emission lines of hydrogen and ionized calcium, show some bright lines of helium as well during the flares. Another example of a flare was the sudden and brief increase of $1\frac{1}{2}$ magnitudes in the light of the normally fainter star of the visual binary Krueger 60 (Fig. 13·16) reported by Peter van de Kamp and Sarah L. Lippincott.

Although the outbursts of flare stars are believed to be confined to small areas of their surfaces, the greater brightness of the flares than that of their dimmer surroundings much increases the total light of these stars. Similar flares in other than red stars would be more likely to escape detection.

ERUPTIVE STARS

Novae are stars that rise rapidly in brightness from comparative obscurity and more gradually decline. They are often designated by the word Nova followed by the possessive of the constellation name and the year of the outburst. Nova Aquilae 1918 is an example. More recently they have been designated by letters along with other variable stars. Thus Nova Herculis 1934 is also Nova DQ Herculis. In addition to typical novae, recurrent novae, and dwarf novae, there are also the rare and even more spectacular supernovae. The account in this chapter is restricted to novae in our galaxy.

13·17. Typical Novae. More than 100 typical, or "ordinary," novae have been recognized in our galaxy, a number that is increasing by one or two in a year. Many escape detection; it is estimated that a total of 25 appear yearly in the Milky Way. Five typical novae in the present century became stars of the first magnitude or brighter. Nova Persei 1901 rose to apparent magnitude +0.1, as bright as Capella. Nova Aquilae 1918 reached magnitude −1.4, as bright as Sirius. Nova Pictoris 1925, Nova DQ Herculis (1934), and Nova CP Puppis (1942) became, respectively, as bright as Spica, Deneb, and Rigel.

Typical novae are subdwarf stars smaller and less massive than the sun. Characteristic of their light variations is a single abrupt rise to maximum brightness and a much slower decline, interrupted by partial recoveries. The rise may exceed 12 magnitudes, representing an increase in brightness of more than 60,000 times,

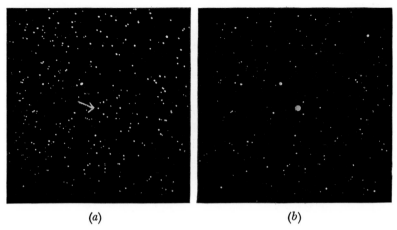

(a)   (b)

FIG. 13·17. Nova Aquilae 1918, Before and After the Outburst. (a) In 1905, as a star of the 11th magnitude. (b) On July 12, 1918, more than a month after the outburst. (*Yerkes Observatory photographs*)

and usually requires only a day or two. The novae return eventually to about the same faint magnitudes they had before the outbursts occurred, suggesting that the effect of the eruptions on these stars is superficial. On their returns they are likely to fluctuate moderately for some time. As many as 20 to 40 years may elapse before they settle down to comparative stability.

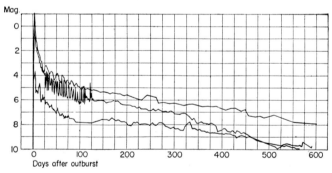

FIG. 13·17A. Light Curves of Nova Aquilae 1918, Nova Persei 1901, and Nova Geminorum 1912. They are designated in order of decreasing brightness at the maxima. (*Harvard Observatory diagram*)

13·18. Recurrent Novae. The novae already described have been observed to erupt only once. *Recurrent novae* have two or more recorded outbursts; otherwise they seem to differ from typical novae only in their less extreme rise in brightness. Six examples are recognized. Their names and the dates of their recorded outbursts are as follows:

Nova T Coronae Borealis rose in 1866 to visual magnitude 2, and in two months thereafter declined to the 9th magnitude; it flared out again in 1946, then to the 3rd magnitude. Nova RS Ophiuchi, normally around the 12th magnitude, rose to the 4th magnitude in 1898 and 1933, and to the 5th magnitude in 1958. Nova T Pyxidis rose from magnitude 13 to nearly naked-eye visibility in 1890, 1902, 1920, and 1944. Outbursts of Nova U Scorpii occurred in 1863, 1906, and 1936; of Nova WZ Sagittae in 1913 and 1946; of Nova Sagittarii in 1901 and 1919.

There is some indication that the amount of the rise in brightness for all recurrent and dwarf novae varies directly as the logarithm of the average interval of time between outbursts. If the relation holds for typical novae, the intervals between their outbursts may be many thousand years. Thus typical novae such as Nova Aquilae 1918 would be expected to flare out again eventually.

13·19. Spectral Changes of Novae. During the initial increase in brightness the spectrum of a typical nova usually contains a pattern of dark lines somewhat like that of a type A star. These lines

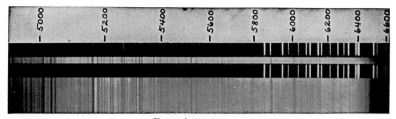

December 23, 1934

January 12, 1935

Fig. 13·19. Spectrum of Nova Herculis 1934 Near and Soon After Maximum Brightness. The unwidened spectrum of the nova between lines of the comparison spectrum is shown above the widened nova spectrum in each case. (*Lick Observatory photographs*)

are much displaced to the violet, showing that the gases in front of the star are rapidly approaching us.

Soon after the nova attains its maximum brightness, broad undisplaced emission lines suddenly appear, having the dark lines at their violet edges. As the light of the nova fades, the bright lines become stronger, and three sets of absorption lines successively make their appearance, each set more displaced to the violet than the preceding one. Radial velocities occasionally exceeding 3000 km/sec are represented by the displacements of the dark lines and the half-widths of the bright ones. With the further decline of the nova the bright lines persist until they resemble the spectrum of an emission nebula, except that the nova lines are wider.

13·20. The Nature of Novae. Novae are currently regarded as stars that are collapsing to become white dwarfs but are too infrequent, according to R. P. Kraft, to constitute a typical stage in stellar evolution. These stars become unstable at times, releasing more internal energy than their small photospheres can radiate. The following account of the nature of novae is taken from the interpretation of their spectral changes as described by D. B. McLaughlin.

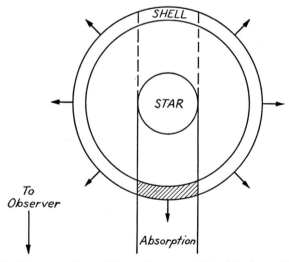

FIG. 13·20. Interpretation of Nova Spectrum After Maximum Brightness. Broad bright lines are produced by light from all parts of the expanding shell. Narrower dark lines at violet borders of bright ones are caused by absorption of the star's light by the part of the shell in front of the star.

A hot subdwarf star in pre-nova state may have remained constant in light or have varied through only a small range for many years. Quite suddenly an excessive amount of energy is liberated below the surface. A superficial layer is then violently ejected, but the main body of the star does not expand. The ejection is not instantaneous; it occurs during an appreciable fraction of the star's rise to maximum brightness. The total mass released in the whole explosion is about 1/10,000 of the star's mass.

The enormous increase in the radiating surface of the ejected shell gives the effect of a rapidly expanding photosphere, causing the star to become much brighter. The dark lines strongly displaced to the violet in the nova's spectrum are produced by absorption in the part of the spreading shell that is in front of the star and is therefore approaching us. The broad emission lines appear soon after maximum brightness of the star when the gaseous shell becomes transparent enough by dilution so that the light begins to come through from all parts of it, some approaching and others receding from us.

The different layers of the shell that have been successively ejected cause the successive patterns of dark lines to appear. The inner layers, having higher speeds of expansion, catch up with the outer one, forming with it the principal shell. This shell produces later the bright nebular lines in the spectrum, when the gases have become sufficiently rarefied by the expansion. The shell of a nearer nova has sometimes grown large enough to be visible directly with the telescope.

13·21. Expanding Envelopes of Novae. The envelope around Nova Aquilae 1918, for example, became visible with the telescope about four months after the star began to brighten. Thereafter, the envelope was observed to increase in radius about 1″ a year. The linear rate of the expansion, as determined from the shortward displacement of the dark lines in the spectrum, or by the half-width of the bright lines, was around 1700 km/sec. Because the tangential velocity, T, of the expansion was presumably the same as the radial velocity and because the angular velocity, μ, was also known, the distance, r, in parsecs of the nova, could be found by the relation (11·11): $r = 0.211\ T/\mu$. The distance of Nova Aquilae proved to be 360 parsecs, or about 1200 light years.

The envelope around Nova Aquilae attained a diameter exceeding 10,000 times the earth's distance from the sun, and disappeared soon afterward. The envelopes around other typical novae have generally vanished only a few years after their appearance. Their rapid expansions and short durations contrast sharply with the slow expansions and long lives of planetary nebulae, such as the Ring nebula in Lyra. The envelopes of supernovae, however, expand rapidly and persist for centuries.

13·22. Supernovae in Our Galaxy. *Supernovae* are stars considerably more massive than the sun, which explode once in the course of their lifetimes. When they explode, they become many million times more luminous than the sun and blow into space gaseous material amounting to at least one solar mass. Six or seven such outbursts were recorded in the Galaxy during the past 2000 years. Allowing for the many that are too remote to be conspicuous, I. S. Shklovsky estimates that supernovae are exploding in the system of the Milky Way at an average rate of one in 30 to 60 years. Novae and supernovae in the exterior galaxies are discussed in Chapter 18.

The apparently brightest supernova on record flared out in Cassiopeia in November, 1572, and was observed by Tycho Brahe. It became at least as bright as Venus and thereafter gradually faded until it disappeared to the unaided eye in the spring of 1574. "Kepler's star" in Ophiuchus in 1604 rivaled Jupiter in brightness. The explosion of a supernova in Taurus in the year 1054 produced the expanding Crab nebula.

13·23. Expansion of the Crab Nebula. The Crab nebula (Messier 1) in Taurus has a radius of about 180″, which is increasing at the rate of 0″.2 a year. At the distance of 3500 light years, the present linear diameter is 6 light years. The nebula is expanding around the site of a supernova recorded in Chinese annals as having appeared southeast of Zeta Tauri on July 4, 1054. The supernova became as bright as Jupiter and remained visible for two years.

The Crab nebula consists of a homogeneous central structure surrounded by an intricate system of filaments (Fig. 13·23). The spectrum of the amorphous central region is continuous. Strong polarization of this light suggests that it is synchrotron radiation (4·26), like that produced by fast-moving electrons revolving in the magnetic field of a laboratory accelerator. The spectrum of the

Fig. 13·23.   Crab Nebula, M 1, in Taurus.   The nebula is expanding around the site of a supernova.   Photographed in red light.   (*Mount Wilson and Palomar Observatories photograph*)

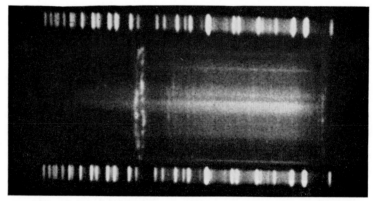

Fig. 13·23A.   Spectrum of the Crab Nebula.   Showing doubling of lines. (*Photograph by N. U. Mayall, Lick Observatory*)

filaments shows emission lines of hydrogen, helium, and other elements observed in the spectra of planetary nebulae. Doubling of these lines (Fig. 13·23A) reveals the expansion of the nebula; the rate of increase of its radius is 1100 km/sec, or about 60 million miles a day.

13·24. Remnants of Other Galactic Supernova Envelopes. Fragments of the expanding envelope around Tycho's supernova, B Cassiopeia, 1572, have been photographed by Minkowski with the Hale telescope. They are described by him as a faint arc and two inconspicuous filaments of nebulosity moving toward the outside. Remnants of Kepler's supernova of 1604 in Ophiuchus similarly photographed are a relatively inconspicuous fan-shaped mass of filaments and several faint wisps of nebulosity. The motions are away from the center of the area. The radio source Cassiopeia A (17·20) is identified in the photographs by many fragments of an envelope spreading from an otherwise unidentified supernova explosion of about the year 1700. The familiar Loop of nebulosity in Cygnus and other partial wreaths of bright nebulosity in this vicinity (Fig. 16·9) are believed to be expanding around the sites of supernova outbursts.

13·25. Dwarf Novae comprise a group of hot subdwarf stars somewhat smaller and fainter than other novae. Typical examples are SS Cygni and U Geminorum. The former star is normally around apparent magnitude 12; it brightens abruptly about 4 magnitudes at irregular intervals and returns to normal brightness in a few days. Over 10-year periods the average interval between outbursts for any one of these stars is about the same, ranging from 13 to 100 days for the group. The stars of a subgroup having Z Camelopardalis as prototype are more erratic in behavior. No evidence is available that dwarf novae eject gases into space at the outbursts.

A. H. Joy's discovery at Mount Wilson Observatory in 1943 that SS Cygni is a spectroscopic binary star may have prepared the way for the eventual understanding of all novae. The revolution period of $6^h 38^m$ shows that the two stars of this binary system are very close together. One component is a larger red star; its smaller white companion is the nova. M. F. Walker observed in 1954 that the typical nova DQ Herculis is also one component of a very close double star. Other dwarf and typical novae have proved to

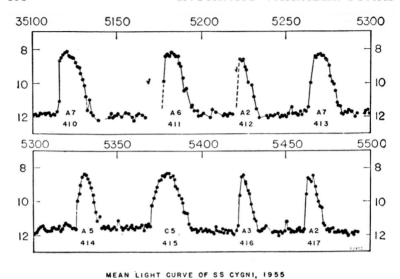

MEAN LIGHT CURVE OF SS CYGNI, 1955

FIG. 13·25. Light Curve of SS Cygni in 1955. Numbers at the top are Julian days 2,435,100 to 2,435,500. Apparent magnitudes are indicated at the right and left. Determined by the American Association of Variable Star Observers. (*Diagram by Margaret W. Mayall*)

be members of binary systems. R. P. Kraft has pointed out the possibility that membership in a certain kind of double system may be a necessary condition for a star to become a nova, and has discussed the evolution of such a system.

REVIEW QUESTIONS

1. Distinguish between three types of pulsating variable stars: classical cepheids, type II cepheids, and RR Lyrae variables.

2. Describe and interpret two changes in the spectrum of a cepheid variable as the star declines from maximum to minimum brightness.

3. What data must be known in order to calculate the distance of an RR Lyrae variable star as accurately as possible?

4. What additional information is needed to obtain the distance of a cepheid variable star?

5. Verify the statement that the upward revision by 1.5 magnitudes in the absolute brightness of classical cepheids multiplied the former values of their distances by the factor 2.

6. State some differences between Mira-type and cepheid variable stars.

7. Explain that veiling may contribute to the irregular variability of red supergiant stars such as Alpha Herculis.

8. Describe the behavior of flare stars.

9. Distinguish between the light variations of typical novae, recurrent novae, and dwarf novae.

10. Discuss the possibility that a star must belong to a certain kind of binary system in order to become a nova.

11. State reasons for the conclusion that the Crab nebula is spreading from the site of a supernova explosion. Compare this nebula with the envelopes around ordinary novae.

12. Explain that typical novae such as Nova Aquilae 1918 might be expected to flare out again after thousands of years.

REFERENCES

Kukarkin, B. V., P. P. Parenago, and others, *General Catalogue of Variable Stars.* Second edition. Moscow, 1958.

Payne-Gaposchkin, Cecilia, *The Galactic Novae.* Interscience Publishers, New York, 1957.

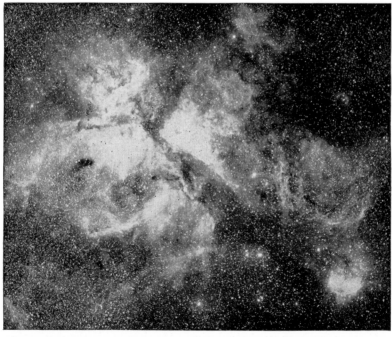

The Great Nebula near Eta Carinae. (*Photograph with the Uppsala Schmidt telescope by Bart J. Bok, Mount Stromlo Observatory*)

14

BINARY STARS

VISUAL BINARIES — SPECTROSCOPIC BINARIES —
ECLIPSING BINARIES — ROTATIONS OF THE STARS

Binary stars are physically connected pairs of stars. The connection is sometimes shown decisively by the mutual revolutions of the two stars, but is more often indicated only by their common proper motion. In the latter case the periods are presumably so long that the revolutions have not progressed far enough to be detected since the pairs were first observed.

Visual binaries are pairs of stars that can be separated with the telescope. *Spectroscopic binaries* appear as single stars with the telescope; their binary character is shown by periodic oscillations of the lines in their spectra. Many spectroscopic binaries have orbits so nearly edgewise to the earth that the revolving pairs undergo mutual eclipses and are *eclipsing binaries* as well.

The rotations of the stars are also described in this chapter because they were first detected in stars of eclipsing binaries.

VISUAL BINARIES

14·1. Optical and Physical Double Stars. The fact that certain stars which appear single to the unaided eye are resolved with the aid of the telescope into double stars was recorded casually by early observers, beginning with the discovery, in 1650, that Mizar in the handle of the Great Dipper is a double star. The reference is not to the naked-eye companion Alcor. The members of such pairs were generally but not always believed to appear close together only by the accident of their having nearly the same direction, until William Herschel, in 1803, reported that the components of Castor were in mutual revolution. He then made the distinction between "optical double stars" and "real double stars," the latter designation referring to two stars actually close together and united by the bond of their mutual gravitation.

Micrometric measuring of double stars was systematized by F. G. W. Struve at Dorpat, Russia, who in 1837 listed 3000 pairs. More recent surveys for the discovery of double stars have been made, particularly at Lick Observatory for the northern hemisphere and at the University of Michigan southern station for the southern hemisphere. A total of 40,000 double stars are known. The pairs having the smaller separations, which are likely to progress more rapidly in their revolutions, can be observed satisfactorily only with the larger telescopes.

14·2. Measurements of Visual Binaries have been made mainly with the position micrometer at the eye-end of the telescope. In this form of micrometer the thread is moved parallel to itself to meas-

FIG. 14·2. Micrometer of the 36-inch Refractor, Lick Observatory.

ure angular distances and can also be rotated to measure directions in the field. The position of the *companion,* or fainter star of the pair, with respect to the *primary star* is obtained by measuring its position angle and distance. Such positions are employed to determine the apparent orbit of the companion relative to the primary.

The *position angle* is the angle at the primary star between the directions of the companion and the north celestial pole; it is reckoned in degrees from the north around through the east. The *distance* is the angular separation of the two stars.

The smallest separation of a binary star that can be accurately measured with the 40-inch Yerkes refractor is 0″.2 and with the 82-inch McDonald reflector is about 0″.1, according to G. Van Biesbroeck. Photography with long-focus telescopes is employed successfully where the separation is greater than 2″, and for smaller separations by use of special methods. From the photographs the similar orbits of the two components can be determined by referring the motions of the two stars to others nearby in the field.

14·3. The Apparent and True Orbits. The *apparent orbit* of the companion relative to the primary star is the projection of the true orbit on the plane at right angles to the line of sight. This observed orbit is an ellipse and the law of areas is fulfilled by the line

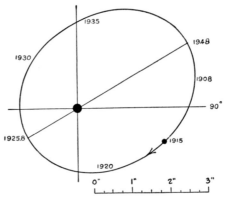

Fɪɢ. 14·3.   Orbit of Krueger 60.   The relative apparent orbit of the fainter star as determined by R. G. Aitken.

joining the two stars, but the primary star is not likely to be at the focus of the ellipse. The *true orbit* is calculated from the apparent orbit by one of several methods. It has the primary star at one focus and may be in any plane at all.

The *elements of the relative orbit* resemble the elements of a planetary orbit (7·26). They are: a, the semi-major axis of the orbit, or the mean distance between the stars, expressed in seconds of arc; T, the time of *periastron* passage, that is, when the stars are nearest; e, the eccentricity; i, the inclination of the orbit plane to the plane through the primary star at right angles to the line of sight; Ω, the position angle of the node that lies between 0° and 180°; ω, the angle in the plane of the true orbit between that node and the periastron point, in the direction of motion. P denotes the period of revolution in years.

When the parallax of the binary is known, the linear scale of the orbit can be found by the relation: a (in astronomical units) = a (in seconds of arc)/parallax. Everything is then known about the orbit, except which end is tipped toward us; it remains to be decided by the spectroscope whether the companion is approaching or receding from us when it passes the node.

14·4. Examples of Visual Binaries. More than 2500 visual binaries have already shown evidence of orbital motion. More than 10 per cent of these have revolved far enough since their discoveries to

| 1908 | 1915 | 1920 |

FIG. 14·4. Binary Star Krueger 60. Between 1908 and 1920 the binary, in the upper left corners, completed about a quarter of a revolution. Note in Fig. 13·16 the further progress of the revolution by 1939. (*Photographs by E. E. Barnard, Yerkes Observatory*)

permit definitive determinations of their orbits. Some characteristics of a few binaries are given in Table 14·I, which is taken mainly from a more extended table by P. van de Kamp.

TABLE 14·I   ORBITS OF VISUAL BINARIES

Name	Visual Magnitudes		Period P	Semi-Major Axis a	Eccen-tricity e	Parallax p	Masses m_1	m_2
BD −8° 4352	10.1	10.3	1.7	0″.22		0″.157	(1.0)	
Delta Equulei	5.2	5.2	5.7	0 .26	0.39	.052	2.0	1.9
42 Comae	5.2	5.2	25.8	0 .66	.52	.051	(2.2)	
Procyon	0.4	10.6	40.6	4 .55	.31	.287	1.8	0.6
Krueger 60	9.8	11.5	44.6	2 .41	.41	.253	0.3	0.2
Sirius	−1.5	8.6	49.9	7 .62	.59	.379	2.3	1.0
Alpha Centauri	0.1	1.4	80.1	17 .66	.52	.760	1.1	0.9
Castor	2.0	2.8	380	5 .84	.37	.074	(3.4)	

BD −8° 4352. This binary has the exceptionally short period of 1.7 years. The average separation of the two stars does not greatly exceed the earth's distance from the sun.

Delta Equulei. Also revolving in a very short period, the components have a separation less than Jupiter's distance from the sun.

42 Comae. The orbit is almost edgewise to the sun. It may not be precisely so, because eclipses have not been observed.

Krueger 60. This binary (Fig. 14·4) has an unusually small mass. The fainter component is a flare star (Fig. 13·16).

Alpha Centauri. The nearest system to the sun, it was one of the first double stars to be discovered. The separation at periastron is a little more than Saturn's distance from the sun, and at apastron is midway between the mean distances of Neptune and Pluto from the sun.

Castor. This familiar double star was the first to be observed in revolution, although its period is nearly 4 centuries. The average separation (Fig. 14·7) is more than twice the mean distance of Pluto from the sun. At periastron in 1968 the two stars will be 55 astronomical units apart.

14·5. Companions of Sirius and Procyon. The discoveries of the faint companions of Sirius and Procyon constitute the first chapter of what has been called the "astronomy of the invisible," namely,

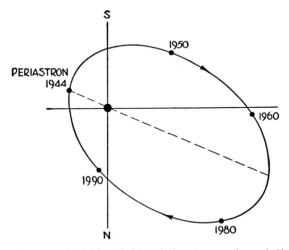

FIG. 14·5. Apparent Relative Orbit of the Companion of Sirius. The two stars were least separated in 1944.

the detection of unseen celestial bodies by their gravitational effects on the motions of visible bodies. The discovery of Neptune (8·37) is another famous example. As in the case of Neptune, the companions of both stars were subsequently observed with the telescope.

F. W. Bessel, at Königsberg in 1844, announced that Sirius did not have the uniform proper motion that characterizes single stars, but was pursuing a wavy course among its neighbors in the sky. Having also found a similar fluctuation in the proper motion of Procyon, he concluded that both stars were attended by unseen companions and that the mutual revolutions of the pairs were causing waves in the proper motions of the primary stars. Later, the orbits of both systems were calculated, although the companion stars had not yet been detected.

The companion of Sirius was first observed, in 1862, by Alvan Clark, a telescope maker who was using the bright star for testing the 18½-inch refractor now at Dearborn Observatory. Despite the brilliance of its primary, the 8th-magnitude companion is not difficult to see with a large telescope, except near its periastron. This star was among the first-known examples of the very dense white dwarf stars. The companion of Procyon proved to be more elusive; it was finally seen at Lick Observatory in 1896.

14·6. Unseen Companions. Variable proper motions of other apparently single stars have been discovered in recent times by photographic means. In one case the fainter companion has since been observed, that of the 11th-magnitude red dwarf star Ross 614 at the distance from us of 13 light years. Calculation of the orbit by S. L. Lippincott showed that the pair would be most widely separated in 1955. The 15th-magnitude companion was then seen and photographed by Walter Baade with the 200-inch telescope. Both stars have very small masses.

There are frequent cases where periodic perturbations of the revolutions of visual binary stars reveal the presence of third bodies in the systems. An example is the binary 61 Cygni, which has been studied by K. Aa. Strand. Here the two visible members revolve in a period of 720 years, while an invisible companion revolves around one of them in a period of nearly 5 years. There are also cases where the orbits of spectroscopic binaries were found to be disturbed and where the spectrum of a third star of the system was subsequently detected. An example is the eclipsing star Algol.

14·7. Multiple Systems. The presence of more than two stars in binary systems is not exceptional. An estimate that 5 per cent of visual binaries are at least triple systems is considered conservative. A common type of triple system is represented by Alpha Centauri, where the binary is attended by a remote companion, Proxima. A similar pattern is found in the system of Castor, except that each of the three stars is a spectroscopic binary.

The familiar double-double Epsilon Lyrae is typical of quadruple systems. Two moderately wide pairs of stars mutually revolve in a period of several hundred thousand years. Another interesting

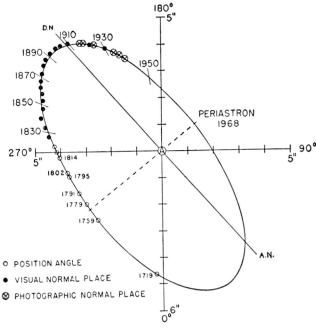

FIG. 14·7. Apparent Orbit of Castor. (*Determined by K. Aa. Strand*)

example is Zeta Cancri, recently studied by C. E. Gasteyer at Dearborn Observatory. Two pairs of stars revolve in periods of 59.7 and 17.5 years, respectively, and move around a common center once in 1150 years. One star of the latter pair, not observed with the telescope, is recognized by the 17.5-year revolution of its companion.

14·8. Masses of Visual Binaries. The mass of a celestial body can be determined whenever its gravitational effect on the motion of another body a known distance away is appreciable. This method does not apply to single stars, which are too far removed from other stars to have their motions affected noticeably; nor to the majority of visual binary stars, which have thus far given no evidence of mutual revolution. It can be used to evaluate the combined masses of binary systems that have progressed far enough in their revolutions so that their orbits have been calculated. This is an important result of the studies of visual binaries.

By the restatement of Kepler's harmonic law (7·22) the sum of the masses, m_1 and m_2, of the two components of a binary system, in terms of the sun's mass (the earth's relatively small mass is neglected), is given by the relation:

$$m_1 + m_2 = a^3/P^2 p^3,$$

where a is the semimajor axis of the relative orbit in seconds of arc, P is the period of revolution in sidereal years, and p is the parallax in seconds of arc.

The sum of the masses is all that can be determined from the relative orbit. When, however, the revolutions of the two stars have been observed with reference to neighboring stars in the field, the individual masses become known. The center of mass of the system is thereby established, and the ratio of the masses is inversely as the ratio of the distances of the two stars from this point.

As an example of the use of the above relation, the sum of the masses of Sirius and its companion is calculated from the data in Table 14·I as follows:

$$m_1 + m_2 = (7.62)^3/(49.9)^2(0.379)^3 = 443/136 = 3.3.$$

The combined mass of Sirius and its companion is 3.3 times the sun's mass.

14·9. The Mass-Luminosity Relation. Studies of binary stars led to the discovery by A. S. Eddington, in 1924, of a simple and useful relation between the masses and luminosities of stars in general. The more massive the star, the greater is its absolute brightness. In Fig. 14·9, the logarithms of the masses of a number of stars in binary systems in terms of the sun's mass are plotted against their absolute bolometric magnitudes. *Bolometric magnitude* refers to the radiation of a star in all wavelengths, which can be derived from the visual absolute magnitude and spectral type with allowance for the absorption of the starlight by the earth's atmosphere. The mass of a single star may be read from this curve if the absolute bolometric magnitude is known and if the star is of the type that conforms to this relation.

Giant and main-sequence stars show in general a close agreement with the mass-luminosity relation. Special groups of stars do not conform. Among these are a number of supergiants and white dwarf stars. Compared with main-sequence stars of equal mass, the white dwarfs are the fainter by several magnitudes.

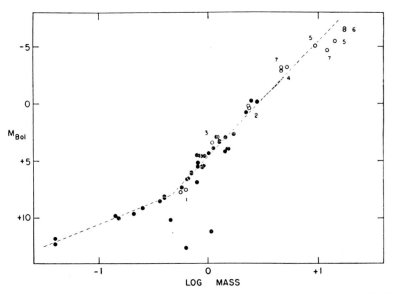

Fig. 14·9. Mass-Luminosity Relation for Stars of Visual Binaries (filled circles) and Spectroscopic Binaries (open circles). The three points below the curve represent white dwarf stars. (*Diagram by K. Aa. Strand*)

14·10. Dynamical Parallaxes. The formula of Section 14·8 in the form:

$$p^3 = a^3/P^2(m_1 + m_2)$$

may be employed to determine the parallaxes of binary systems when the combined masses of the component are already known. An approximate value of the sum of the masses can be used, because the parallax is inversely proportional to the cube root of this sum. Parallaxes of systems so determined are known as *dynamical parallaxes.*

Because the combined mass of a binary system is usually not far from twice the sun's mass, a preliminary value of the parallax is found by putting $m_1 + m_2 = 2$ in the preceding formula, when a and P are known. Given the apparent magnitudes of the two stars and their preliminary distances from us, their absolute magnitudes are calculated, and more nearly correct masses are obtained from the curve of Fig. 14·9. The required parallax of the system is finally found by substituting the new masses in the formula.

By a procedure that depends primarily on the mass-luminosity relation, H. N. Russell and Charlotte Moore calculated the dynamical parallaxes of more than 2000 visual binary systems. Such parallaxes for appropriate systems having well-defined orbits have statistical probable errors of 5 per cent.

SPECTROSCOPIC BINARIES

Binary stars having their components so close together that they appear as single stars with the telescope are discovered and studied in photographs of their spectra. Unless their orbits are at right angles to the line of sight, the revolving stars alternately approach and recede from the earth. The lines in the spectra are displaced by the Doppler effect (4·9) to the violet in the first case and to the red in the second, so that they oscillate in the periods of the revolutions. Spectroscopic binaries are not to be confused with pulsating stars (13·4), where the spectrum lines also oscillate.

14·11. Oscillations of Spectrum Lines. The brighter component of Mizar, the first visual double star to be reported, was the first

FIG. 14·11. Spectrum of Mizar. The lines of the two components of the binary are separated in the upper spectrogram and superposed in the lower one. (*Yerkes Observatory photographs*)

spectroscopic binary to become known, in 1889. The lines in the spectrum of this star were found to be double in some objective prism photographs at Harvard Observatory, whereas they were single in others.

Mizar is an example of spectroscopic binaries having components about equally bright and of the same spectral type. The spectrum shows two sets of lines that oscillate in opposite phase. When one star is approaching us in its revolution, the other star is receding from us. The lines in the spectrum of the first star are displaced to the violet, while those of the second star are displaced to the red, and the lines appear double. About a quarter of the period later, when both stars are moving across the line of sight, the lines of the two spectra have no Doppler displacements caused by the revolutions and are accordingly superposed.

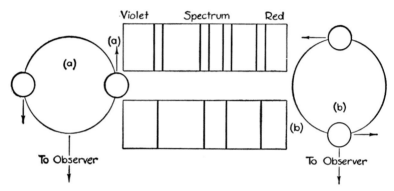

FIG. 14·11A. Doppler Displacements in the Spectrum of Mizar. (a) When one star approaches and the other recedes from us, the lines are double. (b) When both stars are moving across the line of sight, the two sets of lines are undisplaced by the revolution and are superposed.

If one member of a pair is as much as 1 magnitude brighter than the other, which is true of most of these binaries, only the spectrum of the brighter star is likely to be visible. The periodic oscillation of the lines in the spectrum shows that the star is a binary. Examples of spectroscopic binaries among the brighter stars are Spica, Capella, Castor, and Algol.

14·12. The Velocity Curve of one of the stars of a spectroscopic binary shows how the velocity of the star in the line of sight varies during a complete revolution. It is a smooth curve drawn to represent the observed radial velocities of a star at different phases of its revolution; the radial velocities are calculated from the displacements of the spectrum lines measured in photographs taken at the different phases.

If the orbit is circular, the radial velocities are represented by a sine curve. If the orbit is elliptical, the form of the velocity curve depends on the eccentricity of the ellipse and also on its orientation when projected on a plane passing through the line of sight. Fig. 14·12 shows the form of the velocity curve for an ellipse of moderate

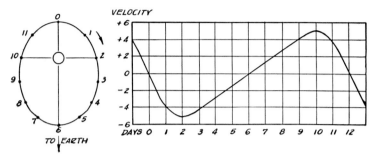

FIG. 14·12. Relation Between Orbit and Velocity Curve of a Spectroscopic Binary. The period of the revolution is 12 days. Only one spectrum appears. The star approaches the earth from phase 0 to 6 days. Maximum radial velocities occur at 2 and 10 days, when the star is crossing the "plane of the sky."

eccentricity, having its projected major axis directed toward the earth. Velocity of recession is denoted by the plus sign and of approach by the minus sign.

Conversely, when the velocity curve is known, the projected orbit of the star can be calculated by an appropriate method. Whenever

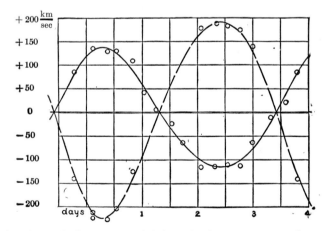

FIG. 14·12A. Velocity Curves of Spica. Both spectra were observed, but the lines of the fainter component were clearly seen only near the times of greatest separation of the lines. (*Publications of the Allegheny Observatory*)

the lines of both spectra are visible in the photographs, it is possible to determine the velocity curves (Fig. 14·12A) and projected orbits of both components of the binary.

14·13. Orbits of Spectroscopic Binaries.   It is the projection of the orbit on a plane through the line of sight that is calculated from the velocity curve.   The inclination, i, of the orbit plane to the plane of the sky cannot be determined from the spectrum.   The semi-major axis, a, of the orbit is derived in combination with the inclination in the quantity $a \sin i$.   Thus the actual size of the orbit remains unknown unless it can be found separately in another way; it can be found if the double star is an eclipsing binary.   The other elements of the orbit are determined uniquely from the radial velocities.

The masses of the two stars of the binary are also uncertain unless the inclination of the orbit plane is known.   When both spectra are visible, the value of $(m_1 + m_2) \sin^3 i$ is found by use of a formula similar to the one previously given (14·8).   In such cases the ratio of the masses, m_1/m_2, is taken from the velocity curves; it varies inversely as the ratio of the velocity ranges of the two stars.

As an example, the velocity range of the brighter component of Spica (Fig. 14·12A) is 252 km/sec, and that of the fainter star is 416 km/sec.   The ratio of the masses, m_1/m_2, is 416/252, or 1.6.   The calculation of the projected orbits gives $(m_1 + m_2) \sin^3 i = 15.4$ times the sun's mass.   If the inclination of the orbits to the plane of the sky is not far from 90°, $m_1 + m_2 = 15.4$; and the mass of the brighter component of Spica is 9.6 times the sun's mass, while the fainter star is 5.8 times as massive as the sun.

Studies of the spectra of certain eclipsing binaries (14·23) by Otto Struve and others have shown that the revolving stars are surrounded by gas streams, which are going around at different speeds from those of the stars themselves.   Dark lines abstracted from the starlight by the swirling gases blend with the dark lines in the spectra of those stars.   Unless the effects of the gas streams around such binaries are allowed for, the radial velocities from the confused lines and the orbits derived from them are subject to considerable error.

14·14. Features of Binary Systems.   Among the characteristics of binary systems that might seem to provide clues as to their origin and development, we note the following:

(1) The great number of such systems informs us that the process which develops them is not unusual. As an example, very nearly half of the 56 stars within 16 light years from the sun are double or triple systems.

(2) The great variety in their separations. There is a gradation from rapidly revolving pairs almost in contact to binaries having so widely separated components that the only observed connection between them is their common motion through space.

(3) The correlation between eccentricity of orbit and length of period. There is a fairly steady statistical increase in eccentricity from nearly circular orbits of binaries having periods of a few hours or days to values around 0.7 for pairs with periods of revolution running into many hundreds of years.

(4) The swirling gas streams surrounding many close spectroscopic binaries.

(5) The systematic difference in spectral type of the components of visual binaries, first reported, in 1923, by F. C. Leonard. If both stars have the same brightness, their spectral types are the same. If they are main-sequence stars of different brightness, the brighter star is generally the bluer; if they are giants, the brighter star is likely to be the redder of the two.

(6) The systematic difference in the speeds of rotation of the components of visual binaries (14·27).

14·15. The Problem of Their Origin has long been debated. The *fission theory*, as explained by J. H. Jeans, G. H. Darwin, and others, was favored in former times, and some recent efforts have been made to revive it in amended form. The theory begins with a single star shrinking under the action of gravity, thus progressively rotating faster and increasing its equatorial bulge until the star approaches instability. We note presently that the rotations of some of the hotter stars are almost fast enough to threaten their stability.

When a critical stage in the process is reached, the theory based on a conventional model suggests that the star's equator might begin to be drawn out into an ellipse. Later, the star might assume the form of a dumbbell, or pear, and finally divide. The resulting pair of stars would at first rotate and revolve in the same period; but further shrinkage could put the two motions out of step, preparing the way for effects of tidal friction. The components might then increase their separation and period of revolution, but to a limited extent unless the binary is supplied in some way with many times its initial angular momentum.

The *separate nuclei theory* carries the problem back to early stages in the formations of stars from turbulent cosmic clouds. It supposes that binary-star patterns are set by mutually revolving proto-stars condensing from the clouds.

ECLIPSING BINARIES

A spectroscopic binary is also an eclipsing binary when its orbit is so nearly edgewise to the earth that the revolving stars undergo mutual eclipses. Because the system appears as a single star with the telescope, what is observed is that the light of the star becomes fainter at regular intervals. Eclipsing binaries are variable stars only because the planes of their orbits happen to pass nearly through the earth's position. To an observer in another part of our galaxy their light might be practically constant, and another group of spectroscopic binaries, to us invariable in brightness, would exhibit eclipse phenomena.

14·16. Algol, the "Demon Star," is the most familiar of the eclipsing binaries and was the first of this type to become known. The discovery that its light diminishes at intervals of about 2 days and 21 hours was made as early as 1783, and the theory was then proposed that the bright star is partially eclipsed by a faint companion revolving around it in this period. The correctness of this view was established in 1889, when a spectroscopic study of Algol showed that it is a binary and that the radial velocity of the bright star changes from recession to approach at the time of the eclipse, as the theory required.

The brighter, B8 component of Algol has 3 times the diameter of the sun. The companion is fainter by 3 magnitudes, but its diameter is 20 per cent greater than that of the brighter star. The centers of the two stars are 13 million miles apart, or slightly more than a third of the average distance of Mercury from the sun. Their orbits are inclined 8° from the edgewise position relative to the earth. Once in each revolution the companion passes between us and the bright star (Fig. 14·16), partially eclipsing it for nearly 10 hours and reducing the light of the system at the middle of the eclipse to a third its normal brightness. The slight decrease in the light midway between the primary eclipses occurs when the companion is partially eclipsed by the brighter star. A third star revolving around the two in a period of 1.87 years, contributes a number of narrow lines to the spectrum of the system.

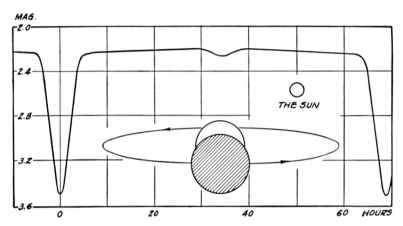

Fig. 14·16. Light Curve and System of Algol. The size of the sun is shown on the same scale. (*Light curve and orbit by Joel Stebbins*)

The periods of eclipsing binaries range from 80 minutes in the case of WZ Sagittae to 27 years for Epsilon Aurigae, and are frequently around 2 or 3 days.

14·17. The Light Variations. The light curve of an eclipsing binary shows how the magnitude of the system varies through a complete revolution. Twice during a revolution the curve drops to a minimum and rises again. The deeper minimum, or *primary minimum,* occurs when the star having the greater surface brightness is being eclipsed; the shallower one, or *secondary minimum,* occurs when that star is eclipsing its companion.

Even when the eclipses are not occurring, the light continues to vary appreciably in many of these systems, mainly because the stars are ellipsoids. They are elongated by mutual tidal action, each of the pair in the direction of the other, a relation that is maintained by the equality of their periods of rotation and revolution. During the eclipses the stars are seen end-on; halfway between the eclipses they are presented broadside, so that their disks are larger and the stars are accordingly brighter. Thus the light of the system rises to maxima midway between the minima (Fig. 14·17). This effect becomes especially conspicuous when the two stars are almost in contact.

The hemispheres of the two stars that face each other are made brighter by the radiation of the other star. The difference is greater for the two hemispheres of the less luminous star, so that

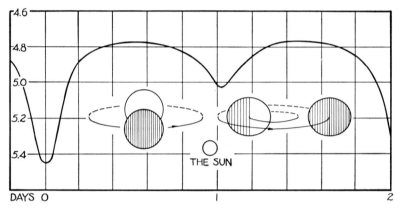

FIG. 14·17. Light Curve and System of the Eclipsing Binary u Herculis. The binary is shown at primary minimum and greatest elongation.

the light curve is higher near the secondary minimum (Fig. 14·17). In the more widely separated eclipsing binaries both ellipticity and radiation effects are so slight that the light curves outside the eclipses are practically horizontal (Fig. 14·18).

14·18. Light Variations During Eclipses. The eclipses of binary stars, like eclipses of the sun, may be total, annular, or partial. During a total eclipse the light remains constant at the minimum, and the duration of this phase is longest as compared with the whole eclipse when the orbit is edgewise to us and when the two stars differ greatly in size. That the light does not vanish during totality (the greatest observed decrease is 4 magnitudes) shows that the larger star is not dark, although it is usually the fainter of the two. When an eclipse is annular, the light may not remain quite constant because the eclipsed star, as in the case of the sun, is likely to be somewhat less bright near the edge than at the center.

When an eclipse is partial, or is total or annular only for an instant, the curve drops to its lowest point and at once begins to rise. In general, the depths and shapes of the light curve during eclipses depend on the relative size and brightness of the two stars and on the inclination of the orbit. The secondary minimum is scarcely discernible in some systems, whereas in others it may equal the primary minimum in depth. The fraction of the period in which the eclipses are occurring depends on the ratio between the sum of the radii of the two stars and the radius of the orbit. If the fraction is large, the stars are revolving almost or actually in contact.

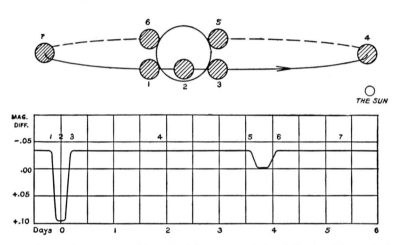

THE SUN

FIG. 14·18. Apparent Orbit and Light Curve of the Eclipsing Binary 1 H. Cassiopeiae. The primary eclipse, of the bright star by its smaller companion, is annular. The secondary eclipse is total. Tidal and reflection effects are inconspicuous, because of the wide separation of the stars.
(Light curve and orbit by Joel Stebbins)

14·19. The Photometric Orbit. For any model of an eclipsing system, in which the inclination of the orbit is specified, it is possible to predict the form of the light curve. Conversely, when the light curve is determined by photometric observations, it is possible to calculate the elements of the orbit and the dimensions of the two stars in terms of the radius of the relative orbit.

One of the elements so determined is the inclination, i, of the orbit to the plane at right angles to the line of sight. If the spectroscopic orbit of each star is also known, we can return to it and supply the value of i in the expressions $a \sin i$, $m_1 \sin^3 i$, and $m_2 \sin^3 i$ (14·13), thus separately determining the radius of the relative orbit and the masses of the stars. Going back to the photometric orbit, in which the dimensions are derived in terms of the radius of the orbit, we have finally the absolute dimensions of the stars themselves. Thus the combination of the photometric and spectro-scopic orbits permits the evaluation of the sizes and masses, and therefore the densities of the stars—data of great value in studies of the constitution of the stars.

In the study of eclipsing systems we have an example of the power of astronomical research. The largest telescope shows any one of these systems only as a point of light fluctuating periodically in brightness. Yet the observations of this light with the photom-eter and spectroscope and the judicious use of analysis lead to fairly complete specifications of the remote binary systems.

14·20. Eclipsing Binaries Having Elliptic Orbits. Most of these systems have nearly circular orbits. In cases where the orbits are

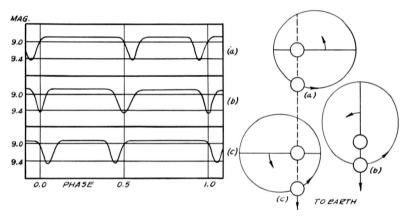

FIG. 14·20. Light Curves and Orbit of the Eclipsing Binary GL Carinae. The major axis of the orbit rotates in a period of 25 years. Note the difference in the light curves corresponding to three different directions of the major axis. (*From data by Henrietta Swope, Harvard Observatory*)

considerably eccentric, additional effects are observed in the light curves, which follow from the law of equal areas (7·15) in its gen-eral form; the stars revolve faster near periastron. Two effects are as follows:

(1) The two eclipses are of unequal durations. The eclipse that occurs nearer periastron is the shorter. The difference is greatest (*b*) when the major axis of the orbit is directed toward the earth.

(2) The intervals between the minima are unequal. The interval including periastron passage is the shorter. This difference is great-

est, as for (a) and (c), when the major axis of the orbit is perpendicular to the line of sight.

In some of these systems the major axis of the orbit rotates rather rapidly in the direction the stars revolve, although in most systems the period of this rotation runs into hundreds of thousand years. The advance of periastron is caused by the oblateness of the stars. Thus in the period of rotation of the axis the light curve exhibits a cycle of the two effects that have been described. As an example, the major axis of the orbit of GL Carinae rotates in a period of 25 years. The primary and secondary minima happen to have the same depth in the light curves of this system (Fig. 14·20).

Other noteworthy features of certain eclipsing binaries are mentioned in a few sections that follow.

14·21. The Eclipsing Binary Zeta Aurigae is one that permits the study of a star's atmosphere at different levels. It consists of a B8 star considerably larger than the sun and a K5 supergiant star. The two stars have nearly the same photographic magnitude. They mutually revolve once in 972 days, or about 3 times in 8 years. The principal eclipse, of the blue star by the red one, is total for 37 days preceded and followed by partial phases, each lasting for 32 hours.

The most remarkable features are presented during the week before the eclipse begins and the week after it ends, while the smaller star is passing behind the atmosphere of the larger one. Fig. 14·21 shows spectra of Zeta Aurigae photographed by D. B. McLaughlin from January 20 to 28, 1948. They begin shortly before the blue star has come out from total eclipse, and end when it has almost risen from behind the upper levels of the red star's atmosphere.

In the first photograph the spectrum of the large red star appears alone. In the third the blue star has completely emerged from behind its companion, adding its spectrum containing strong hydrogen lines. Here we also see dark lines abstracted from the light of the blue star by the red star's atmosphere, and in the later photographs we note how these lines fade as the blue star shines through successively higher levels of that atmosphere.

A detailed study of the spectra has shown that the extensive atmosphere of the red supergiant is arranged in strata. Atoms of neutral metals are prominent in the gases at the lowest levels. Atoms of ionized metals occupy the intermediate levels. Hydrogen and ionized calcium are abundant throughout and display their dark lines up to the highest levels, at distances above the star's surface equal to nearly half its radius.

Three other supergiant eclipsing stars are known that permit similar studies of the atmospheres before and after the eclipses. These are 31 Cygni, 32 Cygni, and VV Cephei.

FIG. 14·21. Spectrum of Zeta Aurigae. On successive evenings from January 20 to 28, 1948, as the blue star emerges from eclipse and shines through increasingly higher levels of the red star's atmosphere. (*Photographs by Dean B. McLaughlin, University of Michigan Observatory*)

14·22. The Binary Epsilon Aurigae presents an interesting case where a periodic reduction in brightness is caused only by the passing of one star behind the cloudy atmosphere of the companion. This binary revolves in a period of 27.1 years. The whole eclipse lasts nearly two years, and the deepest phase, when the light is reduced 0.8 magnitude, has about half that duration. Struve in 1958 accounted tentatively for the eclipse as follows:

The binary consists of a type F supergiant and a relatively small companion, perhaps of type B, which is itself too faint to make an impression in the spectrum. The F star is not eclipsed directly by the companion, but by its enormous cloudy atmosphere. Gas clouds of this atmosphere are ionized by the radiations of both stars and are thereby made opaque enough to cause the observed dimming of

FIG. 14·22. Region of Zeta and Epsilon Aurigae. The arrow points to Zeta in eclipse. In the view at the right the eclipse has ended. Epsilon is the bright star at the top. (*Harvard Observatory photographs*)

the light of the system. The spectrum of the F star remains visible during the eclipse.

The latest eclipse of Epsilon Aurigae began in June, 1955, and ended in May, 1957. A doubling of many lines in the spectrum, observed at that eclipse by Otto Struve and Helen Pillans, is ascribed by them to clouds of gas around both stars, revolving generally in the direction of the orbital motion.

14·23. Gas Streams Around Close Binary Stars. Many close pairs of stars, where the separations are small compared with the diam-

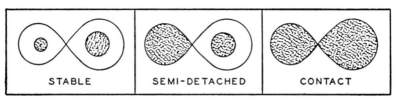

FIG 14·23. Types of Close and Contact Binaries. The stars are shaded. Critical equipotential curves resemble the figure 8. (*Diagram by Zdenek Kopal, University of Manchester*)

eters of the stars themselves, are involved in gas streams. The importance of such streams in the development of those binaries has been shown by F. B. Wood, by Z. Kopal, and by Struve and associates.

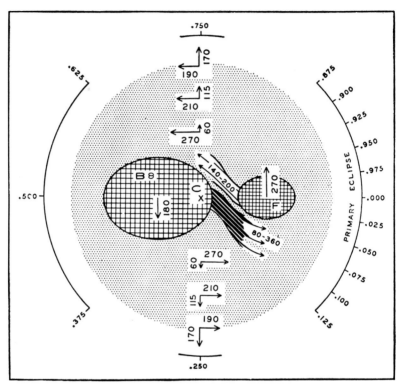

FIG. 14·23A.   Gas Streams Around Beta Lyrae.   The two stars are elongated by each other's attraction.   Arrows for star and gas motions are marked in kilometers per second.   On the outer scale, the phases of the revolution as seen from the earth correspond with those in Fig. 14·24.
(*Diagram by Otto Struve*)

If both stars are well within the critical equipotential surfaces between them (Fig. 14·23), the binary is *stable*. At the point where the surfaces join, the attractions toward the two stars are equal. When one star of a binary expands in its evolution from the main sequence until it fills its equipotential surface, the binary is *semidetached*. Material expelled from this star, as by prominence action, may swirl around the binary and eventually fall into one star or the other. Kopal points out that the less massive component is the first to do so in every known case. Yet the current theory of stellar evolution would lead us to expect exactly the opposite. If both stars expand until they fill their equipotential surfaces, the result is a *contact binary* that is surrounded by gas from both. A numerous class of these is that of the W Ursae Majoris binaries, having periods of revolution around half a day.

14·24. Beta Lyrae Involved in Gas Streams. Beta Lyrae is a well-known example of an eclipsing binary surrounded by gas streams. It consists of a larger B8 star and a smaller F companion, which is

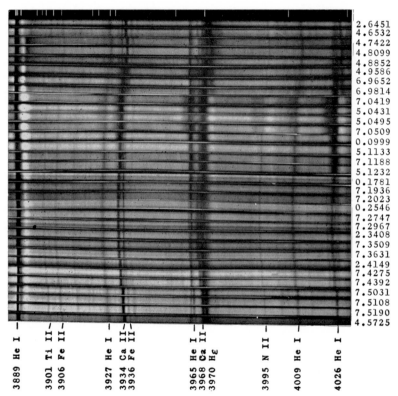

| 2.6451 |
| 4.6532 |
| 4.7422 |
| 4.8099 |
| 4.8852 |
| 4.9586 |
| 6.9652 |
| 6.9814 |
| 7.0419 |
| 5.0431 |
| 5.0495 |
| 7.0509 |
| 0.0999 |
| 5.1133 |
| 7.1188 |
| 5.1232 |
| 0.1781 |
| 7.1936 |
| 7.2023 |
| 0.2546 |
| 7.2747 |
| 7.2967 |
| 2.3408 |
| 7.3509 |
| 7.3631 |
| 2.4149 |
| 7.4275 |
| 7.4392 |
| 7.5031 |
| 7.5108 |
| 7.5190 |
| 4.5725 |

He I — 3889
Ti II — 3901
Fe II — 3906
He I — 3927
Ca II — 3934
Fe II — 3936
He I — 3965
Ca II — 3968
Hε — 3970
N II — 3995
He I — 4009
He I — 4026

FIG. 14·24. Spectra of Beta Lyrae in the Extreme Violet. (*Photographs by Jorge Sahade and Otto Struve with the 100-inch Mount Wilson telescope*)

in front at the primary eclipse and is enough fainter so that its spectrum is not observed. The two stars revolve in a period of $12^d 22^h 22^m$, which is increasing at the rate of about 10 seconds a

year.   Clouds of gas revolving around the binary add their dark
and bright lines to the spectrum.

Spectra of Beta Lyrae in the extreme violet, photographed by
Jorge Sahade and Otto Struve, are arranged in Fig. 14·24 in order
of phase of the binary revolution.   The phase, following the decimal point at the right of each spectrum, is the fraction of a complete revolution counted from the middle of the primary eclipse at
0.0000.   Prominent lines in the spectra are identified by their wavelengths and elements at the bottom.

Stationary interstellar lines, such as the narrow dark calcium line
at wavelength 3934 A, are used to align the spectra vertically.
Thus the displacements of other lines by the orbital motion are
clearly shown.   Note how the broad stellar line at 3934 and many
others form wavy velocity curves turned through 90°.   The broad
dark and bright lines of helium at 3889, however, are examples of
lines that do not follow the curve of the stellar lines.   These are
produced by gas clouds of the system, which swirl around the
binary in the direction but not in the period of the revolution.

ROTATIONS OF THE STARS

Before concluding the account of eclipsing binaries we consider
the evidence that these stars are rotating on their axes.   This brings
us to the rotations of single stars as well, as shown by the widening of their spectrum lines, and finally to the evidence of magnetic
fields in certain stars.

14·25. Rotations of Eclipsing Stars.   The spectroscopic method of
studying the sun's rotation (10·2), by comparing the Doppler shifts
of the lines at opposite edges of the disk, is not applicable ordinarily to stars that show no disks.   The method can be applied,
however, to some eclipsing binary stars.   Preceding the middle of
the eclipse of a star by a much fainter companion, the light comes
mainly from the part of the bright star that is rotating away from
us.   After the middle of eclipse the light comes mainly from the
part of the star that is rotating toward us.

Thus during the initial phase of the eclipse the lines of the star's
spectrum should be displaced farther toward the red, and during
the final phase they should be displaced farther toward the violet
end of the spectrum than can be ascribed to the revolution of the

star. This effect was first detected by Frank Schlesinger at Allegheny Observatory, in 1909, by the irregularity it caused in the velocity curve of the eclipsing binary Delta Librae. It was later observed in the curves of other eclipsing stars.

Beginning with these stars of known rotation and going on to spectroscopic binaries generally, assuming that each pair rotates and revolves in unison, it became possible to verify a Doppler effect that would be predicted for rotating stars. The spectrum lines are increasingly broadened as the speed of the rotation is greater. The way was now prepared for the study of the rotations of single stars.

14·26. Rotations of Single Stars. Otto Struve and C. T. Elvey at Yerkes Observatory, about 1930, were pioneers in the study of the

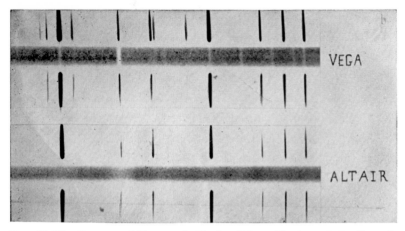

FIG. 14·26. Spectra of Vega and Altair. The widening of the lines in the spectrum of Altair is caused by the rapid rotation of this star. The narrower lines of Vega suggest that its axis is directed nearly toward us. These are negatives. (*Yerkes Observatory photographs*)

rotations of single stars from the contours of the lines in their spectra. The method was to compare the "washed out" lines of a star such as Altair (Fig. 14·26) with the sharp lines of a star of similar spectral type, such as Vega. The latter star is either in very slow rotation or, as seems more likely in this case, its axis is directed nearly toward us.

It was shown that such widening of the lines may be generally attributed to the rotations of the stars. Thus Altair rotates with a speed of at least 240 km/sec at its equator and in a period of 15

hours or less, depending on how nearly its axis is perpendicular
to the line of sight.

14·27. Rotations of Main-Sequence and Giant Stars. If the rotation axes of stars have random directions, it is easy to calculate from
the observed rotation speeds the average actual values for a particular class of stars. Single blue stars of the main sequence are likely
to have high speeds of rotation. Some have equatorial speeds of

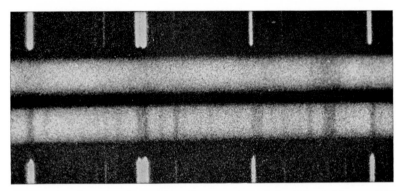

FIG. 14·27. Spectra of the Two Components of the Visual Binary ADS
8257. The lines in the spectrum of the brighter star (above) are much
more widened than are those of the fainter star (below). The bright
comparison lines are of iron. (*Photographs by Otto Struve with the
100-inch Mount Wilson telescope*)

300 km/sec or more; such swiftly rotating stars may not be far
from instability. The yellow and red stars of this sequence have
more moderate speeds, except those that occur in close binary
systems. Struve suggests that these yellow and red single stars may
have imparted much of their original spins to the revolutions of
their planets. If the sun were to absorb its planetary system, the
sun would rotate 30 times as fast as its present equatorial rate of
2 km/sec.

The brighter star of a main-sequence visual binary is likely to
rotate more rapidly than the fainter star, as Struve has observed
from the widening of the spectrum lines. An extreme example is
the binary ADS 8257 (Fig. 14·27). Although the two stars differ in
brightness by a whole magnitude, they are both of type F. The
lines in the spectrum of the brighter star (above) are made diffuse
by a rotation as fast as 100 km/sec at the equator, whereas the

lines of the fainter star (below) are practically unwidened, indicating a low speed of rotation.

Giant stars generally have slower rotations than corresponding main-sequence stars, as would be expected from the conservation of angular momentum (9·30) if they have expanded in their evolution from that sequence. Employing values of rotation speeds of giants determined by Arne Slettebak, Allan Sandage has calculated that when these giants were on the main sequence they were rotating in general as swiftly as do the stars that are now there.

14·28. Magnetic Fields of Stars. The Zeeman effect (10·18) in stellar spectra was discovered by H. W. Babcock at Mount Wilson Observatory in 1946 in the spectrum of the A-type star 78 Virginis. Employing a double polarizing analyzer, he observed a division of the lines corresponding to a polar field strength of 1500 gauss.

Babcock's catalog of 1958 lists 89 stars definitely showing magnetic fields and many others that probably show this effect. They are generally type A stars having sharp and unusually intense spectrum lines of metals such as chromium and strontium, and of rare earths such as europium. All the magnetic fields are variable in strength and some show reversals of polarity in cycles of a few days.

An example is α^2 Canum Ven. The polar magnetic field of this star varies in cycles of $5\frac{1}{2}$ days between extremes of +5000 and −4000 gauss, which are comparable with the strongest fields observed in sunspots. At the first extreme the lines of metals in the spectrum have their greatest intensity, and at the second the lines of the rare earths are the most intense. An unusually strong magnetic field was reported in 1960 in the case of the 8.6-magnitude type A star HD 215,441. The field is positive, varying irregularly from 12,000 to 34,400 gauss.

The proposal is made by Babcock that hydromagnetic fluctuations analogous to the 22-year solar magnetic cycle are occurring in the surface layers of these stars. Strong magnetic fields, as he explains, are the property of all rapidly rotating stars having convective outer zones; but they are observable only in the small proportion of such stars that have the rotation axes directed nearly toward the earth.

1. How is it possible to decide whether two stars that appear very close together are physically connected or accidentally double if their revolution has not been observed?

2. The companion of Sirius was discovered before it was seen, and it eventually proved to be a star of an unusual type. Explain.

3. What must be known about a visual binary in order to evaluate the sum of the masses of the two stars? the mass of each star?

4. Explain that the mass of a single star can be estimated when its absolute brightness is known.

5. Why do the lines in the spectrum of Mizar appear double at times and single at other times?

6. If the lines in the spectrum of a star are always single, how can it be decided whether it is an ordinary star, a spectroscopic binary in which the companion is too faint to show, or a pulsating star?

7. Algol was definitely proved to be an eclipsing binary when observations of its spectrum showed that the radial velocity of the brighter star changes from recession to approach at the time of minimum brightness. Explain.

8. What features of the light curve of Algol (Fig. 14·16) show that (a) the two stars have very unequal surface brightness? (b) the eclipses are partial? (c) the companion is more luminous on the side toward the brighter star?

9. What features of the light curve in Fig. 14·18 show that one eclipse is total and that the two stars are considerably separated?

10. Explain that the eclipsing binary Zeta Aurigae offers opportunity for examining different levels in the atmosphere of the larger star.

11. Repeated studies of the light curves of some eclipsing binaries having orbits of large eccentricity show that the major axes of the orbits are rotating. Explain.

12. Explain that the average rate of rotation of a class of single stars may be determined by the widening of the lines of their spectra.

13. If the lines in the spectrum of a type A star are narrow, the axis of the star's rotation is likely to be nearly in the line of sight. Explain.

14. Assign a possible reason for (a) the slower rotation of yellow and red stars than of blue stars of the main sequence; (b) the slower rotation of giant stars generally as compared with corresponding main-sequence stars.

1. Employing the values a, P, and p in Table 14·I, calculate (14·8) the combined mass of the binary star Alpha Centauri.

Answer: $m_1 + m_2 = 2.0$ times the sun's mass.

2. Employing the values of a, P, and $m_1 + m_2$ in Table 14·I, calculate (14·10) the parallax of Procyon.

Answer: The parallax is $0''.288$.

REFERENCES

Aitken, Robert G., *The Binary Stars*. Second edition. McGraw-Hill Book Company, New York, 1935.

Binnendijk, Leendert, *Properties of Double Stars*. University of Pennsylvania Press, Philadelphia, 1960.

Kopal, Zdenek, *Close Binary Systems*. John Wiley and Sons, New York, 1959.

van de Kamp, Peter, *Basic Astronomy*. The Macmillan Company, New York, 1952.

The 200-inch Telescope of the Palomar Observatory.

15

STAR CLUSTERS

GALACTIC CLUSTERS – GLOBULAR CLUSTERS

Star clusters are physically related groups of stars having their members less widely separated than are the stars around them. The common motion of the members of a cluster through the star fields suggests their common origin by the condensing and fracturing of a large cosmic gas cloud. Because the stars of a particular cluster are practically at the same distance from us, they may be compared fairly one with another. Although their ages are about the same, the members have different masses, and the more massive ones have evolved the faster. Thus the cluster stars can inform us of the course of stellar evolution.

Star clusters are associated with other galaxies as well as with our own. They are of two types: galactic, or open, clusters and globular clusters. An authoritative reference concerning them is Helen Sawyer Hogg's article in *Handbuch der Physik,* volume 53 (1959).

15·1. Types of Clusters. *Galactic clusters,* such as the double cluster in Perseus (Fig. 15·1), are so named because those in our galaxy are near its principal plane. Thus they appear in or near the Milky Way, except some of the very nearest ones, notably the Coma Berenices cluster, which is not far from the pole of the Milky Way. Also known as *open clusters,* they are rather loosely assembled. Their separate stars are distinguished with the telescope, and in some cases the brighter ones are visible to the

FIG. 15·1. Double Cluster in Perseus. (*Yerkes Observatory photograph*)

unaided eye. The nearest clusters, which are likely to have large proper motions, are sometimes called *moving clusters.*

Globular clusters are more compact and are spheroidal in form. The cluster M 13 in Hercules (Fig. 15·11) is an example. They are larger, more populous, and more luminous than the galactic clusters, and those in our galaxy are less confined to the vicinity of the Milky Way.

Star clusters, nebulae, and exterior galaxies were formerly cataloged together. They are often designated by their numbers in one of those catalogs. The great cluster in Hercules, for example, is known as NGC 6205, or as M 13. The first designation is its running number in Dreyer's *New General Catalogue* (1887); this catalog and its extensions in 1894 and 1908, known as the *Index Catalogue* (IC), list over 13,000 objects. The second designation of the Hercules cluster is its number in the catalog of 103 bright objects that the comet hunter Charles Messier prepared for the *Connaissance des Temps* of 1784. A useful list of these objects, with their positions in the sky, is given in *Sky and Telescope* for March, 1954.

GALACTIC CLUSTERS

15·2. Examples of Galactic Clusters. The cluster of the Pleiades, or "Seven Sisters," in Taurus is known to many people. The V-shaped Hyades cluster in the same constellation is also conspicuous in our skies. The brighter stars of both clusters are plainly visible to the naked eye, and those of the Coma Berenices cluster are faintly visible. The Praesepe cluster in Cancer (Fig. 15·7), also known as the "Beehive," the double cluster in Perseus, and a few others appear as hazy spots to the unaided eye and are resolved into stars with slight optical aid. These nearer clusters are well observed with binoculars. Many others can be viewed with small telescopes. Galactic clusters are prominent in photographs of the Milky Way.

About 500 galactic clusters are cataloged in the galactic system. Their memberships range from around 20 to a few hundred, and to more than a thousand in the rich Perseus clusters. Their visibility is limited because of their small memberships and the scarcity of high-luminosity stars in them. Many clusters must be unnoticed against the bright background of the Milky Way or concealed by the heavy dust in these directions. The galactic clusters we observe around us are all within 20,000 light years from the sun, but

Fig. 15·2. Region of the Pleiades. (*Yerkes Observatory photograph*)

they are doubtless as abundant in other parts of the spiral arms of our galaxy as they are in our own neighborhood.

15·3. The Ursa Major Cluster contains the bright stars of the Great Dipper, except its end stars Alpha and Eta, and several fainter stars of the constellation. Although its members are considerably separated in the sky because they are near us, they form a compact group having about the size of the smaller galactic clusters. Surrounding the cluster is a large and sparsely populated stream having so nearly the same motion as the cluster itself that all these stars were formerly believed to comprise together a cluster of extraordinary size.

The stream around the Ursa Major cluster includes such widely scattered stars as Sirius, Alpha Coronae, and Beta Aurigae. Nancy G. Roman's spectroscopic parallaxes at Yerkes Observatory show that this stream envelops not only the sun, which is itself not a member, but two other galactic clusters as well.

15·4. The Hyades Cluster. Just as the rails of a track seem to converge in the distance, so the parallel paths of stars in a cluster are directed toward a convergent point if the cluster is receding from us. This effect of perspective is especially noticeable in the proper motions of the Hyades cluster (Fig. 15·4), which is so near us that it covers an area of the sky 20° in diameter.

The Hyades cluster comprises the stars of the familiar group itself, except Aldebaran, which has an independent motion not shown in the figure, and of the region around it. The cluster has at least 150 members. Its denser part is 10 parsecs in diameter, and its center is 40 parsecs, or 130 light years, from the sun. The space motion of these stars is eastward and away from the sun. The con-

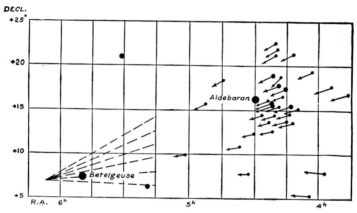

FIG. 15·4. Convergence of the Hyades Cluster. The V-shaped Hyades and neighboring stars in Taurus are converging toward a point in the sky east of Betelgeuse in Orion. Aldebaran is not a member of the moving cluster. The lengths of the arrows represent the proper motions of the cluster stars in an interval of 50,000 years. (*Adapted from a diagram by Lewis Boss*)

vergent point of their paths lies a little way east of Betelgeuse in Orion.

When the convergent point of a moving cluster is known and the proper motion, μ, and radial velocity, V, of one of its stars have been observed, the distance of that star and of any other member of the cluster with known proper motion can be calculated. The space velocity is $v = V/\cos \theta$, where θ (Fig. 15·4A) is the star's angular distance from the convergent point. The tangential velocity is $T = v \sin \theta$. The parallax can now be found from the relation (11·11): $p = 4.74\mu/T$.

As an example, the observed values for Delta Tauri in the Hyades

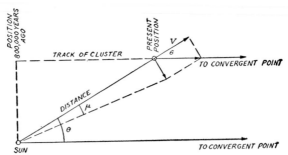

Fɪɢ. 15·4A. Track of the Hyades Cluster. The present distance of the cluster can be found when the proper motion, μ, radial velocity, V, and angular distance, θ, from the convergent point have been determined.

cluster are: $\mu = 0''.115$, $V = +38.6$ km/sec, and $\theta = 29°.1$. The resulting space velocity is 44.0 km/sec, and the parallax is $0''.025$. The distance of the star is therefore 40 parsecs.

The space velocity and θ define the track of the star with respect to the sun. By means of relations easily worked out from Fig. 15·4A it can be shown that the Hyades cluster was nearest the sun 800,000 years ago at the distance of 20 parsecs.

15·5. Color-Magnitude Diagram. Except for the very nearest clusters, the dimensions of star clusters are small enough to be neglected for the present purpose compared with their distances; the stars of a cluster are supposed to be at the same distance from us. Thus the apparent magnitudes, m, of these stars differ from the absolute magnitudes, M, by the same amount: $m - M = 5 \log r - 5$, where r is the distance of the cluster in parsecs.

When the apparent magnitudes of the cluster stars are plotted with respect to their spectral types, the array of points has the same significance as the spectrum-absolute magnitude diagram except for the constant difference $m - M$. When the color indexes are employed instead of the spectral types, we have the equivalent *color-apparent magnitude diagram* (Fig. 15·5).

Comparing this diagram for the Praesepe cluster with the standard spectrum-absolute magnitude diagram of Fig. 11·27 and remembering that color index has a known relation to spectral type, we see how the distance of the cluster may be determined. The method is to match comparable parts of the two arrays, to note the difference between the apparent and absolute magnitudes, and to calculate the distance by the formula given above. Allowance must be made for any dimming of the cluster stars by intervening

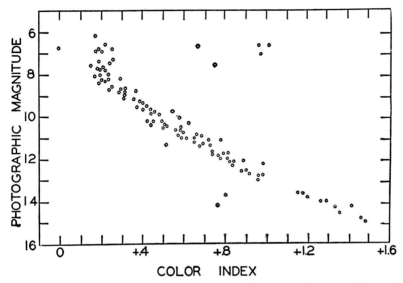

Fig. 15·5. Color-Magnitude Diagram of the Praesepe Cluster. (*Adapted from a diagram by H. L. Johnson*)

TABLE 15·I DISTANCES OF GALACTIC CLUSTERS *

Cluster	Constellation	Parsecs	Light Years
Hyades	Taurus	40	130
Coma	Coma Berenices	80	260
Pleiades	Taurus	126	410
Praesepe	Cancer	158	515
M 39	Cygnus	250	820
IC 4665	Ophiuchus	330	1080
M 34	Perseus	440	1440
M 25	Sagittarius	550	1790
M 67	Cancer	830	2710
NGC 2264	Monoceros	870	2840
M 36	Auriga	1260	4110
NGC 2362	Canis Major	1450	4730
NGC 6530	Sagittarius	1580	5150
NGC 2244	Monoceros	1660	5410
M 11	Scutum	1740	5670
Double	Perseus	2250	7340

* Determined photoelectrically by Harold L. Johnson, Lowell Observatory.

cosmic dust, which would make the calculated distance greater
than the actual distance, and also for any displacement of the
cluster stars in their evolution from the standard main sequence.
The distance of the Praesepe cluster so determined and corrected
is 158 parsecs, or 515 light years.

15·6. Star Clusters of Different Ages. In the color-magnitude diagram of the Praesepe cluster, the top of the main sequence bends
to the right, and a few of the brightest stars are still farther to the
right. Turning now to Fig. 15·6, we see that other clusters break
off the sequence at other places. Main-sequence stars are absent in
galactic clusters above the breaks. The opinion is that the differ-

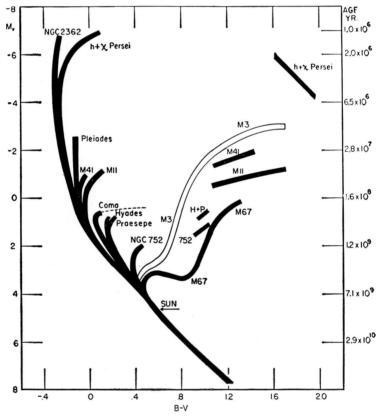

FIG. 15·6. Color-Magnitude Diagrams for 10 Galactic Clusters and the
Globular Cluster M 3 (Fig. 15·15). Color indexes are plotted with respect to absolute visual magnitudes. (*Diagram by Allan R. Sandage*)

ences between such diagrams are mainly effects of advancing age of the clusters and also of their chemical composition.

As the clusters grow older, according to a theory of stellar evolution that is examined further in the following chapter, its stars leave the main sequence and move into the giant sequences. The more luminous stars shift more rapidly, because they are converting their hydrogen to heavier elements at a faster rate. The less luminous stars have not yet had time to show conspicuous shifts.

NGC 2362 is the youngest cluster represented in the figure; its age is given as only 10^6 years. The double cluster in Perseus is also in its youth, according to this view, which seems to find support in the unusually large memberships of these clusters and the extent of the main sequence still intact. The Pleiades cluster is middle-aged, and the Hyades and Praesepe clusters are approaching old age. The cluster M 67 is the oldest galactic cluster represented in Sandage's diagram of 1957; its age is 5×10^9 years by the dating process then employed. Another cluster, NGC 188, was represented in a later diagram as about twice as old; and all the ages were increased by a revised dating process.

15·7. Lifetimes of Clusters. The common motion of the stars of a cluster suggests their common origin, probably by the condensation of a very large cloud of interstellar gas and dust. The maintenance

Fig. 15·7. Praesepe Cluster in Cancer. (*Photograph by William Henry*)

of the common motion shows that the cluster stars are not quickly affected by the field stars through which they pass. Yet at each encounter with a field star the cluster stars are attracted in slightly different amounts depending on how near the intruder they pass. Thus very gradually stripped of members by the field stars and even more effectively by collisions with interstellar clouds, as Lyman Spitzer has shown, the cluster should ultimately be dispersed, generally in a shorter time than the lifetime of the galaxy itself. The more compact clusters and especially those farther removed from the central plane of the star clouds should have the longer lives.

The galactic cluster M 67, where the stars break from the main sequence (Fig. 15·6) along with those of the durable globular cluster M 3, has excellent reason for its long life. This cluster near Alpha Cancri is about 10° from the Praesepe cluster. Both clusters are more than 30° from the central line of the Milky Way. M 67, however, is 5 times as remote as Praesepe and is at an unusually great linear distance above the principal plane of the Galaxy. There it is relatively immune to disturbances which hasten the disruption of clusters; it has retained at least 500 members.

15·8. Very Young Clusters. Some galactic clusters, such as NGC 2362, are even more youthful than the double cluster in Perseus. The upper parts of their main sequences in the color-magnitude diagrams are intact, containing the highly luminous O and B stars, which have arrived there a million years or so after their births. The less luminous stars from the blue down to the red ones lie above the main sequence, presumably because they have not yet had time to arrive. G. H. Herbig reported such variance of the redder stars from the standard main sequence in a heavily clouded region of Taurus, and P. P. Parenago at Moscow found for a group associated with the Orion nebula that stars redder than A5 had not yet reached the vicinity of this sequence.

An example of an extremely young galactic cluster is NGC 2264, about 15° east of Betelgeuse and 870 parsecs from us. M. F. Walker's color-magnitude diagram of this cluster shows the O and B stars on the main sequence. The redder stars depart abruptly from the sequence at A0 and tend to lie about 2 magnitudes above it. Many of these are variable in brightness and have been regarded as T Tauri stars (16·16), which are brightened irregularly by causes associated with their extreme youth.

Other examples of groups of stars recently emerged from nebulae

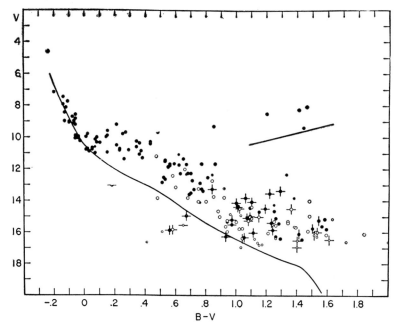

Fig. 15·8. Color-Apparent Magnitude Diagram of Cluster NGC 2264.
The dots represent photoelectric and the circles photographic measures.
Vertical lines denote known variable stars, and horizontal lines stars having bright Hα lines in their spectra. The curve is the standard main
sequence. (*Diagram by Merle F. Walker*)

are the associations of O and B stars, which are recognized by their
rapid spreading from their places of origin.

15·9. Associations of Stars. It has long been known that O and
early B stars tend to occur in groups in the Milky Way, which are
less compact than the galactic clusters. Several years ago, V. A.
Ambartsumian called attention to the temporary existence of such
associations; they are too feebly bound by gravitation to hold together very long, but their stars are evidently so youthful that they
have not had time to disperse. Some associations have been studied
by Adriaan Blaauw, W. W. Morgan, and others, who find that the
stars of each one are spreading rapidly from a common center
where they must have originated.

A group of 17 hot stars in Perseus is an example. It is known
as the Zeta Persei association from the name of its brightest member. The stars in its outskirts are moving at the rate of 14 km/sec
from a center where they were born only 1.3 million years ago.

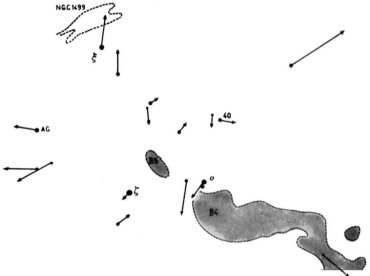

FIG. 15·9. The Zeta Persei Association. Arrows show the proper motions
of stars during the next 500,000 years. An emission nebula is near the
top, and two of the darkest nebulae from Barnard's Atlas are shown
below. (*Photograph and diagram by Adriaan Blaauw, Kapteyn Astronomical Laboratory, Groningen, Holland*)

Another association is centered near the Great Nebula in Orion and at about the same distance from us. Blue stars are withdrawing from the center mainly at the rate of 8 km/sec. But three of the stars, AE Aurigae, Mu Columbae, and 53 Arietis, have velocities of 106, 123, and 59 km/sec, respectively, away from this center. With such high speeds they seem to have escaped into other constellations only a few million years ago. Blaauw calls them "runaway stars." He has experimented with the hypothesis that these three single stars were originally the less massive components of binary systems. The primary stars may have exploded as supernovae, leaving their companions to continue on away from the center of the association with something like their former speeds of revolution in the binary systems. High-velocity stars are withdrawing from other OB associations as well. There are also associations of T Tauri stars (16·16).

GLOBULAR CLUSTERS

15·10. The Brightest Globular Clusters. About 120 globular clusters are recognized in the vicinity of our galaxy. These include a

Fig. 15·10. Globular Cluster Omega Centauri. (*Photograph with 60-inch reflector, Boyden Station of Harvard Observatory*)

dozen faint ones reported in 1955 by A. G. Wilson and G. O. Abell
from the Palomar Sky Survey and remote enough to be regarded
as intergalactic objects. Only a few of the apparently brightest
globular clusters are visible without the telescope.

The southern clusters Omega Centauri (Fig. 15·10) and 47 Tu-
canae are the brightest and also the nearest, at the distance of
22,000 light years. The former appears to the naked eye as a hazy
star of the 4th magnitude; it was recorded as a star by Ptolemy and
was later given a letter in the Bayer system. Because of their low
declinations, these two clusters are not favorably placed for observers anywhere in the United States.

The globular cluster M 13 in Hercules is the brightest and best
known to observers in middle northern latitudes, where it passes
nearly overhead in the early evenings of summer. This cluster and
M 22 in Sagittarius are faintly visible to the naked eye. M 5 in
Serpens, M 55 in Sagittarius, and M 3 in Canes Venatici can also
be glimpsed in favorable conditions.

15·11. The Hercules Cluster is spectacular as viewed with large
telescopes, and especially so in long-exposure photographs with
such telescopes (Fig. 15·11), where it appears not unlike a great

FIG. 15·11. Globular Cluster M 13 in Hercules. (*Palomar Observatory
photograph*)

celestial chrysanthemum. Its diameter in these photographs is about 18′, which at its distance of 30,000 light years corresponds to a linear diameter of 160 light years, or the distance of Spica from the sun. The cluster is estimated to contain 500,000 stars of average mass equal to that of the sun. The red stars of its main sequence have not yet been observed, and the stars in its central region are too congested to be counted separately. Around the center the density of stars may be 100 times as great as the average for the cluster and 50,000 times that of the stars in the sun's neighborhood.

Like other globular clusters, M 13 has an outline that is not quite circular. It is an oblate spheroid presumably flattened at the poles by its slow rotation, although no other evidence of rotation has been detected either directly or with the spectroscope. The apparent oblateness of the cluster is 0.05, or less than that of the planet Jupiter.

15·12. Variable Stars in Globular Clusters. A total of 1612 variable stars were reported, in 1961, by Helen Sawyer Hogg in more than 80 globular clusters that have been searched for such objects. The clusters M 3 and Omega Centauri are the richest in known variable stars, having 189 and 165 examples respectively. No varibles at all have been found in five clusters searched. Ninety per cent of the variables in globular clusters are RR Lyrae stars. The

FIG. 15·12. A Type II Cepheid in the Globular Cluster M 14. The arrows point to the variable star near maximum brightness at the left and minimum at the right. (*Photographs by Helen Sawyer Hogg with the 74-inch telescope, David Dunlap Observatory*)

remainder are of various kinds, most frequently cepheids of both types, Mira-type variables, and irregular variables.

Because the RR Lyrae stars were formerly believed to have the same median absolute magnitudes, the distances of globular clusters could be evaluated from the observed median apparent magnitudes of these variables observed in the clusters. By this means, Harlow Shapley, in 1917, determined the distances of the clusters. He then constructed a model of the cluster system with the idea that the array should be similar in extent and center to the system of the Milky Way.

Shapley's results brought out clearly for the first time the separate status of the Galaxy, and they prepared the way for the recognition of exterior galaxies. His original distances of the clusters and the dimensions of the Galaxy based on them were later reduced, when the importance of correcting for the effect of intervening cosmic dust came to be understood. A further revision of the cluster distances will be required when a new system of median absolute magnitudes of RR Lyrae variable stars (13·9) is firmly established.

15·13. The Array of Globular Clusters. Starlight is dimmed by dust in interstellar space, particularly in the directions of the Milky Way, so that the photometrically determined distances of the stars are greater than the actual ones unless appropriate corrections are made. That the globular clusters of our galaxy are also dimmed and reddened by the dust is shown by the photoelectric measures of Stebbins and Whitford. The clusters far from the Milky Way are of uniform color corresponding to spectral type F6. They become redder toward the Milky Way, until they correspond in the extreme to the color of a type M star. The dimming and reddening of one of the clusters are well shown in Fig. 15·13.

Statistical corrections for the effects of the dust have been obtained by supposing that the obscuring material is spread uniformly in a layer 1000 parsecs in thickness around the principal plane of the Milky Way. The measured distance of each cluster is reduced by an amount that depends on the galactic latitude (17·4) of the cluster and the assumed *optical thickness* of the dust layer, that is, the amount in magnitudes that the light would be dimmed if it should pass vertically through the layer.

Fig. 15·13A illustrates the results where the optical thickness is taken to be 0.46 magnitude. The places of some of the clusters are

FIG. 15·13. Heavily Veiled Region of the Globular Cluster NGC 6553 in Sagittarius. Photographed with nearly equal exposure-times with plates sensitive to blue light (above) and red light (below). (*Photographs by Walter Baade, Mount Wilson Observatory*)

here projected on the plane through the sun and the center of the cluster system and perpendicular to the plane of the Milky Way. The corrections place the clusters mainly within a circle having a radius of 20,000 parsecs and its center about 9000 parsecs, or 30,000 light years, from the sun. A few faint clusters are far outside these limits.

The distribution of globular clusters over the face of the sky shows that the center of the cluster system is in the direction of

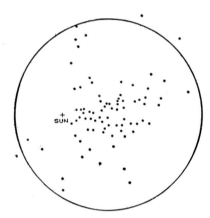

Fig. 15·13A.   Positions of Some Globular Clusters in the Galaxy. These are shown projected on a plane perpendicular to the principal plane of the Galaxy. Distances from the sun are corrected for optical thickness of 0.46 magnitude of absorbing layer. The radius of the circle is 20,000 parsecs.

Sagittarius. Almost all recognized clusters are found in the hemisphere of the sky having its center in that constellation, and fully a third are in the vicinity of the great star cloud of Sagittarius.

15·14. Two Stellar Populations.   The spectrum-luminosity diagram for the stars in the sun's neighborhood differs from the diagram for the stars in globular clusters. Interest in the matter was not fully awakened until 1944, when Walter Baade explained that populations of stars represented by the two diagrams are found in different parts of our galaxy and of exterior galaxies as well. Baade designated the two populations as types I and II respectively.

The *type I population* (Fig. 11·27) is represented by the sun's region of our galaxy, and was accordingly the first to be recognized. It frequents regions where gas and dust are abundant. Its brightest stars are blue stars of the main sequence, which is intact, and its red giants are around absolute visual magnitude zero. This is a young population, comprising stars of relatively high metal content (16·22).

The *type II population* (Fig. 15·14), represented by the stars of normal globular clusters, occurs in regions that are nearly free

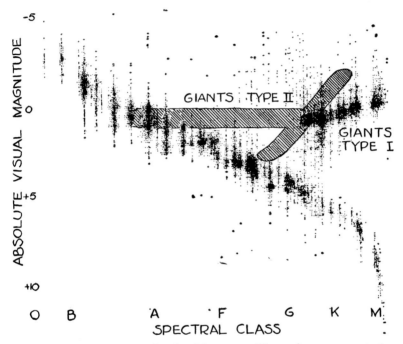

FIG. 15·14. Spectrum-Luminosity Diagrams. The points represent stars of Baade's type I population, as in Fig. 11·27. The shaded strips represent giants of his type II population. (*Adapted from the original diagram by Walter Baade*)

from interstellar gas and dust. Its giant sequence begins at the redder end with K stars of absolute visual magnitude −2.4. On the downward slope in the diagram this sequence divides into two branches, one of which runs horizontally to the left at about magnitude zero. The second branch continues on in nearly the same direction until it joins the type I main sequence. To the left of this junction there are no original main sequence stars of the cluster. This is an old population, comprising stars of low metal content.

The prototypes of Baade's two stellar populations are extreme cases. Intermediate types have been suggested. A possible choice of five different populations in our galaxy is noted later (17·7).

15·15. The Cluster Color-Magnitude Diagram Extended. Baade's original diagram for the type II population has been extended by the investigations of Arp, Baum, and Sandage. Their color-magnitude diagrams of the clusters M 3 and M 92 were derived from photographs with the 100-inch and 200-inch telescopes.

The diagram for M 3 is shown in Fig. 15·15. The nearly vertical giant branch joins the cluster main sequence at type F5, absolute magnitude +3.5. This sequence goes on downward from there, with slightly steeper slope than the normal main sequence, to magnitude +5.6, the limit of these photographs, and is entirely absent above the junction. The horizontal giant branch terminates at

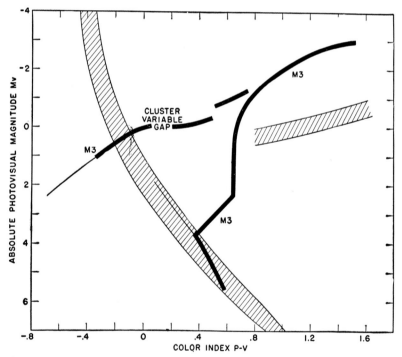

FIG. 15·15. Color-Magnitude Diagram of the Globular Cluster M 3. The type II array of the cluster is shown by the solid lines. The shaded areas represent the main sequence and red giants of the type I population.
(Diagram by H. C. Arp, W. A. Baum, and A. R. Sandage)

the left with extremely blue stars. The omission of the RR Lyrae variables leaves a gap in this branch, indicating that nonvariable stars are not generally present here.

15·16. Variety Among Star Clusters. Globular clusters of our galaxy have been distinguished from galactic clusters by their greater size, compactness, and luminosity. Although the impression long prevailed that globular clusters were very much alike, the present view is that the division of all star clusters into two types is too simple. This is particularly the case when the color-magnitude diagrams are available and when the clusters in exterior galaxies are included.

S. C. B. Gascoigne and G. E. Kron reported in 1952 that the integrated color indexes of objects known as globular clusters in the Magellanic Clouds (18·7) are about equally divided in two groups. The clusters of one group are red, colored by their brightest giant stars; they are more nearly like the normal globular clusters of our own galaxy. The clusters of the second group are blue, corresponding to the colors of their most luminous main-sequence stars; they are unlike the galactic clusters in appearance and content. Brightest of the blue clusters in the Large Magellanic Cloud is NGC 1866, having a population exceeding 10,000 stars.

P. W. Hodge prefers to designate the two groups as "young populous clusters" and "old populous clusters," depending on whether their main sequences extend above absolute visual magnitude zero or fail to do so. H. C. Arp suggests that the term "globular cluster" be reserved for clusters of great age and low metal content, such as M 3.

As assemblages of older stars the red globular clusters of our galaxy have been regarded as free from interstellar gas and dust. Supplies of such material originally possessed by the clusters were believed to have condensed to form stars or to have been exhausted in other ways. Yet the dark regions observed in some of these clusters are caused most likely by clouds of gas and dust in the clusters themselves, according to M. S. Roberts. He concludes that the gas has been shed by stars evolving to the white dwarf stage. The gas may now be condensing into young stars. This, he believes, could account for the few blue main-sequence stars found above the turnoff points in color-magnitude diagrams of certain old clusters.

1. Distinguish between galactic and globular star clusters. Name an example of each type.

2. Why are all known galactic clusters in our galaxy relatively near us?

3. Explain the method of determining the distance of a galactic cluster by observing the spectra and apparent magnitudes of its stars.

4. Show that the distance of a cluster determined by the method of Question 3 is magnified by intervening dust unless allowance is made for this effect.

5. Turning to the color-magnitude diagrams of galactic clusters in Fig. 15·6, explain why the Perseus double cluster is considered youthful, the Pleiades in middle age, and M 67 in old age.

6. A galactic cluster is believed to lose members generally as it ages. Although M 67 is presumably an old cluster, it is among the most populous. Explain.

7. In color-magnitude diagrams of very young clusters, such as NGC 2264 (Fig. 15·8), the most luminous blue stars are on the main sequence, but the redder stars are above the normal position of this sequence. Explain.

8. Associations of stars seem to show that these stars were born only a million years or so ago. Explain.

9. Describe the cluster M 13 in Hercules as a fine example of a globular cluster, in particular: (a) its position in the constellation (Map 3); (b) its appearance to the naked eye and with large telescopes; (c) its distance, linear size, and membership.

10. How may the distance of a globular cluster in our galaxy be determined?

11. How did Shapley demonstrate from the globular clusters the separate status of our galaxy and the sun's eccentric position within the Galaxy?

12. Distinguish between Baade's types I and II stellar populations as represented by his original spectrum-luminosity diagram (Fig. 15·14).

13. Describe the later extension of the type II diagram (Fig. 15·15).

16

INTERSTELLAR GAS AND DUST

DIFFUSE NEBULAE – THE INTERSTELLAR MATERIAL – THE LIVES OF THE STARS

The spaces between the stars in the sun's vicinity contain as much gas as there is in the stars themselves. The gas is accompanied by smaller amounts of dust. Concentrations of the interstellar material produce the more obvious bright and dark nebulae.

DIFFUSE NEBULAE

16·1. Nebulae in General. Faintly glowing spots in the heavens, excluding the comets, were called *nebulae* from early times. Some of these proved later to be remote star clusters. Others seemed to avoid the region of the Milky Way and came to be known as extragalactic nebulae. These are stellar systems outside our own galaxy, which are now more often called exterior galaxies, or simply galaxies. The exterior galaxies are described in Chapter 18.

The nebulae proper in our galaxy and in other galaxies as well are generally of the type known as *diffuse nebulae*. Condensations in the interstellar material, they are clouds of gas and dust having irregular forms and often large angular dimensions. Some are made luminous by the radiations of neighboring stars and possibly by collisions between clouds, whereas others are practically dark. Nebulae of a different type (12·25) are gaseous envelopes around certain hot stars.

Some diffuse nebulae resemble the cumulus clouds of our atmosphere. Others have a filamentary structure that is remindful of our high cirrus clouds. All are turbulent and are also moving as a whole in various directions. Where clouds come together and interpenetrate, the collision velocities are likely to exceed the speed of sound at these low temperatures. Shocks, compressions, and magnetic fields can account for the intricate structure of the nebulae.

16·2. The Great Nebula in Orion is the brightest of the diffuse nebulae in the direct view. Scarcely visible to the naked eye, its place is marked by the middle star of the three in Orion's sword. Through the telescope it appears as a greenish cloud around the star, which itself is resolved into a group of type O stars.

In photographs with large telescopes the Orion nebula is spread over an area having twice the apparent diameter of the moon. At

Fig. 16·2. The Great Nebula in Orion. (*Mount Wilson Observatory photograph*)

its distance of 1600 light years, the nebula as shown in these photographs has a linear diameter of 26 light years, or about the distance of Vega from the sun. It is a prominent concentration of the nebulosity that is spread over much of the region of Orion. The nebula is accompanied by an aggregate of several hundred O and B stars.

Many of the bright diffuse nebulae we see in photographs are invisible in the direct view with the telescope. These objects are intrinsically faint, and not made faint by great distance as a star may be. Close at hand they would not be any easier to detect. Luminous areas have the same brightness per unit angular area regardless of distance.

16·3. The Illumination of Nebulae. The presence of stars near or actually involved in the nebulae is mainly responsible for their shining. In the absence of such stars the nebulae are practically dark. This relation was demonstrated, in 1922, by Edwin Hubble at Mount Wilson Observatory. Particular stars can be selected that are associated with almost every known bright nebula, and in each case the radius of illumination of the nebula is roughly proportional to the square root of the brightness of the star (Fig. 16·3). A star of

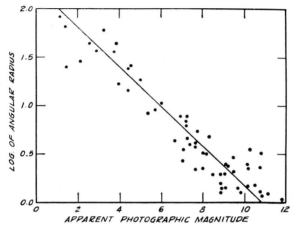

Fig. 16·3. Increase in Extent of Nebular Illumination with Increasing Brightness of Involved Stars. (*Adapted from a diagram by Edwin Hubble*)

the 1st magnitude illuminates the nebula to an angular distance of 100′ in the photographs, whereas the effect of a 12th-magnitude star extends less than a minute of arc.

Another conclusion from Hubble's investigations is the relation between the temperature of the associated star and the quality of the nebular light. If the star is as hot as type B1, the spectrum of the nebula differs from that of the star in having strong emission lines. If the star is cooler than B1, the nebular light resembles the starlight. Bright nebulae are accordingly of two types: emission nebulae and reflection nebulae.

16·4. Emission Nebulae. In the vicinity of a very hot star, where the radiation is largely in the ultraviolet, the hydrogen gas of an interstellar cloud is kept ionized. Radiation from the star of wavelength less than 912 A can remove the electrons from normal hydrogen atoms. When substitute electrons are captured by the positively charged protons, the electrons may land in any one of the possible orbits and reach their lowest level by a series of transitions with the emission of light. Atoms of other elements in this part of the cloud are also excited by such radiations or by collisions with other atoms and contribute to the illumination.

Thus the diffuse nebulae such as the great nebula in Orion, which have hot stars involved in them, are *emission nebulae*. Their light differs in quality from that of the stimulating stars. Other examples are the planetary nebulae, which have central stars of type O or W, and the envelopes of novae when their gases have become sufficiently attenuated by expansion.

Bengt Strömgren has shown that a single O star ionizes almost all hydrogen atoms in a gas of suitably low density to a distance of 50 parsecs, or 160 light years. The Orion nebula has a much smaller radius than this because its density is unusually high, so that the effectiveness of the stars' radiations is more quickly diluted.

16·5. Bright-Line Spectra of Nebulae. The bright lines that characterize the spectra of emission nebulae are mainly lines of

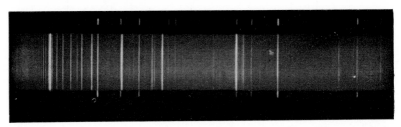

FIG. 16·5. Spectrum of the Orion Nebula. From ultraviolet to blue. The very strong line at the left is the double line of singly ionized oxygen at 3727 A. Short comparison lines above and below are of hydrogen and helium. (*Photograph by Donald E. Osterbrock, Mount Wilson and Palomar Observatories*)

hydrogen, neutral helium, and oxygen and nitrogen in different stages of ionization. Prominent among them are a pair of lines at wavelengths 3726 and 3729 A in the ultraviolet (combined at the left in Fig. 16·5), due to singly ionized oxygen, and a pair at 4959 and 5007 A in the green, due to doubly ionized oxygen. The latter pair gives the greenish hue to such nebulae. Neither pair has as yet been observed in laboratory spectra of oxygen.

The identification of these two pairs of lines, and of additional lines of oxygen, nitrogen, and some other elements, rests on theoretical evidence given, in 1927, by I. S. Bowen. They are "forbidden lines," so called because the electron transitions producing them are much less likely to occur in a gas in ordinary conditions than are the lines normally observed. The reverse is true in the rare and extended gas of the nebulae; the unusual lines are more likely to appear than the normal ones.

The relative strength of the bright lines does not at once show the relative abundance of the chemical elements in the gases of these nebulae. Oxygen and nitrogen are less abundant than hydrogen and helium, but in collisions with other atoms they are able to utilize greater quantities of energy provided by the exciting starlight.

16·6. Reflection Nebulae. Where the stars in the vicinities of the interstellar clouds are cooler than type B1, the nebulae are not noticeably self-luminous. Their spectra are the same as those of the associated stars. Examples are the nebulosities surrounding stars of the Pleiades. The light of such nebulae is starlight scattered by the dust particles that are present in the clouds along with the gas. Scattered starlight is, in fact, a constituent of all nebular light, but its presence in emission nebulae may be unnoticed. The emitted light concentrated in a few bright lines of the spectrum is much more conspicuous than the scattered light, which is spread over all wavelengths.

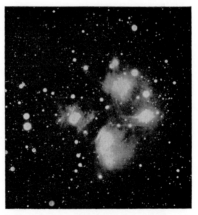

FIG. 16·6. Nebulosities surrounding the Pleiades. (*Photograph by E. E. Barnard*)

The colors of reflection nebulae are nearly the same as those of their associated stars. This is well shown in the photographs (Fig. 16·6A) of a cloudy region in Scorpius, where bright nebulae appear around the stars like the glow around street lamps on a foggy night. Thus the illumination around the red star Antares, which is scarcely noticeable in blue light, becomes conspicuous in yellow light. The opposite is true of the nebulae around the blue B stars.

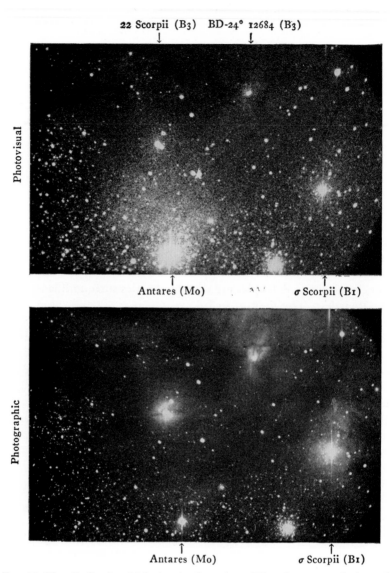

FIG. 16·6A. Reflection Nebulae in Scorpius. The glow around the red star Antares is more conspicuous in yellow light (above), whereas that around blue stars, such as Sigma Scorpii, is stronger in blue light (below).
(Photographs with a Schmidt camera, McDonald Observatory)

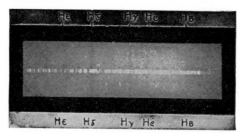

FIG. 16·6B. Spectrum of Nebula Surrounding Merope in the Pleiades. The spectrum of the nebula resembles that of the involved star, showing dark lines especially of hydrogen and helium. A comparison spectrum appears in the middle. (*Lowell Observatory photograph*)

16·7. Dark Nebulae have no stars nearby to illuminate them. They make their presence known by dimming the light of whatever lies behind. Some are visible to the naked eye. The majority are revealed in the photographs by their obscuration of bright regions of

FIG. 16·7. Great Rift in the Milky Way. From Cygnus to Scorpius. (*Mosaic from* Atlas of the Northern Milky Way)

the Milky Way. The darkest clouds are relatively near us at distances of from 300 to 1500 light years. At greater distances their contrast with the bright background is diluted by stars in front of them. Few dark nebulae are known in our galaxy that are more distant than 5000 light years.

A great complex of cosmic clouds is centered in the region of Scorpius and Ophiuchus, and goes on northward to the Northern Cross, forming the Great Rift in the Milky Way. Another extends from Cassiopeia through Perseus and Auriga into Taurus.

In addition to its more conspicuous showing in the bright and dark nebulae, the interstellar material is recognized by the radiation of its neutral hydrogen as recorded with radio telescopes. The presence of intervening gas is also revealed by the dark lines it imprints in the spectra of stars, and that of dust is shown by its reddening and dimming of stars behind it.

16·8. Hydrogen in Interstellar Gas. Hydrogen is the most abundant element between the stars as it is in the stars themselves. It is accompanied by helium and by heavier gases in much smaller amounts. Where an interstellar cloud surrounds a hot star, the hydrogen is ionized and set glowing in a spherical region around the star, having a radius that is greater as the involved star is hotter. The part of the cloud outside the sphere is not ionized and is normally dark. Strömgren has called the two parts of the clouds the H-II and H-I regions.

The H-II Regions. The presence of clouds of ionized hydrogen over large areas of the Milky Way, in addition to the more obvious emission nebulae, was first observed by Struve and Elvey at McDonald Observatory, in 1937. They had devised a fast nebular spectrograph for detecting the faint emission lines and found them more often where large numbers of B and O stars are present in the vicinities. Other emission regions have since been found in photographs with wide-angle cameras, taken with plates sensitive to the part of the spectrum around the red hydrogen line. The emission nebulosities and associated blue stars are being employed with optical telescopes to trace the spiral arms of our galaxy (17·12). About 5 per cent of the gas in these arms is in the H-II form.

The H-I Regions. The clouds of neutral hydrogen are invisible by optical means. Their only known radiation is at wavelength 21 cm, which is recorded with radio telescopes.

The lowest level of the hydrogen atom is really a pair of levels where the electron may be, depending on whether its magnetic spin is parallel or opposed to that of the nucleus of the atom. Transition of the electron from the upper to the lower level produces the radiation at 21 cm. Observable radiation of the clouds at this wavelength, predicted by van de Hulst in 1944, was first detected by the Harvard physicists H. I. Ewen and E. M. Purcell, in 1951. This radiation has effective use with radio telescopes in tracing spiral arms of the Galaxy (17·21) and in other investigations within and beyond the Galaxy.

16·9. Hydrogen Wreaths in Cygnus. The region of the Northern Cross exhibits a bewildering array of bright and dark clouds. We

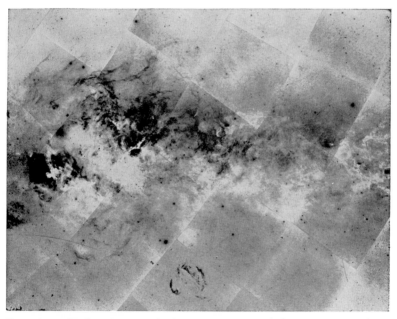

Fig. 16·9. Hydrogen Wreaths in Cygnus. A mosaic of negative photographs of the region of the Northern Cross. The Great Rift runs horizontally through the middle. The Loop of nebulosity is below. (*Copyright by National Geographic Society-Palomar Observatory Sky Survey. Courtesy of J. L. Greenstein*)

view this region along the arm of the Galaxy that includes the sun. Most remarkable in the display are the wreaths formed by filaments of faintly luminous nebulae. The smallest and brightest of these is the familiar Loop of nebulosity near Epsilon Cygni, of which the brightest parts are the filamentary nebulae **NGC** 6960 and 6992. Other wreaths appear only as arcs of circles that may be mostly concealed by other nebulae. The larger wreaths were unknown until they were revealed in a mosaic of photographs (Fig. 16·9) with the 48-inch Palomar Schmidt telescope. They are Sky Survey photographs with red-sensitive plates, which bring out the faint nebulae more clearly.

All these formations suggest expanding shells. The Loop itself, at the distance of about 2500 light years, is known to be increasing in radius, and it may have been slowed considerably from the original rate by resistance of dark material outside it. The expansion has been ascribed to the outburst of a supernova that may have occurred as much as 100,000 years ago, but the central star has not been identified. The illumination of this nebulosity is believed to be caused by collision of the expanding shell with the surrounding interstellar material.

16·10. Interstellar Lines in Stellar Spectra. Many years ago, a "stationary" dark line was observed in the spectrum of the binary star Delta Orionis; this line is narrower than the lines in the spectrum of the star itself and does not oscillate with them in the period of its revolution. It was the first known example of *interstellar lines,* which are absorbed in the spectra of stars by intervening cosmic gas. The recognized constituents of the interstellar gas are neutral atoms of sodium, potassium, calcium, and iron, singly ionized atoms of calcium and titanium, and the cyanogen and hydrocarbon molecules, including singly ionized hydrocarbon.

Interstellar atomic lines arise only in electron transitions from the lowest levels in the atoms. Such lines are likely to appear in the far ultraviolet where they are usually unobservable. This is true of hydrogen and some other elements such as carbon, nitrogen, and oxygen. Absorptions by molecules so far identified also involve transitions from their lowest levels; each band of their usually complex spectra is represented by only one or two narrow lines. In addition, there are a number of diffuse lines, which might be mistaken for stellar lines except for a difference in radial velocity. Their identifications are not as yet established.

The frequent division of the interstellar lines into two or more components was shown by earlier studies of W. S. Adams at Mount Wilson. The division was later given clear and important interpretation by Guido Münch, whose results were derived from spectra of distant stars photographed with the 200-inch telescope. They show that the material producing the interstellar lines is situated in or near the spiral arms of our galaxy.

Where two arms intervene between the star and observer, the lines may be divided into two main components by Doppler effects of the rotation of the Galaxy, effects which we examine in the following chapter (17·16). A line produced by the gas of each arm may be further divided into several components by turbulence of the material. As the starlight passes through the arm, it may be absorbed by clouds moving at different speeds in the line of sight and thus causing different Doppler displacements of the lines.

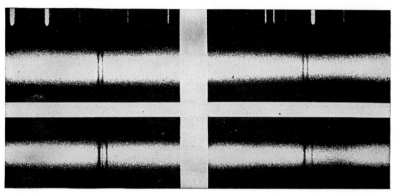

Fig. 16·10. Interstellar Lines in the Spectra of Kappa Aquilae (above) and HD 167264 (below). The K line of calcium is shown at the left and the H line at the right. The lines are divided. (*Mount Wilson Observatory photographs*)

Some gas clouds are situated as much as 3000 light years from the principal plane of the Galaxy; these have velocities of the order of 50 km/sec toward or away from the plane.

16·11. Dust Located by Counts of Stars. Interstellar dust dims the light of the stars beyond. Whether or not the dust is conspicuous in the photographs, its distance and effect can be determined by counts of stars in that area of the sky.

If the stars were equally luminous and uniformly distributed in the space around us, and if the space itself is perfectly transparent, the total number of stars brighter than a limiting apparent magnitude would increase 4 times for each fainter magnitude to which the limit is extended. Consider the total number of stars brighter than the 12th magnitude as compared with the total number brighter than the 11th magnitude.

Because the apparent brightness of equally luminous stars varies inversely as the squares of their distances from us, a 12th-magnitude star, which is apparently 1/2.5 as bright as an 11th-magnitude star, would be the square root of 2.5, or 1.6, times as far away. Thus the stars brighter than the 12th magnitude would occupy a volume of space around us that is 1.6^3, or nearly 4, times as large as the space occupied by the stars of the 11th magnitude; and with the assumption of equal distribution they would be 4 times as numerous. It is true that the stars are not equally luminous; but the luminosity function (11·31) can replace that assumption.

As an example, suppose that the total numbers of stars brighter than successive magnitudes are counted in a certain area and that the ratio of the numbers remains 4 up to the 11th magnitude but is reduced to 2 at the 12th magnitude. We conclude that the stars are uniformly distributed and that space is transparent to the distance represented by the 11th-magnitude stars. From there the stars either thin out or are dimmed by dust, or both. Other evidence is needed for the decision.

16·12. Reddening of Stars; Color Excess. Interstellar dust not only dims the stars beyond, but it makes them appear redder than their normal colors by scattering their blue light more than their red light. Similarly, the scattering of sunlight in our atmosphere reddens the setting sun. If in a particular part of the sky the stars more distant than 300 parsecs are reddened, there is dust at that distance.

The *color excess* of a star is the difference in magnitude by which the observed color index, blue minus visual, exceeds the accepted value for a star of its spectral type (Table 12·II), it is a measure of the reddening of the star by the dust. When the color excess is multiplied by an appropriate factor, we have the *photographic absorption,* that is, how much in magnitudes the star is dimmed by the dust as photographed with a blue-sensitive plate. A useful survey of color excesses is that of Stebbins, Huffer, and Whitford, who employed a photoelectric cell and color filters to determine the colors of 1332 O and B stars.

The distance of a reddened star, r in parsecs, is calculated by the formula: $5 \log r = m - M + 5 - K$, where m is the apparent photographic magnitude, M is the corresponding absolute magnitude for a star of this particular spectral class, and K is the photographic absorption.

16·13. The Dust Grains.   The reddening of stars by intervening cosmic dust is attributed to particles smaller than 10^{-5} cm in diameter.   Dust grains of this size would scatter the starlight in inverse proportion to the wavelength, which is not far from the observed relation in the light of the reddened stars.   The origin of the grains is not clearly understood; whether they form from gas in the interstellar medium or are particles blown into the medium from upper atmospheres of stars, or both, is conjectural.   The dust contributes only one or two per cent to the total mass of the interstellar material.

Starlight is frequently polarized in its passage through the dust clouds, as J. S. Hall and W. A. Hiltner discovered independently in their photoelectric studies.   Leverett Davis and J. L. Greenstein have explained that this effect could be produced in the light by elongated grains rotating around their short diameters; the axes of the rotations would set themselves along magnetic lines of force.   The implication that our galaxy has a magnetic field has opened exciting possibilities that have not as yet been completely explored.

16·14. Globules of Dark Nebulae.   Photographs in many parts of the Milky Way show small dark nebulae against backgrounds of star-rich regions and bright nebulosity.   Some are like wind-blown wisps; others are oval or nearly circular, as if they had been inked in the photographs with a fine-pointed pen.   B. J. Bok and others have drawn attention to the great numbers of such "globules."   We see them, for example, projected upon the diffuse nebula M 8 (Fig. 16·14), and an average of one per square degree throughout that vicinity wherever the background is sufficiently bright.   None at all, however, is reported in the region of the Orion nebula.

The globules have apparent diameters of from 5″ to 10′ or more, and linear diameters of the order of 10^4 to 10^5 astronomical units.   Their photographic absorptions range from at least 5 magnitudes for the smaller objects to 1 magnitude for the larger ones.   Cosmologically the globules have great interest if it can be shown that they represent a stage of evolution preceding the birth of stars.

THE LIVES OF THE STARS

Two features of stellar evolution have persisted in the successive theories of the past two centuries.   The first is that stars condense from nebulae; the second that energy derived from gravitational

Fig. 16·14. Nebula M 8 in Sagittarius. (*Photograph by N. U. Mayall with the Crossley reflector, Lick Observatory*)

contraction is the guiding process throughout the evolution. A third feature, that the stars are "cosmic crucibles" in which lighter chemical elements are built up into heavier ones, was prominent around the beginning of our century. It appears again in the latest theories, which also stress the importance of the interchange of material between stars and nebulae.

The literature of this recently revived and rapidly developing subject is already extensive. The brief account in the following sections may be supplemented, for example, by G. R. and E. M. Burbidge's review article on Stellar Evolution in *Handbuch der Physik*, Volume 51, 1958, and by Martin Schwarzschild's *Structure and Evolution of the Stars*.

16·15. Birth of Stars in Interstellar Clouds. It is supposed that a star is formed by the contraction under gravity of a rather dense cloud of gas and dust a light year or so in diameter. When this material has condensed to a diameter of the order of 10,000 astronomical units, the "protostar" may perhaps be observed as a dark globule. More highly heated by further contraction, the star finally becomes hot enough to shine; and it may then blow away enough excess dust around it so that we can better see what is going on.

Where the process begins with interstellar material of normal density, the cloud requires a mass of at least 1000 suns in order to condense under its own gravitation. It is likely to fracture later into many parts. Thus we have the beginning of a cluster or an association of stars.

16·16. From Nebulae to the Main Sequence. After a star has begun to shine, it goes on contracting and moves across the color-magnitude diagram from the right until it reaches the main sequence. During this contraction the decrease in the radiating surface is compensated by its increasing temperature, so that the star's luminosity remains nearly constant. Half the potential energy released by the contracting gas is radiated away; the remainder goes into heat, raising the star's internal temperature to values where nuclear reactions become effective.

This initial phase is of such short duration compared with the lifetime of a star that relatively few stars might be expected to be observed in transition to the main sequence. We have seen (15·8), however, that the yellow and red stars of some very young clusters seem not yet to have had time to reach this sequence.

Stars on their way to the main sequence vary irregularly in brightness. A. H. Joy called attention to these *T Tauri stars* in 1945. He observed that the light variations of 40 stars in a heavily clouded region of Taurus are accompanied by bright lines and continuous emission of varying intensity in their spectra. More recently, G. Haro, G. H. Herbig, and others observed similar emission in the spectra of yellow and red dwarf stars in clouded regions of Taurus, Monoceros, and Orion. These effects are believed to be caused by instability of the young stars rather more than by their interactions with the dust clouds.

When a group of youthful stars approaches the main sequence of the color-magnitude diagram, the most massive stars settle in the bluest parts of the sequence; they arrive in advance of the others because they contract the more rapidly. The less massive stars array themselves later in order of decreasing mass along the redder parts of the sequence. The cores of all these stars are now hot enough to promote the synthesis of hydrogen into helium with the release of sufficient energy to keep the stars shining. Contraction is halted for a time at this stage; the stars change little in size, temperature, and brightness. Here is the reason why the majority of stars in the sun's vicinity are members of the main sequence.

16·17. Evolution of Cluster Stars. A star remains in the original main sequence as long as the release of energy in its interior is just

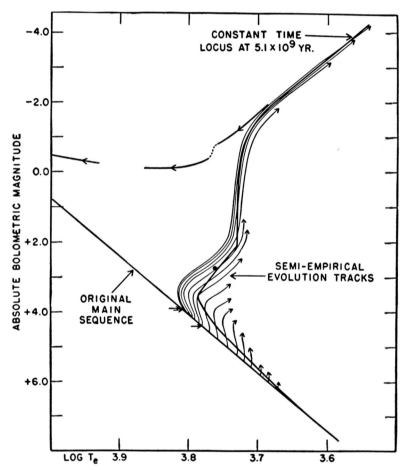

FIG. 16·17. Semiempirical Evolution Tracks of Stars in M 3. Values of log T_e correspond to the following spectral types: 3.9 to A5; 3.8 to F5; 3.7 to K0 for main sequence and G0 for giants; 3.6 to K5 for main sequence and K0 for giants. (*Diagram by Allan R. Sandage*)

enough to supply a constant rate of radiation. When the hydrogen in the core is nearly exhausted, the core resumes its contraction, growing hotter and promoting further nuclear reactions outside it. The outer layers expand. The star then becomes brighter and begins to more upward and to the right in the diagram.

Because the evolution is faster as the stars are bluer, the slope of the new main sequence becomes steeper, as Chandrasekhar and Schönberg have shown, up to the point where the stars have left the sequence entirely. Although this effect is less conspicuous where the stars are continually being born, it shows clearly in the galactic clusters, as we have seen (15·6), and also in the globular clusters.

Allan Sandage has determined empirically the evolutionary tracks (Fig. 16·17) in the globular cluster M 3 of stars in the interval of 5.1×10^9 years since they left the original main sequence with absolute magnitudes between +3.98 and +4.5. By comparing the present luminosity function of the cluster with the initial function (Fig. 11·31) for the main-sequence stars, he found the final magnitude for each track, and located each end-point horizontally in the diagram by use of the color-magnitude diagram of this cluster. The heavier curve through the points so determined lies along the more nearly vertical branch of the type II giant sequence.

A supergiant star of magnitude −4.0 at the top of this curve was originally of magnitude +3.98. The original main-sequence stars brighter than +3.98 may now be moving toward the left on the horizontal giant branch or may already have collapsed to become white dwarfs.

16·18. Abundances of the Chemical Elements. The present abundances of the elements offer one of the most powerful clues to the history of the stars. Hydrogen accounts for about 93 per cent of all the atoms and 76 per cent of all the mass of matter in the universe. Helium is second with about 7 per cent of the atoms and 23 per cent of the mass. All the other elements together contribute only a little more than 1 per cent to the mass.

Fig. 16·18 shows how the logarithms of the relative abundances are arrayed with respect to the atomic numbers of the elements in the sun and stars. The zigzag line represents the corresponding abundances in the earth and meteorites.

The abundance curve drops rather abruptly for the lighter elements and then levels off at number 60. Most of the points define a curve well enough to promote inquiry about a few more conspicuous departures. The atoms of lithium and beryllium (numbers 3 and 4, below the curve) undergo nuclear disintegration at temperatures around a million degrees; they are likely to unite with protons and then to separate into helium atoms. The atoms of iron (number 26, above the curve) are quite stable except at very high temperatures, above 2 billion degrees.

Two theories of the origin of the chemical elements have received considerable attention. The first, by George Gamow and associates, supposes that the elements were built up from neutrons all in the course of half an hour following a possible explosion that initiated the expanding universe. Although the observed abun-

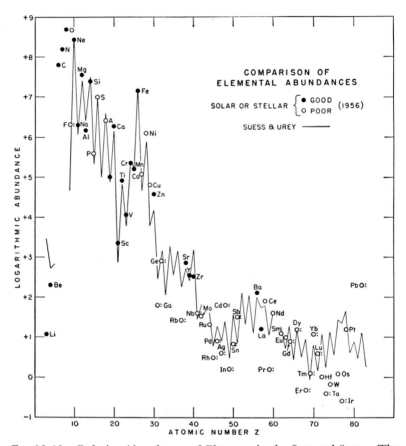

FIG. 16·18.   Relative Abundances of Elements in the Sun and Stars. The zigzag line represents the corresponding abundances in the earth and meteorites. (*Diagram by Jesse L. Greenstein*)

dance curve agrees in general with their theoretical curve, based on successive neutron captures, it has seemed doubtful to some other investigators that this process could have gone successfully beyond the bottlenecks of the unstable helium isotope, weight 5, and beryllium, weight 8.

The second and more recent theory, as explained particularly by W. A. Fowler and associates, supposes that the elements have been and are still being synthesized in the interiors of evolving stars.

16·19. Synthesis of Helium in the Sun. The more recent theory of the origin of the chemical elements begins with the proton-proton reaction in the cores of stars while they are approaching the main sequence. At 5 million degrees the protons are fusing into deuterons. These later collide with other protons to form He^3, which finally combine to produce ordinary helium, He^4. This reaction goes on effectively at central temperatures, about 13 million degrees, of ordinary stars such as the sun. When some carbon is present and when the temperature becomes as high as 20 million degrees, the carbon cycle is an additional means of burning hydrogen. The fusion of hydrogen into helium is the main process in all stars and is the only one that is expected in a main-sequence star not considerably more massive than the sun.

The sun itself, estimated to be 6 billion years old, is scheduled to remain near the main sequence for an equal period in the future. By the end of that period the core of the sun, originally containing 12 per cent of the total hydrogen supply, will have become pure helium, according to the theory. Having run out of available fuel, the core will contract rapidly and grow much hotter. The expanding mantle around it will then burn its hydrogen at a furious rate.

Relatively soon thereafter at a central temperature of 100 million degrees the sun will be a red giant 30 times its present diameter and 100 times its present brightness. Its hydrogen will be nearly exhausted and its temperature will not be high enough for any considerable burning of helium. This evolution track is obtained by Sandage by transformation from the color-magnitude diagram of the galactic cluster M 67, where the stars have masses about equal to that of the sun.

With little fuel remaining, the sun will presumably contract as quickly as it had expanded. It may move to the left across the middle level of the color-magnitude diagram, from red to yellow to blue, and may then fade to a faintly glowing cinder of its former splendor.

16·20. Synthesis of Elements in More Massive Stars. Stars more massive than the sun, and particularly the bluest stars of the main sequence, have shorter and more spectacular careers. They attain higher central temperatures, which may run into billion degrees when they become supergiants. Such stars are considered capable

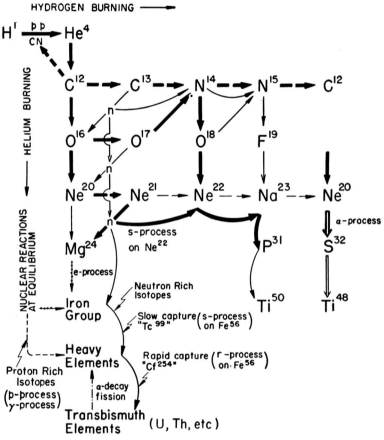

FIG. 16·20. Synthesis of Elements in Stars. Hydrogen burning is the main process. In the more massive stars helium burning may build up heavier elements, and neutron capture may extend the synthesis to the heaviest elements. This chart appeared in an article by G. R. Burbidge, E. M. Burbidge, W. A. Fowler, and Fred Hoyle in *Reviews of Modern Physics,* volume 29. (*Courtesy of W. A. Fowler*)

of building up practically all known chemical elements. The synthesis of elements may proceed mainly in three successive stages (Fig. 16·20).

(1) *Hydrogen burning.* The fusion of hydrogen into helium in the cores of these more massive stars may be principally by means of the carbon cycle. The synthesis of helium spreads into the mantles and is practically complete at the central temperature of 100 million degrees.

(2) *Helium burning.* The fusion of helium into heavier elements can occur at 150 million degrees. Helium nuclei may then combine to form carbon, the reverse of a process already accomplished in the laboratory. Carbon may then fuse with other helium to form oxygen, neon, and magnesium. At a temperature of 5 billion degrees the build-up may go as far as iron, the final synthesis that can release energy for the stars' radiations.

(3) *Neutron capture.* The building of elements from iron on may occur by successive fusions with neutrons, as in the Gamow theory. Neutrons are now abundant, having been released in syntheses of the second stage.

At the extreme internal temperatures required for iron to form, a star is likely to explode as a supernova. By this and other means the star must dispose of any original mass exceeding 1.4 times the mass of the sun, as Chandrasekhar has explained, before it can complete its evolution along with the less massive stars.

16·21. Interchange of Material Between Stars and Nebulae. The stars are believed to be formed by condensation of interstellar material, we have seen. The stars also keep returning gas and perhaps solid particles as well to the interstellar medium. Material issues explosively from supernovae and novae. It streams away continuously from Wolf-Rayet stars, P Cygni stars, red supergiant stars, main-sequence stars like the sun, and from rapidly rotating single stars and close double stars.

A supernova can blow into space material equal to 1 or 2 solar masses. A normal nova returns less than a thousandths of this amount in a single explosion; but such novae are far the more numerous, and explosions may occur repeatedly in the same star. A. J. Deutsch estimates that a red supergiant is losing material at the rate of 1 solar mass per 10 million years. He concludes that of the "dead stars" in the sun's vicinity, which have left the main sequence and have already completed their evolutions, half of their original mass has been returned to the cosmic clouds and the other half is now in the form of white dwarf stars.

16·22. Metals in Successive Generations of Stars. If, as is now supposed, the heavier chemical elements are formed in evolving stars, then the interstellar medium is being enriched more and more in these elements. If the stars of the first generation condensed from cosmic gas that was pure hydrogen, if they built up metallic atoms in their interiors and eventually returned much of the enriched gas to the cosmic clouds, the second-generation stars formed in these clouds would contain a percentage of metals from the start. Third-generation stars, such as the sun is said to be, would begin their evolutions with a higher percentage of metals than did the second generation.

This conclusion seems to be supported by studies of stellar spectra. Strömgren has reported that the percentage content of metals is from 0.1 to 1 in old stars, 2 in stars of middle age, and 3 in very young stars.

16·23. The White Dwarf Stage (11·29) is believed to be the final luminous state of a star. When the star's supply of available fuel is almost exhausted, so that not enough energy is being released in the interior to keep it inflated, the star collapses. In this drastic experience it may explode repeatedly as a normal nova, until it settles down to shine feebly for a long time as a small and dense white dwarf. The star then cools at a constant radius, which is theoretically inversely proportional to its mass, continuing to shine only at the expense of its internal heat previously acquired.

The final cooling stage requires many billion years. Through this long period of time the white dwarf becomes increasingly faint and red, until it ultimately must cease to shine. The question has been asked as to whether our galaxy is yet old enough to contain any "black dwarf" stars at all.

16·24. Planetary Systems Attending Other Stars are considered probable, although they have not been observed. Recent hypotheses of the origin of the solar system suggest evolutionary processes that might be repeated frequently throughout the universe. Conditions in the vicinities of many stars might also be favorable to the evolution of life and even of intelligent life. Su-Shu Huang points out that stars suitable for this result must be hot enough to warm deep habitable zones around them. Such stars must continue to shine for a long enough time as well. Here on earth, he remarks, rational animals evolved from inanimate matter in about three billion years. Most favorable of all would be single main-sequence stars of late F, G, and early K types, which constitute 10 per cent of all types of stars.

A possible indication that the sun is not unique in possessing a family of planets has been mentioned (14·27). Blue main-sequence stars are likely to rotate swiftly, whereas corresponding yellow and red stars have more moderate speeds. The break from fast to slow rotation comes abruptly at type F5. It would seem that the redder stars have planetary systems to which they have imparted much of their original angular momentum. Thus the sun rotates in a period of about a month, and carries only 2 per cent of the entire momentum of the solar system.

The distance in light years at which strong radio transmission of the present can be detected equals the diameter in feet of the receiving antenna divided by 10, according to F. D. Drake of the National Radio Astronomy Observatory. Thus the 85-foot radio telescope of this observatory could detect intelligent life transmissions from the distance of Sirius. With this telescope Drake and associates looked first to Tau Ceti and Epsilon Eridani, two solar type stars about 11 light years away. After 150 hours of observing they had obtained no evidence for strong radio signals from the vicinities of these stars. Early success in this remarkable project was not expected.

REVIEW QUESTIONS

1. State and account for the difference between the light of emission nebulae and of reflection nebulae. Name an example of each kind of nebulae.

2. Why is cosmic hydrogen gas bright in the vicinity of a very hot star and dark outside that region?

3. By what means may an optically dark cloud of neutral hydrogen be recorded with a radio telescope?

4. Account for the interstellar dark lines in the spectra of stars and the frequent divisions of these lines into several components.

5. If counts of stars in a photograph of an area of the sky show that the number brighter than apparent magnitude 15 is considerably less than 4 times the number brighter than magnitude 14, what are two possible conclusions?

6. Define the color excess of a star. If a star having a type A spectrum appears as red as a normal K star, what is inferred?

7. What would be the character of cosmic dust if it dimmed but did not redden the light of stars beyond it?

8. State the possible evidence that the condensing of cosmic clouds into stars is being observed.

9. State the observational evidence that certain stars may now be in transition from the nebulae to the main sequence.

10. Outline the current theory of the evolution of stars after they have reached the main sequence.

11. Explain that the heavier chemical elements may be built up from hydrogen in the evolving stars.

12. State some means by which the stars are returning much gas and perhaps dust as well to the cosmic clouds.

13. The conclusions from Questions 11 and 12 suggest that stars of successive generations may contain an increasing percentage of metallic gases. Explain.

14. Give reasons for supposing that the white dwarf stars represent the final stage in the lives of the stars.

REFERENCES

Aller, Lawrence H., *Gaseous Nebulae*. John Wiley and Sons, New York, 1956.

Rush, J. H., *The Dawn of Life*. Hanover House, Garden City, N. Y., 1957.

Schwarzschild, Martin, *Structure and Evolution of the Stars*. Princeton University Press, Princeton, 1958.

Struve, Otto, *Stellar Evolution*. Princeton University Press, Princeton, 1950.

17

THE GALAXY

THE MILKY WAY — STRUCTURAL FEATURES OF THE
GALAXY — ROTATION OF THE GALAXY — RADIO VIEW
OF THE GALAXY

The *galactic system,* or system of the Milky Way, is so named
because a prominent feature of our view from inside it is the band
of the Milky Way around the heavens. The system is a spiral
galaxy of stars. Its spiral arms, one of which includes the sun, contain much gas and dust as well as stars. It is commonly called *the
Galaxy* in distinction from the multitudes of exterior galaxies.

This chapter begins with a description of the Milky Way as it
appears to the naked eye and in the photographs. The appearance
suggests that the main body of the Galaxy is much flattened and
that the sun is far from the center. The galactic structure and
rotation are next considered, and finally the progress being made
in exploring the Galaxy with radio telescopes.

THE MILKY WAY

17·1. The Milky Way of Summer. The *Milky Way* is the glowing
belt of the sky formed by the combined light of vast numbers of
stars. Its central line is nearly a great circle of the celestial sphere,
which is highly inclined to the celestial equator. Because of its
inclination, the course of the Milky Way across the sky is quite
different at different hours of the night and at the same hour
through the year.

At nightfall in the late summer in middle northern latitudes, the
Milky Way arches overhead from the northeast to the southwest
horizon. It extends through Perseus, Cassiopeia, and Cepheus as
a single band of varying width. Beginning in the fine region of the
Northern Cross overhead, it is apparently divided into two parallel
streams by the Great Rift, which is conspicuous as far as Sagittarius
and Scorpius. The western branch of the Milky Way is the broader
and brighter one through Cygnus. Farther south, in Ophiuchus,

Fig. 17·1. The Milky Way in Cygnus. The bright star at the right of the North America nebula is Alpha Cygni. The other stars of the Northern Cross are shown, except Beta Cygni at the foot of the Cross, which is out of picture at the lower right. (*Yerkes Observatory photograph*)

this branch fades and nearly vanishes behind the dense dust clouds, coming out again in Scorpius. The eastern branch grows brighter as it goes southward and gathers into the great star clouds of Scutum and Sagittarius. Here, in Barnard's words, "the stars pile up in great cumulus masses like summer clouds."

17·2. The Milky Way of Winter.   In the evening skies of the late
winter in middle northern latitudes the Milky Way again passes
nearly overhead, now from northwest to southeast.   The stream
is thinner here and undivided.   From Cassiopeia to Gemini it is
narrowed by a series of nearby dust clouds, which cause a pronounced obscuration north of Cassiopeia and angle down through
Auriga to the southern side of the band in Taurus.   The Milky

FIG. 17·2.   The Milky Way in Centaurus and Crux.   The Southern Cross
and the Coalsack are near the center.   The two bright stars at the extreme left are Alpha and Beta Centauri.   The globular cluster Omega
Centauri (Fig. 15·10) appears near the upper left corner.   (*Photograph
by Margaret Harwood at the Arequipa Station of Harvard Observatory*)

Way becomes broader, weaker, and less noticeably obscured as it passes east of Orion and Canis Major down toward Carina.

The part of the Milky Way nearest the south celestial pole is either quite out of sight or else too near the horizon for a favorable view anywhere in the United States. This part is conspicuous for observers farther south as it passes through Centaurus, Crux, and Carina; and the Great Rift continues the division as far as Crux (Fig. 17·9). There is a fine star cloud in Norma and another in Carina, and there is the black Coalsack near the Southern Cross.

17·3. Photographs of the Milky Way. The general features of the Milky Way are best displayed to the naked eye or with very short-focus cameras. The details are well shown in the photographs with wide-angle telescopes. E. E. Barnard was a pioneer in this field. Fifty of his finest photographs are contained in his *Photographic Atlas of Selected Regions of the Milky Way*. These were made with the 10-inch Bruce telescope at Mount Wilson and Williams Bay. A more recent collection is available in the *Atlas of the Northern Milky Way*, prepared by F. E. Ross and Mary R. Calvert; these photographs were taken with a 5-inch Ross camera at Mount Wilson and Flagstaff.

The latest and most penetrating representation of the Milky Way, north of declination $-27°$, is contained in the negative prints of the National Geographic Society-Palomar Observatory Sky Survey (4·16) made in blue and red light with the 48-inch Schmidt telescope.

Photographs reproduced in this chapter and elsewhere in the book illustrate the variety in different parts of the Milky Way. Fig. 17·1 shows the region of the Northern Cross. Fig. 17·2 shows the region containing the Southern Cross and the Coalsack. Fig. 17·6 shows the most spectacular part of the Milky Way, from Scutum to Scorpius; the Scutum and Sagittarius star clouds and the Ophiuchus dark cloud are prominent features of this region. The heavy veiling by dust clouds is also seen, for example, in Figs. 17·8 and 17·9.

17·4. Galactic Longitude and Latitude. In studies relating to the Galaxy it is often convenient to denote the position of a celestial body with reference to the circle of symmetry of the Milky Way. For this purpose we define a system of circles of the celestial sphere in addition to the three systems described in Chapter 1. This system is based on the plane of the galactic equator, which passes through the sun.

The north and south *galactic poles* are the two opposite points that are farthest from the central circle of the Milky Way. By international agreement they are respectively in right ascension 12^h 49^m, declination +27°.4 referred to the equinox of 1950, in Coma Berenices, and 0^h 49^m, −27°.4, south of Beta Ceti.

The *galactic equator* is the great circle halfway between the galactic poles; it is inclined 63° to the celestial equator, crossing from south to north in Aquila and from north to south at the opposite point east of Orion. The galactic equator passes nearest the north celestial pole in Cassiopeia and nearest the south celestial pole in the vicinity of the Southern Cross.

Galactic longitude was formerly measured in degrees from the intersection of the galactic and celestial equators in Aquila, near R. A. 18^h 40^m. By decision of the International Astronomical Union in 1958, the zero of galactic longitude is changed to the direction of the galactic center (17·10) on a slightly revised galactic equator, in R. A. 17^h 42^m.4, Decl. −28° 55′ (1950) in Sagittarius. As before, the longitude is measured around through 360° in the counterclockwise direction as viewed from the north galactic pole; its new values equal the former ones plus about 32°.

Galactic latitude is measured from 0° at the galactic equator to 90° at its poles and is positive toward the north galactic pole. In the sections that follow it will be specified whether the galactic coordinates are given in the former or the new system.

STRUCTURAL FEATURES OF THE GALAXY

17·5. The Early Problem of the extent and structure of the stellar system began when the stars came to be regarded as remote suns at various distances from us. The problem took the following form: Do the stars extend indefinitely into space, or is the system of stars around us bounded? If it is limited in extent, what are the size and the form of the system? The philosopher Imanuel Kant, in 1755, was one of the first to imagine that the system has finite boundaries and that the nebulae might be other "universes."

William Herschel, in England, was the pioneer in the observational approach. His first attempt to determine the "construction of the heavens" was described by him in 1784. It was based on counts of all stars visible in the field of his telescope when it was directed to different parts of the sky. He supposed that the extension of the system in any particular direction was proportional to the cube root of the number of stars counted in that direction. Herschel's results contributed little more than the obvious conclusion that the stellar system is much extended toward the Milky Way. Analysis of star counts, however, long remained the favored method of the exploration.

17·6. The Recent Advances. The modern era in the studies of the galactic structure began, in 1917, with Harlow Shapley's researches on the globular clusters. Shapley showed that the system of the Milky Way has finite dimensions and that the sun is far from its center. Edwin Hubble's demonstration, in 1924, that the hitherto mysterious spirals and associated "nebulae" are other galaxies placed our own galaxy in proper perspective. Another forward step was made by R. J. Trumpler, in 1930. His investigations of galactic clusters revealed for the first time that dimming of the view in many directions by cosmic dust must be allowed for.

Meanwhile, the studies of many astronomers with optical and radio telescopes are providing an increasingly clear picture of the Galaxy. The principal features are as follows:

The Galaxy is an assemblage of 100,000 million stars together with much gas and dust. Its spheroidal central region is surrounded by a flat disk of stars 80,000 light years in diameter, in which spiral arms of stars, gas, and dust are embedded. The galactic center is about 30,000 light years from the sun in the direction of Sagittarius. This flat main body of the Galaxy is rotating around an axis joining the galactic poles. Around the main body is a more slowly rotating and more nearly spherical halo containing "high velocity" stars and the globular clusters.

17·7. Stellar Populations in the Galaxy. Baade's recognition of his two types of stellar population in the universe was promoted by his studies of the spiral galaxy M 31 in Andromeda, which structurally resembles our own galaxy. His conclusion was that stars in the spiral arms of that exterior galaxy, where there is an abundance of interstellar gas and dust, belong to the young type I population. Stars in the central region, where little gas and dust remain, belong mainly to the old type II population. A similar situation seemed to exist in our own galaxy.

Meanwhile, the accumulation of observational data and the de-

FIG. 17·6. Toward the Center of the Galaxy. The Milky Way from Scutum to Scorpius. The Scutum star cloud is near the upper left corner. The great cloud in Sagittarius is just below the center. At the left of this cloud the inverted bowl of the "Milk Dipper" is conspicuous, and at the right are the dark nebulosities of southern Ophiuchus. The pair of stars marking the sting of the Scorpion is near the lower right corner. (*Mount Wilson Observatory photograph*)

velopment of an attractive theory of stellar evolution have suggested a gradation of types, the precise number being a matter of convenience. The following sequence of five types of population in the Galaxy in order of increasing age of the stars was proposed by a conference of astronomers at Rome in 1957.

1. *Extreme population I.* This very young population is contained in the spiral arms, where much gas and dust is still uncondensed into stars, and to a limited extent around the center of the Galaxy as well. Its brightest members are blue supergiant stars, such as Rigel, only a few million years old.

2. *Intermediate population I* comprises somewhat older stars, such as Sirius, situated near the principal plane of the Galaxy, but not confined to the arms.

3. *Disk population.* The majority of the stars between the arms and many in the central region of the Galaxy belong to this type; they range from 3 to 5 billion years in age. The sun is believed to be a member.

4. *Intermediate population II* comprises many older stars in the halo and central region of the Galaxy.

5. *Extreme population II,* the oldest population, is represented by the older globular clusters and the separate stars of the halo. An age of at least 7 or 8 billion years is assigned to this group.

17·8. The Central Region of the Galaxy is a spheroidal concentration of stars 12,000 light years or more in diameter. Here the stars are crowded rather uniformly two or three times as closely as they are in the sun's vicinity. This region near the borders of Sagittarius, Scorpius, and Ophiuchus would be remarkably bright if it were not mostly obscured from the direct view and ordinary photography by dense dust clouds of the Great Rift. The bright star cloud of Sagittarius is an exposed portion.

Radiation from the central region has been recorded through the dust by use of a photocell and an infrared filter, together especially sensitive to radiation having a wavelength of 10,300 A. Employing this apparatus on the 60-inch Mount Wilson telescope, Joel Stebbins and A. E. Whitford made a series of sweeps across the part of the Rift immediately west of the Sagittarius cloud. They recorded an area of maximum radiation extending 8° in galactic longitude, 4° or 5° in latitude, and centered in longitude 326°.5.

Jean Dufay and associates at the Haute Provence Observatory in France have made infrared photographs of the central region with

FIG. 17·8. The Central Region of the Galaxy in Blue Light (above) and
in Infrared (below). The brighter star of the pair near the center is 45
Ophiuchi. North is at the top. (*Photographs by Jean Dufay, Haute
Provence Observatory, France*)

a 12-inch Schmidt telescope, which are in general agreement with
the photoelectric sweeps. These show the region divided, at the
left in the lower photograph of Fig. 17·8, where the infrared radiation from stars behind did not penetrate the dust.

17·9. The Flat Disk of the Galaxy. The appearance of the Milky
Way itself tells of two features of our galaxy. First, the disk of
stars surrounding the central region is much flattened; second, the
sun is far from the center of the disk.

The stars crowd toward the Milky Way. From the dull regions
around the galactic poles the numbers of stars in equal areas of the
sky generally increase with decreasing galactic latitude. The stars
visible to the naked eye are 3 or 4 times as numerous near the

Fig. 17·9. The Southern Milky Way from Sagittarius to Crux. The total
field is 140° in diameter and is centered on the star Antares. (*Photograph
by Arthur D. Code at Bloemfontein, South Africa, with a Greenstein-
Henyey wide-angle camera*)

galactic equator as they are near its poles; and the increase exceeds 40-fold for stars visible with large telescopes, despite the greater obscuration by dust in the lower latitudes.

The concentration of stars toward the Milky Way shows that the main body of the Galaxy is flattened in the direction of its poles and is widely extended toward its equator. When we look toward the equator, we are looking the long way out through the Galaxy and therefore at many more stars. Thus the band of the Milky Way.

The similarity of the numbers of stars in corresponding latitudes north and south of the galactic equator shows that the sun is not far from the plane of this equator.

17·10. Eccentric Position of the Sun. Although the sun is near the principal plane of the Galaxy, it is about three fourths of the distance from the center toward the edge of the disk. A frequently cited value of the distance is 8200 parsecs, or about 27,000 light years, as determined by Baade from his observations of RR Lyrae stars near the center and by the Leiden radio astronomers from their analysis of the galactic rotation. It seems possible, however, that this value is somewhat too small. A provisional distance of as much as 35,000 light years may be indicated by recent observations of B stars and cepheid variables by A. E. Whitford, A. D. Code, and J. D. Bahng.

The place of the center was originally located by Shapley in galactic longitude 325° and latitude 0°, in Sagittarius; he supposed that this center has the same direction from us as the center of the system of globular clusters, which he had determined. Shapley also remarked that from our place in the suburbs of the Galaxy the greatest brightness and complexity of the Milky Way is observed in this direction, and the dullest aspect in the opposite direction, in Auriga and Taurus, where we look the shortest way out through the Milky Way.

The more recent determinations have placed the galactic center remarkably close to the position originally assigned it. The center, marked by the radio source Sagittarius A, is in galactic longitude 327°.8, latitude −1°.4 in the former system, or in right ascension 17^h 42^m.4, declination −28° 55′ (1950). Note in Map 3 the location of the center between the characteristic star-figures of Scorpius and Sagittarius.

17·11. The Spiral Structure. Two arms emerge from opposite sides of the central region of the Galaxy and coil around it in the same sense and in about the same plane. This spiral is considered to be of intermediate type in respect to the closeness of its coiling, resembling the great Andromeda spiral. The arms contain much gas and dust as well as stars.

These features of the galactic structure became definitely known only a few years ago. After Hubble, in 1924, had demonstrated the existence of exterior galaxies, it began to seem possible that our galaxy might have a spiral structure similar to that of some of the galaxies outside it. This possibility strengthened to a probability in the minds of many astronomers and finally, in 1951, became established fact.

The tracing of the spiral arms of the Galaxy in the heavens is in progress by at least three means: (1) by direct photography of emission nebulae and the hot stars associated with them (17·12), which are also prominent in the arms of exterior spirals; (2) by studies of interstellar lines in stellar spectra (17·16); (3) by radio reception from neutral hydrogen in the otherwise dark gas clouds of the arms (17·21) and also from ionized hydrogen in the bright clouds.

17·12. Spiral Arms Traced by Photography. The first tracing of the spiral arms of the Galaxy was announced in 1951 by W. W. Morgan, Stewart Sharpless, and D. E. Osterbrock at Yerkes Observatory. Employing a wide-angle Greenstein-Henyey camera and a filter for transmitting the light of the red line of hydrogen, they had photographed the part of the Milky Way that could be observed from that latitude. The positions and distances of emission nebulae and associated blue stars shown in the photographs permitted the tracing in space of two lengths of arms and the suggestion of a third. The three parts of the arms and the names originally assigned them are as follows.

The *Orion arm* was at first supposed to extend from Cygnus past Cepheus, Cassiopeia, Perseus, and Orion to Monoceros. It included the North America nebula, the Great Nebula in Orion, the Great Rift as part of its dark inner lining, and it passed near the sun. Some later observers have considered this arm as passing through the sun's position and extending from here in a somewhat different direction. They have renamed it the Carina-Cygnus arm and have regarded as one of its spurs the part in the Orion region.

The *Perseus arm* was so named by Morgan because it contains

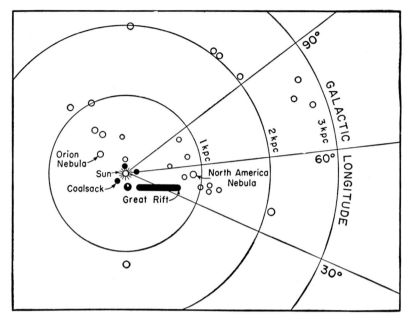

Fig. 17·12. Parts of Spiral Arms of the Galaxy. Traced by directions and distances of emission nebulae. (*Adapted from a model by W. W. Morgan, Stewart Sharpless, and D. E. Osterbrock, Yerkes Observatory*)

the double cluster in Perseus. Outside the first arm, it passes about 7000 light years from the sun. Emission nebulae are less conspicuous in this arm and probably would be difficult to trace in any arm outside it.

The *Sagittarius arm* is nearer the center than the sun's distance. Not well placed for observation in northern latitudes, its tracing was extended optically by B. J. Bok and associates at Bloemfontein. Hydrogen emission is very strong from Sagittarius through Scorpius and into Norma. From there to the Southern Cross it is weak, suggesting a break in the spiral structure. The arm goes on with some interruptions through Carina and Canis Major to Monoceros.

Optical tracing of the arms of the Galaxy is made difficult by the obscuring dust of the Milky Way. The tracing of the spiral pattern has since been extended by radio reception (17·21), which is not hampered by the intervening dust.

ROTATION OF THE GALAXY

The flattened form of the main body of the Galaxy indicates its rotation. Other effects of the rotation are found in the two star streams, in the trend of the motions of stars of high velocity and of the globular clusters, and in the systematic changes in the radial velocities of distant stars with changing galactic longitude. We note these effects in the order of their discoveries.

17·13. The Two Star Streams. Up to the beginning of the present century, no evidence of the systematic motions of the stars had been presented, aside from the apparent drifting of stars away from the standard apex of the solar motion and the common motions of stars in binary systems and clusters.

In 1904, the Dutch astronomer J. C. Kapteyn announced that the peculiar motions of stars (from which the effects of the solar motion are eliminated) around us are not random. There are two streams of stars moving in opposite directions in the plane of the Milky Way with a relative speed of 40 km/sec. With something like the convergence of the Hyades cluster, the stars of the two streams are closing in toward two opposite points in the heavens.

The convergent point of one stream is in right ascension $6^h 15^m$ and declination $+12°$, in Orion, and of the other is in $18^h 15^m$ and $-12°$, in Scutum. The line joining them is in the plane of the galactic equator and is not far from the direction of the galactic center.

This preferential motion of the stars is a consequence of the rotation of the Galaxy, as B. Lindblad, at Stockholm, was the first to explain. Most stars move in slightly eccentric orbits around the galactic center. Lindblad showed that these stars have a greater spread in their motions toward and away from the center than at right angles to this direction. The effect for us is the star streaming.

17·14. The Motions of High-Velocity Objects. The majority of the stars in the sun's vicinity have space velocities of the order of 20 km/sec, which are directed in general away from the standard apex in Hercules. These stars are moving along with the sun in the rotation of the Galaxy, and all have moderate individual motions as well. Exceptional stars, having speeds exceeding 60 km/sec, are known as *high-velocity stars;* their motions were first studied extensively by G. Strömberg at Mount Wilson and J. H. Oort at Leiden.

The motions of high-velocity stars in the galactic plane, when they are corrected for effects of the sun's motion toward Hercules, are directed away from the half of the Milky Way having Cygnus at its middle. Different classes of these objects have different average speeds. For example, the RR Lyrae variables are moving at the rate of 100 km/sec, and the globular clusters, the swiftest of all, are going twice as fast relative to the sun.

Previous to these studies the motions of the globular clusters seemed surprisingly rapid. Now it is understood that we ourselves are the ones who are moving so swiftly. The sun is speeding toward Cygnus in the whirl of the highly flattened disk of the Galaxy at the rate of 216 km/sec, the value commonly adopted. The less flattened array of RR Lyrae stars is rotating with the lower speed of 116 km/sec and is therefore falling behind us at the rate of 100 km/sec. The more nearly globular assemblage of the globular clusters (Fig. 15·13A) is turning even more slowly. The idea of subsystems of the Galaxy, rotating on a common axis at different rates and thus having different degrees of flattening, was proposed by Lindblad.

17·15. Differential Effects of the Rotation. Two extremes in the distribution of material through the Galaxy would produce the following effects in the rotation: (1) If the material is uniformly distributed, the Galaxy would rotate like a solid wheel. All parts would rotate in the same period, keeping the same relative positions. Evidence of such rotation would be difficult to observe except by reference to the external galaxies.

(2) If most of the material is concentrated around the center, the rotations of the outer parts would resemble the revolutions of the planets around the sun. The periods would increase and the speeds would diminish with greater distance from the center. Thus the stars nearer the center than the sun's position would go around faster than the sun's speed, so as to overtake and pass on ahead of us. The stars farther from the center than the sun's position would move more slowly and would therefore fall steadily behind us in the rotation.

J. H. Oort, in 1927, was the first to show more nearly the second effect of the galactic rotation in the radial velocities of stars in different parts of the Milky Way. He observed that stars having

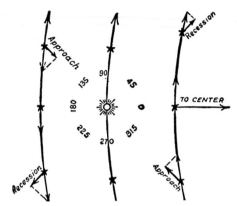

Fig. 17·15.   Effect of the Rotation of the Galaxy on the Radial Velocities of Stars.   Stars nearer the center than the sun's distance are going around faster and are passing by the sun.   Stars farther from the center are moving more slowly and are falling behind the sun.   Thus stars having directions 45° and 225° greater than that of the center are receding from the sun, and stars around 135° and 315° are approaching the sun.

galactic longitudes 45° and 225° greater than the direction of the center (Fig. 17·15) are receding from us with the greatest speeds. Stars having longitudes 135° and 315° greater than the direction of the center are approaching us with the greatest speeds.

The differential effect, V, in the radial velocities of stars is expressed by the formula:

$$V = rA \sin 2l,$$

where r is the difference between the star's and the sun's distance from the galactic center. A is Oort's constant, 18.6 km/sec per 1000 parsecs, which is the rate of velocity change with increasing distance difference.   The quantity l is the star's galactic longitude measured from the direction of the galactic center.   The result for a particular distance difference, where the radial velocities are plotted against the longitudes, is a curve with a double wave, having two maxima and minima around the circle of the Milky Way.

The differential effect in the observed radial velocities, whether of approach or recession, increases with the difference of distance between the star and the sun from the center of the Galaxy, and its amount can inform us of this difference.   This is the basis for tracing spiral arms of the Galaxy by radio reception (17·21).

17·16. Interstellar Gas in the Spiral Arms. A spectroscopic survey of a large section of the Milky Way by Guido Münch with the 200-inch Palomar telescope has shown that the interstellar lines in stellar spectra (16·10) are caused by gas in the spiral arms of the Galaxy. These studies have located parts of two arms at different distances beyond the sun's distance from the center of the Galaxy. These are the Carina-Cygnus arm and the Perseus arm.

Because the gas in the more distant of these two arms is moving the slower relative to the sun's motion in the rotation of the Galaxy,

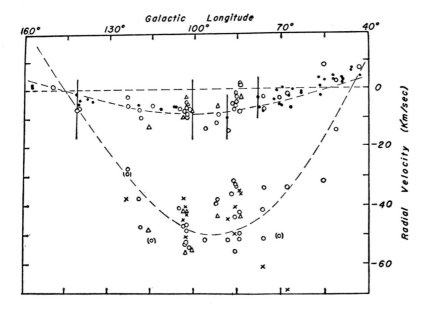

FIG. 17·16. Differential Radial Velocities from Interstellar Lines in the Spectra of Stars of the Northern Milky Way. The circles and triangles denote the velocities from the strong components of calcium and sodium lines respectively. The crosses represent more distant stars. The curves show the rotation effect at distances of 400 and 3000 parsecs from the sun. (*Diagram by Guido Münch, Mount Wilson and Palomar Observatories*)

the dark lines it absorbs in the spectra of remote stars have the greater Doppler displacements. Thus the interstellar lines are divided into two components. The corresponding radial velocities for the two sets of lines are plotted in Fig. 17·16 with respect to the galactic longitudes of the stars in the former reckoning. The two arrays of points are well represented by sine curves showing the differential effects of the galactic rotation at distances of 400 and 3000 parsecs, which are evidently the distances of the two arms from the sun in these directions. The distance of the nearer arm is in practical agreement with its distance derived in other ways.

The maximum values of approach to the sun occur in about galactic longitude 100° (about 135° from the direction of the galactic center), as Fig. 17·15 shows that they should. The departures of the points from the sine curves of Fig. 17·16 and the frequent further splitting of the interstellar lines into several parts are ascribed to turbulent velocities of the gas in the two arms; these are more conspicuous in the more distant arm.

17·17. Rotation of the Galaxy. Viewed from the north galactic pole, the direction of the galactic rotation is clockwise. As we in the northern hemisphere look from our place in the Galaxy toward its center, the direction of the rotation between us and the center of the Galaxy is toward the left. The period of the rotation is probably about the same throughout the central region. In the disk it becomes greater with increasing distance from the center. At the sun's distance the period is of the order of 200 million years. If the Galaxy is 10 billion years old, it has rotated 50 times in our vicinity since its beginning. The difference in the rotation at different distances from the center is enough to efface the spiral arms in the course of a single rotation, according to Oort. The question remains as to how the dispersed spiral pattern is restored.

The sun's velocity in the rotation is generally taken to be 216 km/sec, or 134 miles a second, toward galactic longitude 55° in the former reckoning, in Cygnus. This is the value given by van de Hulst, Muller, and Oort in 1954 from their radio records. It is based on the sun's distance of 8200 parsecs from the galactic center; and some other investigators have reported values of this order. From the radial velocities of galaxies of the local system, however, N. U. Mayall, in 1946, and M. L. Humason, in 1955, derived the sun's velocity as about 296 km/sec, or 184 miles a second. H. F. Weaver points out that the wide discrepancy in these results could be lessened by adopting a greater distance of the sun from the center.

RADIO VIEW OF THE GALAXY

Radio astronomy has provided in the past few years an unexpected and completely new approach in the studies of the Galaxy.

Improved apparatus and methods are giving increasingly detailed views of the radio Galaxy. The use of the 21-cm emission line in the spectra of the otherwise dark hydrogen clouds permits the tracing of the spiral arms.

17·18. An Early Radio Survey. After Jansky, in 1932, had reported radio reception from the Milky Way at 14.7 meters, Grote Reber completed, in 1944, the first extensive radio survey of the Milky Way. With a 30-foot paraboloidal antenna and apparatus for recording at 1.85 meters, he scanned the Milky Way as it passed his meridian. Reber's pioneer equipment could not distinguish separately sources of radiation closer together than 12°. Although the view was accordingly blurred, it revealed some of the brightest features of the radio Milky Way. His antenna is now remounted at the National Radio Astronomy Observatory at Green Bank, West Virginia.

Reber's original results are shown in the contour map of Fig. 17·18, where the intensities of the radiation are indicated with respect to the galactic longitudes of their origins. We note that regions of equal intensity are roughly symmetrical relative to the

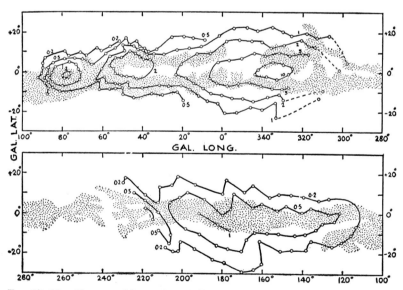

Fig. 17·18. Contour Lines of Equally Intense Radiation from the Milky Way at 1.85 Meters. The galactic coordinates are in the former system. (*Diagram from Reber's radio data prepared by R. E. Williamson and Ruth J. Northcott, David Dunlap Observatory*)

galactic equator. The greatest intensity, 10 on Reber's scale, was recorded from the direction of the galactic center, about longitude 330° by the former reckoning. Secondary maxima of intensity 2 were found in Cygnus, longitude 50°, and in Cassiopeia, 80°; these are now known to be effects of two strong radio sources in the former constellation and one in the latter.

Later surveys with improved apparatus have been made at a variety of wavelengths. The Milky Way is the dominant feature of all the radio maps, but radio sources appear instead of individual stars of the optical view. The radio records differ, depending on the wavelengths with which they are obtained. At the shorter lengths, where the thermal radiation (4·26) is most intense, the Milky Way is narrower and the sources are mainly emission nebulae. At the longer wavelengths, where the nonthermal radiation is most intense, the Milky Way is broader and the sources are of less usual types.

17·19. A Recent Radio Map, completed in 1957 with the 96-foot helix antenna of Ohio State University (Fig. 4·30), covers practi-

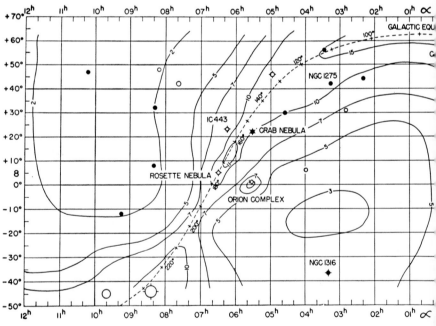

FIG. 17·19. Radio Map of the Sky at 1.2 Meters.

cally all of the heavens accessible from Columbus. The contour
lines of equal radio "brightness" at 1.2 meters (Fig. 17·19), plotted
in right ascension and declination for the epoch 1950.0, show the
background radiation. The numbers on the contour lines indicate
the brightness on a power scale above a reference level. The
dashed line represents the former galactic equator, which is marked
at intervals with degrees of galactic longitude in the earlier reckoning. Along this equator the radio brightness increases toward
the galactic center, in longitude 328°.

The background radio radiation consists of three parts, according
to Ko and Kraus: (1) A belt about 3° wide nearly in the galactic
plane; (2) a fainter surrounding zone about 15° wide; (3) a still
fainter approximately uniform distribution over the sky.

The open circles in the figure show the positions of more extended radio sources, and the filled circles indicate sources less
than 1° in diameter. The stars are invisible. Aside from the Milky
Way, which is more prominent here, the radio view at 1.2 meters
has practically no resemblance to the view with the naked eye.

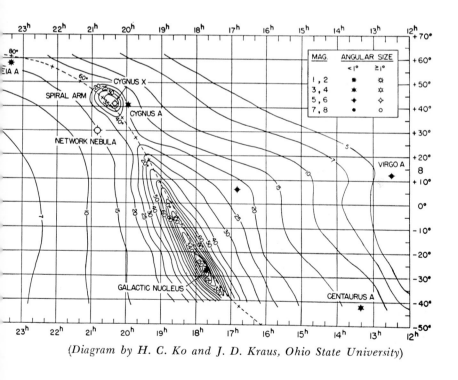

(Diagram by H. C. Ko and J. D. Kraus, Ohio State University)

17·20. Discrete Radio Sources are emission sources of limited angular dimensions ranging from 1″ to more than 1° in diameter. The most familiar sources are generally known by the name of the constellation followed by a letter. In the form of designation adopted by the International Astronomical Union in 1955, Cassiopeia A, for example, is recorded as 23N5A. This indicates that the right ascension is 23 hours and the declination is between 50° and 60° North. The letter A denotes that the source was the first recognized in that region. The stronger sources are concentrated toward the Milky Way, whereas the weaker sources are more uniformly distributed over the sky. Optical identifications of several have already been made. A few of the most prominent sources are the following.

Cassiopeia A (R.A. 23ʰ 21ᵐ, Decl. +59°), situated in our galaxy, is a source of very powerful radiation in the meter wavelengths; the strength of the radio reception is comparable with that from the sun, although the distance of the source is 11,000 light years. Photographs with the Hale telescope show many fragments of a

Fɪɢ. 17·20.   NGC 5128, the Optical Counterpart of Radio Source Centaurus A. (*Photograph with the Hale telescope, Palomar Observatory*)

nebulous shell that is expanding at the rate of 7500 km/sec from the site of a type II supernova, according to Minkowski. If the rate has remained uniform, the outburst occurred about the year A.D. 1700.

Centaurus A ($13^h 22^m$, $-43°$) is associated optically with the unusual elliptical galaxy NGC 5128. The dark band across this object (Fig. 17·20) has been interpreted by Minkowski as belonging to an edgewise spiral colliding centrally with the elliptical galaxy.

Cygnus A ($19^h 58^m$, $+41°$) is identified optically (Fig. 18·11) with two condensations having their centers 2″ apart and surrounded by a large faint halo. The interpretation of this object and of NGC 5128 as pairs of galaxies in collision has not received complete approval (18·11).

Sagittarius A ($17^h 42^m$, $-29°$) represents the direction of the galactic center (17·10).

Taurus A ($5^h 32^m$, $+22°$) is situated in our galaxy; it is the most intense radio source in the winter sky. This is the Crab nebula, which is expanding around the site of a supernova explosion of the year 1054.

Virgo A ($12^h 28^m$, $+13°$) is the elliptical galaxy M 87 (NGC 4486) in the Virgo cluster of galaxies. It is surrounded by many globular star clusters and is unique in having a brilliant jet projecting from it. The optical radiation of this object is mainly of the synchrotron type, resembling the diffuse light of the Crab nebula.

Other optically identified radio sources are remnants of envelopes expanding around supernovae observed in our galaxy by Tycho in 1572 and by Kepler in 1604.

17·21. Tracing of Spiral Arms by Radio. Surveys of the spiral structure of the Galaxy with radio telescopes began soon after the detection of the emission line at 21 cm from the otherwise dark clouds of neutral hydrogen that are abundant in the arms. The original survey by H. C. van de Hulst, C. A. Muller, and J. H. Oort with the 25-foot radio telescope at Kootwijk, Holland, reported in 1954, shows features of the spiral pattern between former longitudes 340° to 135° and 160° to 220° beyond the sun's distance from the center of the Galaxy.

As an example of how the tracing is done, consider a particular pointing of the radio telescope toward the central line of the Milky Way in Cassiopeia, in longitude 80° in the former system, or 112° from the galactic center. The hydrogen clouds in this direction

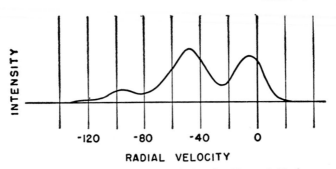

FIG. 17·21. Line Profile of Radio Emission by Neutral Hydrogen at 21 cm in Galactic Longitude 80° in the Former System. The maxima represent hydrogen lanes in three spiral arms in this direction. (*Diagram by C. A. Muller and G. Westerhout, Leiden Observatory*)

are relatively approaching the sun. As the distances of the clouds from us are greater, their speed of approach, and accordingly the Doppler shift of the spectrum line to shorter wavelengths, increases.

Thus by tuning the radio telescope first to 21 cm and then to shorter wavelengths successively, the survey reaches to greater and greater distances in this direction. Where the signal becomes stronger, there are the hydrogen lanes of a spiral arm. The line profile (Fig. 17·21) recorded by the telescope shows three maxima. The corresponding radial velocities reveal the distances from the sun, which in this case are given as 500, 3200, and 7500 parsecs.

17·22. Spiral Structure of the Galaxy. The hydrogen lanes traced by Dutch radio observers in recent years in longitudes available to them are shown in Fig. 17·22. The center of the Galaxy is marked by a cross and the sun's position by a dot above the cross. In the direction 80° from the sun we note three hydrogen lanes, which trace three spiral arms. The first is the Carina-Cygnus arm and the second is the Perseus arm. The lane tangent to the 18° direction from the sun is the Sagittarius arm.

The view in this figure is from the north galactic pole, from which the direction of the galactic rotation is clockwise. The distances of the Carina-Cygnus and Sagittarius arms from the center increase with increasing longitude, showing that the arms are trailing in the rotation. The narrow gap in the lanes just above the sun's position represents directions near the anticenter where the radial velocities are so nearly zero that their differences are not significant.

The composite diagram of Fig. 17·22A shows the spiral arms

traced by the radio observers in Holland (slightly retouched) and at the Radiophysics Laboratory in Australia. In the Sydney pattern the larger dots represent the more reliable observed positions.

Radio studies of the galactic structure other than with the 21-cm spectrum line can employ the continuous nonthermal radiation (4·26) from the spiral arms. Having separated this type of radia-

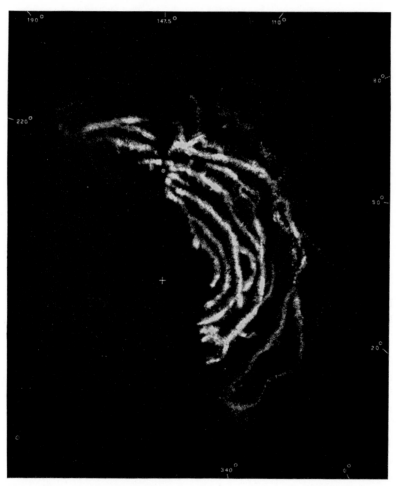

FIG. 17·22. Spiral Structure of the Galaxy. Traced with the 25-foot radio telescope at Kootwijk, Holland. The galactic center is marked by a cross and the sun's position by a circle above it. The numbers are galactic longitudes in the former system. (*Diagram by M. Schmidt and G. Westerhout, Leiden Observatory*)

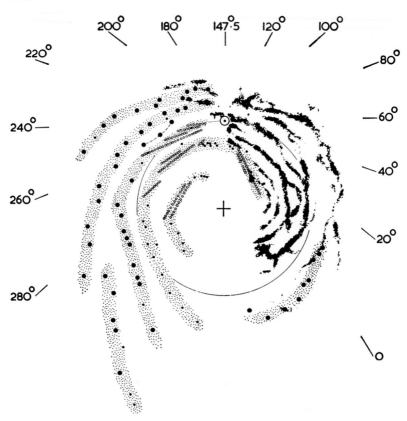

FIG. 17·22A. Spiral Structure of the Galaxy. Composite diagram of the
part of the radio pattern traced at Leiden (right) and at Sydney (left).
The numbers are galactic longitudes in the former system. (*Diagram
by J. L. Pawsey, Radiophysics Laboratory, Sydney, Australia*)

tion from the rest, B. Y. Mills at the Radiophysics Laboratory in
Sydney has constructed a model of the spiral arms that resembles in
a general way the optical and other radio models.

17·23. Gas Around the Galactic Center. A significant addition to
the radio picture of the Galaxy is recorded by J. H. Oort and associates with the 82-foot paraboloid at Dwingleloo. They find that
the radio source Sagittarius A marking the galactic center is a region of neutral hydrogen 2° in diameter enclosing a few clouds of
ionized hydrogen. Gas streams are moving outward from here with
speeds of from 50 to 200 km/sec and are also turning in the gen-

eral rotation of the Galaxy. A bright ring of gas around the center with a radius of 12,000 light years glows by the synchrotron process. How this gas originates and is being replenished as it streams outward is unknown, unless it keeps falling in from the rare gaseous medium of the galactic halo. The opinion is being expressed that we may have here a clue to the evolutionary process by which a galaxy develops spiral arms.

17·24. The Origin of the Galaxy. A hypothesis by C. F. von Weizsäcker of the evolution of the Galaxy offers a convenient means of reviewing the present information about the system of the Milky Way. Weizsäcker's tentative account begins several billion years ago with a large turbulent cosmic cloud, mainly of hydrogen gas, in rotation around its center. The original cloud condensed until it fractured into smaller clouds. Most of the clouds eventually fell in toward the equatorial plane of the rotating mass, forming the flat disk of gas in which spiral arms would develop and also condensing into the stars of the Milky Way.

Some of the smaller clouds remained in the nearly spherical halo of the Galaxy to evolve into globular clusters of stars. Statistical studies by Weizsäcker and others based on Mayall's radial velocity measures showed that the globular clusters are revolving in highly eccentric orbits around the galactic center, somewhat remindful of the orbits of comets around the sun. By Kepler's law of equal areas, the clusters spend most of their lives near their present positions far from the center, where they are practically immune to disturbing influences. After long intervals each revolving cluster dips for relatively short times into the crowded central region of the Galaxy. By collisions here the interstellar gas of the cluster is heated and thereby dissipated, but the formation of the cluster stars themselves is not likely to be seriously affected.

Review Questions

1. Why does the Milky Way have different positions in the sky at the same hour through the year? At what seasons does it pass near the zenith in the early evening in middle northern latitudes?

2. Define the terms: galactic poles; galactic equator; galactic longitude and latitude.

3. How does the appearance of the Milky Way suggest that our galaxy is in general a much-flattened structure? that the sun is far from the center of the Galaxy?

4. Name (a) a constellation in the direction of the galactic center; (b) a constellation in the opposite direction.

5. Describe the first tracing of the spiral arms of the Galaxy by direct photography.

6. Give the names of three arms as assigned them by the original investigators and by some other astronomers. State some features of each arm.

7. What is the evidence that the outer parts of our galaxy rotate more slowly with increasing distance from the center?

8. Describe the sun's share in the rotation of the Galaxy, giving the present direction of its motion, the order of its speed, and the period of a complete rotation.

9. Explain that the observed high speeds of globular clusters result from our own swift motion in the rotation of the Galaxy.

10. Explain (Fig. 17·15) that stars having longitudes around 112° greater than that of the galactic center are approaching us faster in the rotation of the Galaxy as the stars are more remote.

11. Explain that the gas which produces the strong components of the interstellar lines in stellar spectra (Fig. 17·16) is situated in two spiral arms of our galaxy.

12. Contrast the view of the heavens as observed optically and as recorded with radio telescopes.

13. Describe the method of tracing the spiral arms of the Galaxy with radio telescopes.

14. State the nature of some optically identified discrete radio sources.

15. Summarize the current information about the structure, dimensions, and composition of our galaxy.

REFERENCES

Bok, Bart J., and Priscilla F. Bok, *The Milky Way*. Third edition. Harvard University Press, Cambridge, 1957.

Brown, R. Hanbury, and A. C. B. Lovell, *The Exploration of Space by Radio*. John Wiley and Sons, New York, 1958.

Davies, R. D., and H. P. Palmer, *Radio Studies of the Universe*. D. Van Nostrand Company, Princeton, N. J., 1959.

Pawsey, J. L., and R. N. Bracewell, *Radio Astronomy*. Oxford University Press, New York, 1955.

Pfeiffer, John, *The Changing Universe*. A popular account of radio astronomy. Random House, New York, 1956.

Ross, Frank E., and Mary R. Calvert, *Atlas of the Northern Milky Way*. University of Chicago Press, Chicago, 1936.

Shklovsky, I. S., *Cosmic Radio Waves*. English translation. Harvard University Press, Cambridge, 1960.

Smith, A. G., and Carr, T. D., *Radio Exploration of the Planetary System*. Concise treatment in paperback. Published in the Momentum Series, D. Van Nostrand Company, Princeton, N. J., 1963.

18

THE EXTERIOR GALAXIES

STRUCTURES OF GALAXIES – PARTICULAR FEATURES OF
GALAXIES – DISTRIBUTION OF GALAXIES – SPECTRA OF
GALAXIES – THE PHYSICAL UNIVERSE

Other galaxies outside our own are scattered through space as far
as the largest telescopes can explore. These major building blocks
of the physical universe are structurally of three main types: elliptical, spiral, and irregular galaxies. They are generally assembled
in large clusters and in smaller groups such as the local group to
which our galaxy belongs. Their obscuration by the dust clouds
of the Milky Way led to the original designation of the exterior
galaxies as "extra-galactic nebulae." The redward displacements
of their spectral lines, which increase as the galaxies are more distant from us, provide the principal observational basis for the
studies of the expanding universe.

STRUCTURES OF GALAXIES

18·1. Three General Types. Galaxies are divided into three broad
types. (1) *Elliptical galaxies* are ellipsoidal masses of stars, which
are densest around the centers and thin out toward the edges.
Their outlines range in ellipticity from nearly circular to lenticu-
lar. (2) *Spiral galaxies* have lens-shaped central regions surrounded
by flat disks, in which spiral arms are embedded; the arms contain
gas and dust as well as stars. Spiral galaxies are of two kinds:
normal spirals and barred spirals. (3) *Irregular galaxies* have no
particular forms, except that some of them appear to be flattened.

The following more detailed accounts of the different kinds of
galaxies are based on Edwin Hubble's structural classification. A
modification proposed by W. W. Morgan, which also considers the
central concentrations and related stellar populations of the galaxies, is described later (18·20).

Fig. 18·1. Elliptical and Spiral Galaxies. Part of a group in Leo, show-ing an elliptical galaxy, a normal spiral, and a barred spiral. Photograph with the Hale telescope. (*Mount Wilson and Palomar Observatories photograph*)

18·2. Elliptical Galaxies are so named because the nearer ones appear through the telescope as elliptical disks. They are desig-nated by the letter E followed by a number, which is 10 times the ellipticity (2·3) of the disk. The series runs from the circular class E0 to the most flattened E7, which looks like a convex lens viewed edgewise. If all the ellipticals were of the most flattened class, their disks would show the observed range of ellipticity, depending on how they were presented to us. The frequencies of the different classes, however, are not consistent with this supposition. Some elliptical galaxies are actually nearly spherical, although it is im-possible to decide for a particular individual whether it is more flattened than it seems to be.

Extreme types of elliptical galaxies, E0 and E7, are shown in Fig. 18·2. M 32, one of the two companions of the Andromeda spiral (Fig. 18·4), is an example of the slightly flattened class E2, and the other companion, NGC 205, is of class E5.

These are systems of stars, generally dust-free and of Baade's type II population. Almost all the gas and dust available for star-

Fig. 18·2.   Extreme Types of Elliptical Galaxies.   NGC 4278 (left) has a nearly circular disk.   NGC 3115 (right) is among the most flattened elliptical galaxies.   Photographs with the Hale telescope.   (*Mount Wilson and Palomar Observatories photographs*)

Fig. 18·2A.   Elliptical Galaxy NGC 185.   The brightest stars are visible in the outer parts.   (*Photograph by Walter Baade, Mount Wilson Observatory*)

building would seem to have been exhausted. Small dust clouds remain in some systems and have young stars in their vicinities. The nearer ellipticals, including NGC 185 (Fig. 18·2A), are resolved into stars in the Mount Wilson and Palomar photographs.

The richer systems have their stars highly concentrated toward their centers. The Sculptor system is an example of the less populous objects that have more moderate concentration. This and the Fornax system were the first of the kind to be discovered. Other dwarf ellipticals were found later.

18·3. Normal Spiral Galaxies have lens-shaped central regions, from opposite sides of which two arms emerge and at once begin to coil around the centers in the same sense and the same plane. The central regions are brighter than the arms, and in many cases are directly visible with the telescope. The fainter and bluer arms can be seen to advantage only in the photographs.

Normal spirals are divided into three classes. *Class Sa* spirals have large central regions and thin, closely coiled arms; an example is NGC 4594 (Fig. 18·5). In *class Sb* the central regions are smaller, and the arms are larger and wider open. The great spiral in Andromeda is typical of this class to which our own galaxy belongs. In *class Sc* the central regions are reduced to small kernels, and the arms are large and loosely coiled. M 33 in Triangulum (Fig. 18·3) is representative of this class.

18·4. The Great Spiral in Andromeda, M 31, is the brightest and may also be the nearest of the exterior spiral galaxies. An elongated hazy spot to the naked eye, it is marked in Map 4 with its original name, the "Great Nebula" in Andromeda. It is the central region that appears to the naked eye and, for the most part, to the eye at the telescope. Fainter surrounding parts come out clearly in the photographs, where this galaxy is shown in its true character as a flat Sb spiral inclined 13° from the edgewise presentation.

Because of its inclination, the nearly circular spiral appears oval to us. Its length in the photograph is about 3°, and the gradual fading at the edge suggests greater dimensions. Baade's studies of the faint outskirts increase the diameter to 4°.5, which at the distance of 2.2 million light years corresponds to a linear diameter of 180,000 light years.

Separate stars in the arms of the Andromeda spiral were first observed by Hubble in his photographs with the 100-inch Mount

Fig. 18·3. Spiral Galaxy M 33. Photograph with the Hale telescope. (*Mount Wilson and Palomar Observatories photograph*)

Wilson telescope. Hubble also discovered the halo of globular clusters surrounding the spiral. Separate stars in the central region and in the disk outside the conspicuous arms were first observed by Baade with the same telescope. The spiral arms of that galaxy contain all the features found in the Milky Way right around us. These include dark dust clouds and emission nebulae made luminous by the radiations of type O and B stars in their vicinities.

Except for its larger dimensions, the neighboring Andromeda spiral seems to resemble closely our own spiral galaxy. The relations between the structural features can be more clearly observed in the view from outside. What has been learned about the An-

FIG. 18·4. The Great Spiral in Andromeda, M 31. Two elliptical companions are M 32 (above) and NGC 205 (below). (*Photograph by N. U. Mayall, Lick Observatory*)

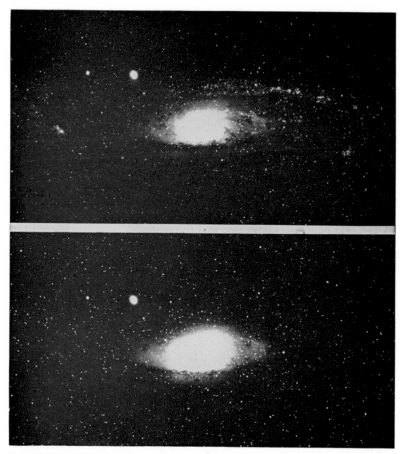

FIG. 18·4A. The Andromeda Spiral in Ultraviolet (above) and Red Light (below). Blue stars in the spiral arms appear in ultraviolet light. The central region is more conspicuous in red light. (*Photograph by Freeman D. Miller, University of Michigan Observatory*)

dromeda spiral has served to guide the investigations of the system of the Milky Way itself.

18·5. Edgewise Spirals. Many spiral galaxies are presented with their flat disks edgewise to us, or nearly so, as would be expected. They show clearly (Fig. 18·5) the polar flattening of the central region and the fidelity with which the material of the disk keeps to the principal plane. Characteristic of the edgewise spirals is the dark streak that sometimes seems to cut them in two. Just as the

F_IG. 18·5. Edgewise Spirals. NGC 4565 in Coma Berenices (above) and NGC 4594 in Virgo (below). (*Mount Wilson Observatory photographs*)

dust near the principal plane of our galaxy prevents us from looking out along this plane, so the dust in the arms of exterior galaxies obstructs the view from outside them.

18·6. Barred Spirals. More than two thirds of the recognized spiral galaxies are of the normal type. The remainder are *barred spirals*. Instead of emerging directly from the central region, the arms of this type usually begin abruptly at the extremities of a broad bright bar that extends through the center. Barred spirals are arranged in Hubble's classification in a series paralleling that of the normal type. The classes are designated SBa, SBb, and SBc.

As the series of barred spirals progresses, the arms build up and unwind. In class SBa the arms are joined to form an elliptical ring, so that the galaxy resembles the Greek letter theta (θ). In class SBb the ring is broken and the free ends are spread, so that

Fig. 18·6. Barred Spiral NGC 1300 in Eridanus. Photograph with the Hale telescope. (*Mount Wilson and Palomar Observatories photograph*)

the galaxy is more nearly like the normal spiral. In class SBc the ends are so far separated that the galaxy has the form of the letter S.

Some spiral galaxies of both types have bright rings inside the spiral patterns. These rings, from which the arms begin tangentially, are said to have so nearly the same linear diameters that they might serve as distance indicators.

18·7. The Magellanic Clouds. Nearest of the exterior galaxies and regarded as satellites of our own galaxy, the two Magellanic Clouds are plainly visible to the unaided eye, but are too close to the south celestial pole to be viewed clearly north of the tropical zone. They were mentioned by early voyagers into the southern hemisphere and are named in honor of the navigator Ferdinand Magellan.

The Large Cloud is in the constellation Dorado. As it appears in the photograph (Fig. 18·7) its apparent diameter is 12°, or half the length of the Great Dipper. The Small Cloud is in Tucana, and its apparent diameter is 8°. At distances somewhat greater than 150,000 light years the optical linear diameters of the two

FIG. 18·7. The Large Magellanic Cloud. (*Photograph by K. G. Henize with the Mount Wilson 10-inch refractor at Bloemfontein, South Africa*)

objects are, respectively, 32,000 and 25,000 light years. A quantity of neutral hydrogen equal to a billion solar masses occurs in and around both Clouds, also forming a link between them, as F. J. Kerr and associates at Sydney have found.

The Magellanic Clouds have been classed generally among the irregular galaxies. However, the Australian radio astronomers have observed the rotations of both Clouds, and G. De Vaucouler's photographs with a small camera at Mount Stromlo seem to him to show that the Clouds are flat one-armed barred spirals having larger angular dimensions than were previously assigned them. H. M. Johnson sees in his photographs of the Large Cloud some resemblance to an asymmetrical Sc spiral galaxy.

18·8. Irregular Galaxies lack the orderly structure that characterizes the elliptical and spiral systems. They constitute a relatively small class among the galaxies where the forms can be observed with present instruments. Aside from the Magellanic Clouds, the nearest examples are NGC 6822 in Sagittarius and IC 1613 in Sex-tans. These are examples of a type that contains O and B stars and emission nebulae.

Several hundred irregular and otherwise peculiar galaxies are recognized in the Palomar sky-survey with the 48-inch Schmidt telescope. Some of these are being studied by E. M. and G. R. Burbidge in their photographs with the 82-inch telescope of the McDonald Observatory. In a preliminary report these investigators conclude that the irregular galaxies represent very early stages of evolution, because they cannot last long in their present form and have not yet attained rotational symmetry. The existence of such youthful types implies that galaxies may be forming even today.

18·9. Sequence of Regular Galaxies. The separate series of galaxies having rotational symmetry were joined by Hubble into a continuous sequence. From the compact spherical form at one end to the most open spirals at the other, it might be considered a progression of expansion. At the termination of the elliptical series the sequence divides into parallel branches of normal and barred spirals. Classes S0 and SB0, not represented in Fig. 18·9, were introduced later after the division before the spiral structures begin.

This sequence provided a basis for thinking about the evolution of galaxies. A progression from left to right in the figure might suggest the streaming of material from opposite sides of the most flattened elliptical systems and the gradual building up of the spiral arms at the expense of the central regions. A progression in

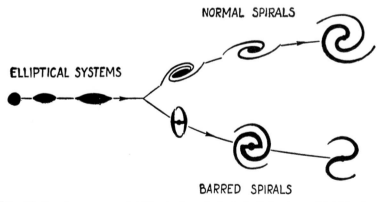

FIG. 18·9. Sequence of Elliptical and Spiral Galaxies. Hubble later placed the classes S0 and SB0 near the division of the sequence into two branches. (*Adapted from a diagram by Edwin P. Hubble*)

the opposite direction, however, is suggested by the trend of the stellar compositions of galaxies (18·20).

18·10. The Status of S0 Galaxies.   The earliest interpretation of S0 galaxies was suggested by their introduction in Hubble's sequence between the flattest ellipticals and the most compact spirals. It seemed that the S0 galaxies might be an intermediate stage in the evolution between ellipticals and spirals.   The greater abundance of these galaxies in the denser clusters of galaxies, however, led to a different interpretation.   Following the hypothesis of Lyman Spitzer and of Baade, the S0 galaxies came to be regarded as the central regions of former spiral galaxies.

Although the ratios of the diameters of galaxies to the distances of their nearest neighbors are much greater than are those of the stars, they still average small enough to preclude the possibility of frequent collisions of galaxies in general.   In the denser clusters, however, it was estimated that the random motion of a galaxy might bring it into collision with another galaxy several times in

FIG. 18·10.   Part of the Coma Cluster of Galaxies.   S0 galaxies are frequent.   Photograph with the Hale telescope.   (*Mount Wilson and Palomar Observatories photograph*)

the course of a billion years. Collision of a spiral galaxy with a neighbor could be violent enough to heat the gases of the spiral arms intensely, accelerating the atomic motions to exceed the velocity of escape from the galaxy. Thus the gas and dust would be dissipated by the collisions, but the loss of the stellar structure of the arms would require further explanation.

Two objections to the collision hypothesis are: (1) that S0 galaxies are observed in less dense clusters as well, and (2) that collisions even in the denser clusters could become insignificant if the distance scale of the universe needs sufficient enlarging, which may be the case. A current interpretation of S0 galaxies is that they are the oldest of the ellipticals and are especially abundant in the denser clusters because in such environment they age more rapidly.

Another trend away from the collision hypothesis of galaxies is found in the present explanation of radio sources such as Cygnus A.

18·11. Radio Source Cygnus A. A powerful source of radio emission, known as Cygnus A because it was the first of these to be recognized in the constellation Cygnus, has its optical counterpart as photographed in Fig. 18·11. The photograph shows a pair of overlapping condensations centered about 2″ apart and surrounded by a large dim halo. The object is one of the brightest members of a remote rich cluster of galaxies. Baade and Minkowski interpreted the condensations as two colliding galaxies that have interpenetrated until their centers are only a few thousand light years apart. Their gases are intensely heated; almost half of the optical radiation appears in the spectrum as widened bright lines of hydrogen and other elements.

The collision hypothesis for Cygnus A and some other abnormal galaxies, such as NGC 5128 (Fig. 17·20), was accepted by most astronomers until 1960, when apparent discrepancies began to be noticed. It was found that the radio emission comes from two regions centered about 80″ on either side of the optical object in Cygnus, which itself is only 30″ in its longest diameter. The Soviet radio astronomer I. S. Shklovsky concluded that the optical feature corresponding to Cygnus A is most likely a double galaxy with the nucleus forming a close pair and that the components are generically related. From his calculations and those of G. R. Burbidge it seemed improbable that the very strong radio emission of Cygnus A could result from the collision of galaxies. Instead, Shklovsky

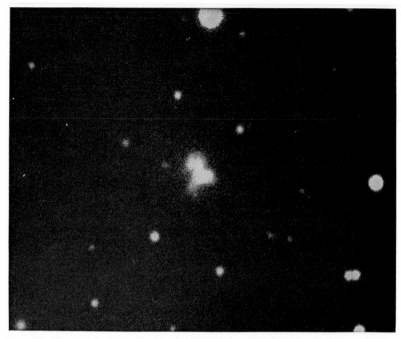

Fig. 18·11. Optical Counterpart of Radio Source Cygnus A. Photograph with the Hale telescope. (*Mount Wilson and Palomar Observatories photograph*)

attributed this radiation to tenuous gas clouds spreading from the sites of earlier supernovae outbursts.

An equally dramatic hypothesis of the instability of systems of galaxies was proposed in 1954 by V. A. Ambartsumian. The hypothesis conjectures that at least some clusters of galaxies possess enormous and unexplained energy that is tearing them apart. The implications of the proposal might extend from clusters to individual galaxies and their evolution. Radio sources such as Cygnus A are viewed as violently exploding galaxies; their nuclei are dividing to produce new galaxies.

18·12. Interactions Between Galaxies. Some objections have been noted to earlier ideas that S0 galaxies might be former spirals which lost their arms in collisions and that radio sources such as Cygnus A might be powered by interpenetrating galaxies. Although collisions between galaxies are perhaps rare enough to be disregarded, effects of interactions between close pairs of galaxies are frequently observed. In some cases the structural features of the galaxies are distorted; a familiar example is the "Whirlpool nebula," M 51, comprising a spiral galaxy and a small elliptical companion. In other cases bright filaments join the components of pairs or appear in their vicinities. The original negative of the pair NGC 4038 and 4039 (Fig. 18·12) shows long filaments above and below the galaxies.

F. Zwicky, of Mount Wilson and Palomar Observatories, has observed many pairs of interacting galaxies in photographs with the 48-inch Schmidt telescope. The Soviet astronomer B. A. Vorontsov-Velyaminov published in 1959 a catalog of 355 such pairs, with an atlas in which nearly all the illustrations are enlargements of Palomar Sky Survey photographs. The interacting pairs are believed to be revolving binary systems.

FIG. 18·12. Interacting Galaxies NGC 4038 and 4039. (*Photograph with the 48-inch Schmidt telescope, Palomar Observatory*)

18·13. Distance Indicators of Galaxies.   Edwin Hubble, in 1924, established the spirals and other extragalactic nebulae as stellar systems beyond our Milky Way.   His photographs with the 100-inch Mount Wilson telescope showed the arms of the spirals M 31 and M 33 partly resolved into stars.   Some of the stars proved to be classical cepheid variables.   Hubble observed that the curve representing the logarithms of the periods of the light variations of these cepheids plotted against their median apparent magnitudes seemed to have the same form as Shapley's log(period)-absolute magnitude curve.   It remained to determine the modulus, the difference $m - M$ between corresponding ordinates of the curves in the two cases.   The distance, r, in parsecs, could then be found by the useful formula: $\log r = (m - M + 5)/5$.   The great distances that resulted showed conclusively for the first time that the two spirals are exterior to our own galaxy.

Hubble later extended his measures of the distances of galaxies in three steps: (1) By use of cepheid variables that he found in five other nearby galaxies; (2) by the apparent magnitudes of what seemed to be the most luminous stars in somewhat more distant galaxies where cepheids were too faint to be seen in his photographs; (3) by the total apparent brightness of entire galaxies on the assumption that galaxies of the same class had the same absolute brightness.   More recent investigations with the 200-inch telescope have shown the need for revising the original distance scale of galaxies, as Hubble himself had considered quite possible.

The upward revision of the luminosities of classical cepheids by Baade in 1952 required multiplication by the factor 2 of the previously assigned distances of almost all galaxies; and the factor was soon raised to 3 for other reasons.   In addition, it became evident that the period-luminosity curves of classical cepheids occupy a band at least 1 magnitude wide (Fig. 13·9) instead of being on the same line, so that the luminosity of a cepheid derived from the original single curve may give a distance as much as 25 per cent in error.

Sandage's red photographs with the 200-inch telescope seem to have demonstrated that the supposed brightest stars originally employed as distance indicators in intermediate galaxies were frequently bright nebulae (Fig. 18·13).   He estimates that the nebu-

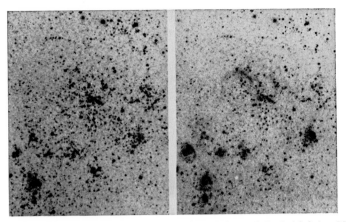

FIG. 18·13. Part of Spiral M 33 in Yellow (left) and Red (right). Negative photographs by A. R. Sandage with the 200-inch telescope. The red photograph shows several H-II regions that with a smaller telescope might resemble single bright stars. (*Mount Wilson and Palomar Observatories photographs*)

lous spots may appear 1.8 magnitudes brighter than the brightest stars in a particular galaxy.

In his paper of 1962 on the distance scale, Sandage adopts classical cepheids as primary indicators of distances of the nearer galaxies. He employs an improved calibration of the period-luminosity relation for the cepheids and more precise photometric measures of very faint stars in and near these galaxies. The new determination for the Andromeda spiral suggests a 50 per cent increase in the distances of the nearer galaxies (Table 18·I) over the values accepted after the revision of 1952.

18·14. Novae in Exterior Galaxies. The normal novae that flare out in the exterior galaxies resemble the galactic novae (13·17) in the order of their luminosity at maximum brightness and in the character of their light variations. Hubble published in 1929 a survey of 82 novae in M 31, and H. C. Arp reported in 1956 on his studies of 30 other novae, which he had discovered in that galaxy with the 60-inch Mount Wilson telescope. Because the distance factor is eliminated, such surveys in a single galaxy give a clearer account of the behavior of novae.

Arp concludes that about 26 normal novae appear annually in the Andromeda spiral; one fourth of these are likely to be concealed by dust clouds of that galaxy or else within its more congested central region. The durations of the observed nova outbursts, while they were brighter than magnitude 20, ranged from 5 to 150 days, and the corresponding absolute magnitudes at the maxima from −8.5 to −6.2. The faster novae faded more smoothly after the maxima than did the slower ones.

18·15. Supernovae sometimes rise to considerable fractions of the total brightness of the galaxies in which they appear. The first of these to be recorded in the exterior galaxies flared out in 1885 near the central region of the Andromeda spiral; at greatest brightness it appeared as a star of the 6th visual magnitude.

Supernovae are stars more massive than the sun, which in the later stages of their evolution attain very high central temperatures and explode. In the explosions they blow off into space excess gaseous material that may amount to as much as one or two solar masses. The outbursts occur in all types of galaxies at the average rate of one per galaxy in 200 to 300 years, according to Zwicky; this frequency is less than has been estimated for our own galaxy (13·22), partly because ours is larger than average. The outbursts of supernovae are most likely to be detected in repeated photographs of clusters of galaxies. Supernovae are of two types:

Fig. 18·15. Supernova in the Spiral Galaxy NGC 4725. Before and during the outburst. (*Mount Wilson Observatory photograph*)

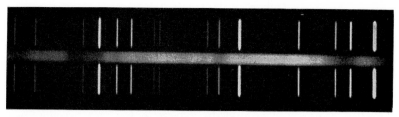

Fig. 18·15A. Spectrum of Type I Supernova in the Irregular Galaxy NGC 4214. (*Photograph, June 24, 1954, by R. Minkowski, Mount Wilson and Palomar Observatories*)

Type I. The members of this type rise to about absolute magnitude −15.5, or more than 100 million times as luminous as the sun. After a rapid drop for 100 days following maximum brightness, they decline less rapidly and more smoothly. The extreme width of the lines in the spectra (Fig. 18·15A) testify to the violence of the explosions. Supernovae of type I are particularly deficient in hydrogen.

Type II. The members of this type attain about absolute magnitude −13.5, and may blow away most of the original mass. They decline after maximum brightness more slowly at first than do those of the first type.

18·16. Globular Clusters Around Galaxies. Hubble was the first to report the presence of at least 250 fuzzy disks projected against and near the borders of the Andromeda spiral. He believed that they were globular clusters of stars like those in the halo around our galaxy, as they proved to be; the outer parts of two of them were later resolved into stars with the 200-inch telescope. The clusters of M 31 are as luminous as our own clusters. On the former scale of distances they seemed to be less luminous than ours, one of the several indications that the scale was too small. Globular clusters are observed around other exterior galaxies as well.

These great clusters are presumably as old as the galaxies themselves. Massive enough to remain stable under their own gravitation, they may provide important clues to the early history of the galaxies.

DISTRIBUTION OF GALAXIES

18·17. Their Surface Distribution. The diagram of Fig. 18·17 represents the results of a photographic survey by Hubble with the Mount Wilson telescopes. He counted the galaxies visible in each of 1283 sample areas over three fourths of the heavens. The numbers are greatest around the galactic poles; they become fewer with decreasing galactic latitude, until near the equator there are almost no galaxies to be seen.

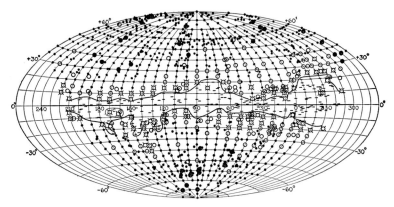

FIG. 18·17. Obscuration of Exterior Galaxies by Dust Clouds of the Milky Way. In this representation of the whole celestial sphere the numbers around the edge are galactic latitudes. Filled dots indicate regions where the galaxies are more numerous than average, circles where they are less numerous than average, and dashes where they are not seen at all. The obscuration is nearly complete in an irregular band along the galactic equator, and is partial for some distance north and south of this "region of avoidance." (*Diagram by Edwin P. Hubble, Mount Wilson Observatory*)

The counts near the poles average 80 galaxies per unit area. Obscuration of 1 magnitude in their brightness would reduce the number to 20, 2 magnitudes to five, and 3 magnitudes to not much more than one visible galaxy per area. The conclusion is that the dimming of the exterior systems by the dust in our galaxy is not less than 3 magnitudes near the galactic equator. The dust in front of the galactic center reduces the photographic brightness of the galaxies behind it as much as 8 to 10 magnitudes.

18·18. The Local Group. The galactic system is a member of a group of at least 17 galaxies, which occupy an ellipsoidal volume of space more than 2 million light years in its longest dimension. Our galaxy and M 31 are near the two ends of this diameter; these and M 33 are the normal spirals of the group. The Magellanic Clouds and two smaller systems have usually been classed as irregular galaxies. The remaining 10 are elliptical galaxies. Six dwarf ellipticals are typified by the Sculptor and Fornax systems discovered by Shapley in 1938. Four others, two in Leo and one apiece in Draco and Ursa Minor, were found more recently in photographs with the Palomar 48-inch Schmidt telescope. Henrietta Swope, who with Baade studied his photographs of the Draco galaxy, reports that it contains over 260 variable stars, almost all of the RR Lyrae type. In having so many of these variables and in the general features of its color-magnitude diagram this galaxy re-

TABLE 18·I   THE LOCAL GROUP

Designation	Type	Distance (light years)	Apparent Diameter	Linear Diameter (light years)
Galactic system	Sb	. . . .	. . . .	80,000
Large Mag. Cloud	I	* 160,000	12°	32,000
Small Mag. Cloud	I	* 190,000	8°	25,000
Ursa Minor system	E	300,000	55′	4,000
Draco system	E	320,000	48′	4,000
Sculptor system	E	340,000	45′	4,000
Fornax system	E	680,000	50′	10,000
Leo II system	E	1,200,000	10′	3,000
NGC 6822	I	1,400,000	20′	9,000
NGC 185	E	1,600,000	14′.5	7,000
NGC 147	E	1,600,000	14′.1	7,000
Leo I system	E	1,800,000	10′	4,000
IC 1613	I	* 2,200,000	17′	10,000
M 31	Sb	* 2,200,000	4°.5	180,000
M 32	E2	* 2,200,000	12′	7,000
NGC 205	E5	* 2,200,000	15′.8	10,000
M 33	Sc	* 2,400,000	62′	50,000

* New values of distances from data by Sandage.

sembles the globular clusters of stars, but it is much larger and less dense than the clusters.

The members of the local group are listed in Table 18·I, which contains their types, their distances from us corrected for absorption by intervening dust, and their diameters. The distances marked with asterisks are from new data supplied by Allan Sandage. The distance of the Draco system and also of M 31 are as determined by Henrietta Swope. For the remaining galaxies of the group the distances given in the previous edition of this book have been multiplied by the factor 22/15, an expedient intended to make them conform more nearly to the scale established by the new value of the distance of M 31. The diameters of all these galaxies have been revised to correspond.

18·19. Clusters of Galaxies. Many, and perhaps all, galaxies occur in clusters that fill all space, according to Fritz Zwicky. The cluster populations range up to several thousand galaxies. His catalog of galaxies and clusters of galaxies lists about 10,000 rich clusters north of declination $-30°$, which can be recognized on yellow-sensitive photographs with the 48-inch Schmidt telescope of Palomar Observatory. Individual clusters are designated here by the equatorial coordinates of their centers; an example is Cl 1215.6 + 3025, where the first number is the right ascension in hours and minutes, and the second is the declination in degrees and minutes. A few of the most prominent clusters are commonly known by the names of the constellations in which they appear; an example is the Virgo cluster.

The Virgo cluster, at a distance previously estimated as 20 million light years, is the nearest and most conspicuous of the larger clusters. Its center is in right ascension $12^h 24^m$, declination $+12°$. Spiral galaxies are numerous in this only moderately compact cluster, and their brightest stars can be observed in photographs with large telescopes. The Coma Berenices cluster is reported to have an apparent diameter of 12° and a membership of 9000 galaxies. This and the Corona Borealis cluster are examples of rich and compact clusters. Their most congested central regions contain a preponderance of S0 galaxies. No evidence of any systematic expansion or rotation of the clusters has been found in extensive spectroscopic studies by Zwicky and Humason.

FIG. 18·19. The Corona Borealis Cluster of Galaxies. Photograph with Hale telescope. (*Mount Wilson and Palomar Observatories photograph*)

SPECTRA OF GALAXIES

The spectra of galaxies are composites, as would be expected for assemblages of stars. The spectrum lines are widened and weakened by the different radial velocities of the individual stars. Doppler effects in the spectra show the rotations of galaxies, and redshifts of the lines increase as the distances of the galaxies from us are greater.

18·20. A Modified Classification of Galaxies, devised by W. W. Morgan, is based on studies of direct photographs and spectrograms of many galaxies. The principal feature of this later classification is the increase in the evolutionary age of the stellar population as the galaxies are more highly concentrated toward their centers. At one extreme are the slightly concentrated irregular and Sc galaxies; their composite spectra contain strong hydrogen lines characteristic of blue stars of Baade's population I. These galaxies are designated as group a. At the other extreme are the highly concentrated spirals and giant ellipticals; their spectra show prominent lines of ionized calcium and molecular bands characteristic of yellow and red giant stars of population II. These galaxies are designated as group k.

Increasing central concentration of the galaxies is represented in the newer system by a succession of groups: a, af, f, fg, g, gk, and k, the lettering being in the same order as in the sequence of types of stellar spectra. The particular population group for a galaxy is followed by a capital letter denoting the form: S for normal spiral, B for barred spiral, E for elliptical, and so on. Finally, a number from 1 to 7 denotes the inclination to the plane of the sky, from flatwise, or else spherical, galaxies to edgewise presentation of flat objects. Thus the Sc spiral M 33, having rather small central concentration and younger stellar population, is classified as fS4. The Sb spiral M 31, having high central concentration and older population, is gkS5.

The population group assigned in each case is determined entirely by inspection of the central concentration of luminosity of the galaxy; but an equivalence with spectral type is expected in the average. The implication is that galaxies having higher central concentration are more advanced in evolution.

Morgan has listed 642 galaxies with their NGC numbers and their classes in the new system. His catalog, prepared mainly from the original negatives of the Palomar Sky Survey, includes practically all galaxies brighter than magnitude 13.1 north of declination −25°.

18·21. Rotations Shown by the Spectra. The flattened forms of regular galaxies suggest their rotations. Definite evidence of the rotations is found in the spectra of spiral galaxies where the equators are presented nearly edgewise to us. When the slit of the spectroscope is placed along the major axis of the inclined spiral,

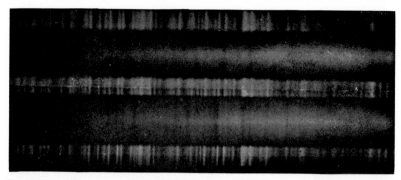

Fɪɢ. 18·21. Spectra of Two Spiral Galaxies. The spectrum of NGC 4594 (Fig. 18·5) is above and of M 31 (Fig. 18·4) is below. The dark lines are displaced toward the red (right) in the upper spectrum and toward the violet (left) in the lower one. The lines slant noticeably in both spectra, showing that the spirals are rotating. Bright comparison lines of vanadium and iron appear above and below the spectra of the spirals. *(Photographs by V. M. Slipher, Lowell Observatory)*

the spectrum lines slant (Fig. 18·21) at an angle from the vertical that depends on the speed of the rotation. It is the same Doppler effect that appears in the spectrum of a rotating planet (Fig. 8·33).

Since the pioneer work of V. M. Slipher, the rotations of several spirals have been studied in this way, particularly by N. U. Mayall and associates at Lick Observatory. The inner part of a spiral rotates like a solid, all in the same period, showing the uniform distribution of material there. In the outer parts the period increases with distance from the center, resembling the rotation of our own spiral galaxy (17·15).

18·22. The Redshifts in the Spectra. Edwin Hubble, in 1929, announced a remarkable relation between the radial velocities and distances of galaxies. With appropriate corrections to the observed values, he discovered that the redshifts of the spectrum lines increase linearly as the distances of the galaxies are greater. This linear relation persisted when the inquiry was later extended to what was then the limiting distance for the 100-inch telescope. More recently, M. L. Humason extended the distance range of the observations toward the limit for the 200-inch telescope.

Humason, Mayall, and Sandage, in 1956, reported the progress on the program to that time. The redshifts had then been observed for galaxies of 26 clusters and for several hundred field galaxies. The clusters range from the Virgo cluster relatively nearby to the remote Hydra cluster. The redshifts of the spectrum lines considered as Doppler effects correspond to velocities of recession varying from 700 to 38,000 miles a second, or to one fifth the speed of light. The rate of increase in the velocities, then given as 180

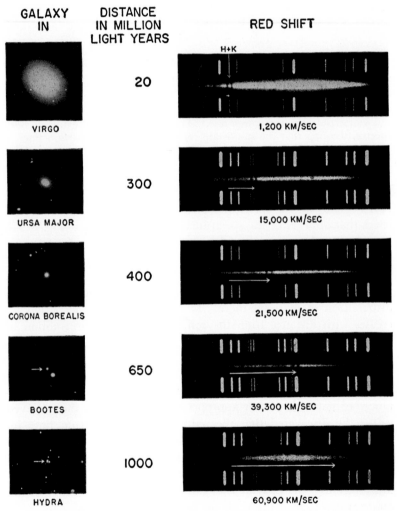

FIG. 18·22. Redshifts in the Spectra of Exterior Galaxies. The arrows show the shifts of the H and K lines of calcium to the red (right). The distances, already increased by a factor 3 from original values, may require further increase. (*Mount Wilson and Palomar Observatories photographs*)

km/sec per 1 million parsecs, or about 35 miles a second per 1 million light years, has been reduced to a little more than half of these values by a revision of the distance scale.

The problem of the expanding universe is not completely solved. Some approaches to the solution by observation and theory are noted in the sections that follow.

18·23. The Expanding Universe. Considered as Doppler effects, the redshifts of the spectrum lines show that the universe of galaxies is expanding in all directions at a rate that increases very nearly in direct proportion to the distance from us. The systematic expansion, however, does not operate within the galaxies themselves or within the groups and clusters.

Fig. 18·23 represents the 18 faintest clusters in which the red-

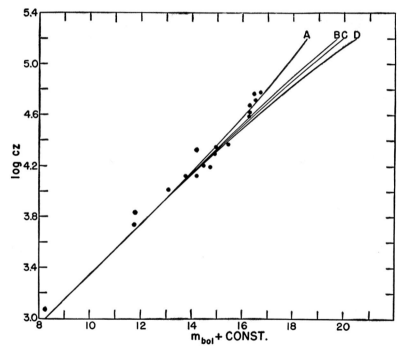

FIG. 18·23. Different Possibilities for an Expanding Universe. The logarithms of the rates of recession are plotted against the integrated magnitudes of galaxies, which are functions of their relative distances from us. A universe represented by line C expands forever at the same rate; by a line between C and B is open and infinite; by line B is Euclidean and infinite; by line A, which these observed shifts seem to follow, is closed and finite. (*Diagram by Allan R. Sandage*)

shifts had been measured. The logarithms of the amounts of the shifts are plotted here with respect to the integrated bolometric magnitudes of the galaxies, which are functions of the relative distances from us.

Where the curve of the figure divides at the top, the calculated line B represents what the effect would be in flat Euclidean space. To the left of B the universe would be closed and finite, like the surface of a sphere. Between B and C it would be open and infinite. Line C represents a universe expanding forever at the same rate of increase in the speed with distance; this line is curved because we view the progress of the expansion at different times. To the left of C the expansion must slow down by an amount depending on the average density of matter in the universe. Line D represents a steady-state universe.

More recently, in 1960, Minkowski photographed the spectrum of a very faint galaxy in Boötes, believed to be the optical counterpart of the radio source 3C295. If the identification of the only available line was correct, the spectrum was shifted to the red farther than for any galaxy previously observed. The corresponding velocity of recession was found to be 46 per cent of the speed of light and the distance of the galaxy was estimated as 6 billion light years.

18·24. The Expansion Implied by the Observed Redshifts. The redshifts for the six most remote clusters of galaxies for which the spectra are observed are represented by the line A of Fig. 18·23. The rate of expansion of the universe seems accordingly to be diminishing; it was faster by 6000 miles a second when the light left those remote galaxies a billion years ago than it is at present. The decrease in the rate of expansion might be expected to continue until contraction sets in. When an excessive density of the material is reached in the subsequent contraction, the universe might begin to expand again, and the oscillation might continue forever. Thus the universe would be finite in space and of infinite duration.

This preliminary interpretation of the observed redshifts, as it was described by Sandage, requires confirmation by velocities and distances of still more remote galaxies, and also a decision as to the correct distance scale. In its present form it implies an average density in the universe 300 times as great as is obtained from the masses assigned to the galaxies alone.

18·25. The Progressive Reddening of Galaxies with their increasing distance from us provides another means of observing the expansion of the universe. The Doppler effect of the recession of the galaxies displaces their spectral energy curves (10·6) toward longer wavelengths and therefore causes the light of the galaxies to become redder as their velocities of recession are greater. This effect has been studied by W. A. Baum from his six-color measures with a photon counter on the 200-inch telescope. His diagram of the velocities so determined is shown in Fig. 18·25 for galaxies in eight clusters. Here the logarithm of the recession velocity for each cluster is plotted with respect to the mean bolometric magnitude of the galaxies, which is a function of the distance of the cluster.

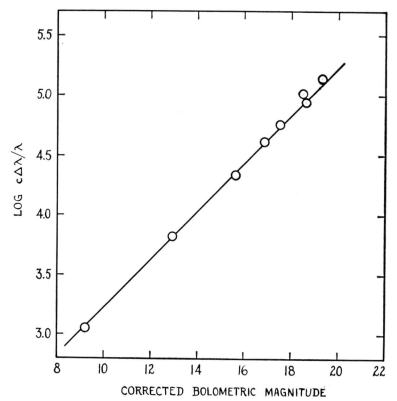

Fɪɢ. 18·25. Velocity-Distance Relation for Eight Clusters of Galaxies. From the relatively nearby Virgo cluster to the very remote cluster 1410. For the mean of the galaxies observed in each cluster the logarithm of the rate of recession is plotted against the bolometric magnitude. (*Diagram by William A. Baum, Mount Wilson and Palomar Observatories*)

Cluster 1410, the most remote of the eight, is represented by the single galaxy corresponding to the radio source 3C295 (18·23). Baum's value for the velocity of recession for this galaxy is 44 per cent of the speed of light, or about 82,000 miles a second. The points for the 8 clusters fall very nearly on a straight line; but their positions are preliminary, requiring certain further corrections not yet evaluated.

18·26. A Hyperbolic Universe. George Gamow has described a theory of a universe expanding, on line C, in open and infinite space. This universe had previously been contracting for an indefinite time. At length it had reached a superdense state where all its structure, including the atomic structures, was shattered. Only elementary particles and a vast store of energy remained when the material could contract no further and began to expand.

The chemical elements, at least the lighter ones, were formed during the first half hour of the expansion, according to this theory. After 250 million years the spreading mass of turbulent gas separated into millions of protogalaxies having degrees of spin that determined the forms the galaxies have retained ever since. When the protogalaxies ultimately condensed into galaxies of stars, these continued to separate at rates exceeding the velocities necessary for their mutual escape and will go on doing so forever. This type of expansion limits the gravitational restraint to a quantity of intergalactic material not greater than 7 times the mass of the galaxies.

18·27. A Steady-State Universe. A theory by Cambridge astronomers, described by Fred Hoyle and others, proposes the continuous emergence of matter, preferably in the form of hydrogen atoms. The addition of the new material causes the universe to expand steadily in Euclidean space at such a rate as to keep the density constant. This steady state may be maintained forever.

Such a universe has no beginning and no end. Nor will the space within our present view become more and more nearly blank. The galaxies we see now will be replaced by about the same number formed from the newer material. The continuous emergence of hydrogen would answer the question of why any hydrogen remains if it is continuously being transformed in the stars into heavier elements.

THE PHYSICAL UNIVERSE

The unfolding of knowledge of the universe has revealed a scene of ever-increasing grandeur. It began with the anthropocentric view in which the observer was the central figure. Around him was a flat earth and over him bent a sky full of stars, which rose and set daily and marched westward with the changing seasons.

In the geocentric view of the early Greek scholars the stationary globe of the earth was the dominant feature. The sun, moon, and planets revolved around the earth within the rotating sphere of the "fixed stars." Next, the heliocentric view, dating formally from the time of Copernicus, established the planetary system on a more nearly correct basis and brought the sphere of the stars to rest. Then emerged the idea that the stars are other suns, many of them perhaps attended by planetary systems.

The invention and development of the telescope extended the inquiries into the star fields and promoted the first attempts to determine the structure of the universe. The discovery of the law of gravitation inaugurated dynamical interpretations of what goes on in the heavens. The recognition of physically related pairs of stars, of star clusters, of nebulae that seemed not of a starry nature, and of other nebulae that seemed to avoid the Milky Way— these and other features of the sidereal scene presented problems for study with the eye at the telescope and later in photographs made with telescopes.

Astrophysics, the "new astronomy," extended techniques of the terrestrial physical laboratories to the laboratory of space, with benefit to the findings of both. It employs the spectroscope, the photographic plate, the photoelectric cell, the filters for transmitting celestial radiations at various wavelengths, the radio telescope, and other devices. Apparatus sent above the earth is recording and relaying to the ground celestial information not previously available to us under the blanket of the atmosphere.

In recent years, as we have seen, the picture of the universe is unfolding with spectacular rapidity. Our galaxy, having the sun in its suburbs, now stands out clearly as a spiral structure in the foreground of the celestial scene. The formerly mysterious spirals and associated "extragalactic nebulae" are established as exterior galaxies, often gathered into groups and larger clusters. Attractive theories are available as to how stars are born in the cosmic clouds and how they continue to shine and to build up heavier chemical elements in their interiors, until they end in the celestial cinder heap.

REVIEW QUESTIONS

1. Describe the three general types of galaxies, naming an example of each.

2. Enumerate several points of resemblance between our galaxy and the great spiral in Andromeda.

3. State reasons for supposing that the Magellanic Clouds may be spirals. How far south must we be (Map 6) to observe the Clouds?

4. Describe Hubble's sequence of regular galaxies.

5. Describe and account for the S0 galaxies that are frequent in compact clusters of galaxies.

6. What is the observational evidence that galaxies collide?

7. Distinguish between supernovae and normal novae as to the frequency and violence of the outbursts. Why are repeated photographs of clusters of galaxies useful in the discovery of supernovae?

8. Name some members of the local group of galaxies. Distinguish between a group and a cluster of galaxies.

9. The dark lines in the spectra of spiral galaxies are rather wide and are sometimes slanting. Bright lines appear as well. Explain.

10. Describe the redshifts of the lines in the spectra of increasingly remote galaxies. Account for the shift to the violet in the spectrum of the Andromeda spiral.

11. Explain an alternate method of observing the redshifts from photoelectric records of the brightness of galaxies at different wavelengths.

12. State the reason (a) why previous values of the distances and diameters of most galaxies were increased in 1952 by the factor 2; (b) why a further revision of the distance scale was necessary.

REFERENCES

Gamow, George, *The Creation of the Universe*. The Viking Press, New York, 1952.

Hoyle, Fred, *Frontiers of Astronomy*. Harper and Brothers, New York, 1955.

Hubble, Edwin P., *The Realm of the Nebulae*. Paperbound edition, Dover Publications, New York.

Sandage, Allan, *The Hubble Atlas of Galaxies*. Carnegie Institution of Washington, Washington, D. C., 1961.

Shapley, Harlow, *Galaxies*. Revised edition. Harvard University Press, Cambridge, 1961.

Shapley, Harlow, *The Inner Metagalaxy*. Yale University Press, New Haven, 1957.

Current contributions to the literature of astronomy appear in periodicals such as:

The Astronomical Journal. Published for the American Astronomical Society at the rate of 10 numbers a year by the American Institute of Physics, 335 East 45th Street, New York 17, N. Y. Editorial office: Yale University Observatory, New Haven 11, Connecticut.

Publications of the Astronomical Society of the Pacific. Published bimonthly by the Society. Address: California Academy of Sciences, Golden Gate Park, San Francisco 18, California. The Society also publishes monthly Leaflets written in popular style by various astronomers.

The Astrophysical Journal. An international review of spectroscopy and astronomical physics. Published bimonthly. University of Chicago Press, 5750 Ellis Avenue, Chicago 37, Illinois.

The Journal of the British Astronomical Association. Published ten times a year. 303 Bath Road, Hounsley West, Middlesex, England.

The Observatory. A Review of Astronomy. Published monthly. The Editors, Royal Greenwich Observatory, Herstmonceux Castle, Hailsham, Sussex, England.

Monthly Notices of the Royal Astronomical Society. Published monthly. Also *Quarterly Journal of the Royal Astronomical Society.* Burlington House, London, W. 1, England.

The Journal of the Royal Astronomical Society of Canada. Published bimonthly. 252 College Street, Toronto, Ontario. The Society also publishes annually *The Observer's Handbook,* a reference for astronomical data and events of the coming year.

Scientific American. Contains frequent articles on astronomy and allied sciences. Published monthly by Scientific American, 415 Madison Avenue, New York 17, New York.

Sky and Telescope. Published monthly. Sky Publishing Corporation, Harvard Observatory, Cambridge 38, Massachusetts.

Appendix

UNITS OF MEASUREMENT

Any measure may be expressed as the product of two factors: (1) a number and (2) the unit that is employed. Examples are 10 feet; 6 hours. The many different *derived units* of measurement can be obtained by combining three *fundamental units* of length, mass, and time. In the United States the legal system of fundamental units is the *English system,* in which the standard units are the yard, the pound, and the second of time. These and other familiar related English units are often used in this book, especially for measures in the solar system. The *metric system* of units also has frequent use in this book, because its units of length and mass progress on the decimal plan and are accordingly more suitable for calculations. The standard fundamental units of the metric system are the meter, the kilogram, and the second of time. A variation is the cgs system, in which the units are the centimeter, the gram, and the second. The same units of time (Chapter 3) are employed in both the English and the metric system.

Astronomical measures often involve very large and very small numbers, which are more conveniently expressed by powers of 10. Examples are the light year, which equals 5.878×10^{12} miles, and the mass of the hydrogen atom, which equals 1.66×10^{-24} gm. Here the exponent shows the number of digits that the decimal point is moved to the right for a positive exponent and to the left for a negative exponent. Thus $10^3 = 1000.$ and $10^{-3} = 0.001$.

Some units of length and mass and their conversion from one system of units to the other are the following.

UNITS OF LENGTH | *English* | *Metric*

1 statute mile (mi)	= 5280 feet	= 1.6093 kilometers
1 foot (ft)	= 12 inches	= 0.3048 meters
1 inch (in)		= 2.54 centimeters

	Metric	*English*
1 kilometer (km)	= 1000 meters	= 0.6214 miles
1 meter (m)	= 100 centimeters	= 39.37 inches
1 centimeter (cm)	= 10 millimeters	= 0.3937 inches
1 millimeter (mm)	= 1000 microns (μ)	= 0.0394 inches

UNITS OF MASS | *English* | *Metric*

| 1 ton | = 2000 pounds | = 907.2 kilograms |
| 1 pound (lb) | = 16 ounces | = 453.6 grams |

	Metric	*English*
1 kilogram (kg)	= 1000 grams	= 2.2046 pounds
1 gram (gm)	= 1000 milligrams	= 0.0353 ounces

ANGULAR MEASURE AND TEMPERATURE SCALES

The unit of angular measure used mainly in this book is the degree (°) and its subdivisions the minute (′) and second (″) of arc. The circumference of a circle is divided into 360 degrees, the degree into 60 minutes, and the minute into 60 seconds. Another unit of angular measure is the *radian* (11·3), which is the angle subtended by the radius of a circle laid off along its circumference. The radian equals 57°.3, or 3437′.7, or 206,264″.8.

Two temperature scales are the *Fahrenheit* (F), which is commonly used in civil life in the United States, and the *centigrade* (C), which is used for scientific purposes in all countries. In the familiar mercury thermometer the heights of the mercury column are marked on the glass tube for the ordinary freezing and boiling points of water. Between these two marks the tube is divided evenly into 180 parts for the Fahrenheit scale and into 100 parts for the centigrade scale. The space between two adjacent divisions represents 1° change in temperature. Hence 1°F = 9/5 of 1°C. Water freezes at 32°F, or 0°C, and boils at 212°F, or 100°C. Thus to convert a temperature reading from the centigrade to the Fahrenheit scale, multiply by 9/5 and add 32°.

The absolute centigrade, or *Kelvin* (K), scale of temperature starts at −273°C as absolute 0°K. Water freezes at 273°K and boils at 373°K.

SOME USEFUL DATA

	English	Metric	Section
Earth's equatorial radius	= 3963 miles	= 6.378×10^8 cm	2·3
Earth's mass	= 6.6×10^{21} tons	= 5.98×10^{27} gm	2·4
Velocity of light	= 186,300 mi/sec	= 2.998×10^{10} cm/sec	4·1
Moon's mass	= $\frac{1}{81} \times$ earth's mass	= 7.35×10^{25} gm	5·1
Moon's radius	= 1080 miles	= 1.74×10^8 cm	5·1
Moon's mean distance	= 238,857 miles	= 3.844×10^{10} cm	5·4
* 1 astronomical unit	= 92,900,000 miles	= 1.495×10^{13} cm	7·16
Sun's mass	= $\frac{1}{3}$ million $\times$ earth	= 1.99×10^{33} gm	10·1
Sun's radius	= 432,000 miles	= 6.96×10^{10} cm	10·1
1 light year	= 5.88×10^{12} miles	= 9.46×10^{17} cm	11·3
1 parsec	= 1.92×10^{13} miles	= 3.08×10^{18} cm	11·3

* This value, generally adopted since 1896, is about 50,000 miles smaller than the value derived in 1961 by timing radar echoes from Venus.

INDEX